Steve

Reliability-centred Maintenance

Reliability-centred Maintenance

John Moubray

BUTTERWORTH
HEINEMANN

Butterworth-Heinemann Ltd
Linacre House, Jordan Hill, Oxford OX2 8DP

ℛ A member of the Reed Elsevier Group

OXFORD LONDON BOSTON
MUNICH NEW DELHI SINGAPORE SYDNEY
TOKYO TORONTO WELLINGTON

First published 1991

Reprinted 1992, 1993, 1994 (twice)

© John Moubray 1991

British Library Cataloguing in Publication Data
A catalogue record for this book is available
from the British Library

ISBN 0 7506 0230 9

Typeset by the author
Printed in England by Clays Ltd, St Ives plc

For Edith

Contents

Preface

To an increasing extent, humanity depends on the wealth generated by the continued operation of highly mechanised and automated businesses. It also depends increasingly on services such as the uninterrupted supply of electricity or trains which run on time. More than ever, these depend in turn on the continued integrity of physical assets.

Yet when these assets fail, not only is this wealth eroded and not only are these services interrupted, but our very survival is threatened. Equipment failure has played a part in some of the worst accidents and environmental incidents in industrial history – incidents which have become bywords, such as *Amoco Cadiz*, Chernobyl, Bhopal and Piper Alpha. As a result, the processes by which these failures occur and what must be done to manage them are rapidly becoming very high priorities indeed, especially as we begin to realise just how many of these failures are caused by the very activities which are supposed to prevent them.

The first industry to confront these issues was the international civil aviation industry. On the basis of research which challenges many of our most firmly and widely-held beliefs about maintenance, this industry evolved a completely new strategic framework for ensuring that any asset continues to perform as its users want it to perform. This framework is known within the aviation industry as MSG3, and outside it as Reliability-centred Maintenance, or RCM.

Reliability-centred Maintenance was developed over a period of thirty years. One of the principal milestones in its development was a report commissioned by the United States Department of Defense from United Airlines and prepared by Stanley Nowlan and the late Howard Heap in 1978. The report provided a comprehensive description of the development and application of RCM by the civil aviation industry. It forms the basis both of this book and of much of the work done in this field outside the airline industry over the past ten years.

Since the early 1980's, RCM has been applied in hundreds of industrial locations around the world. It is rapidly becoming as fundamental to the practice of maintenance management as double entry book-keeping is to financial management, or precedence networks to project management.

This book provides a comprehensive introduction to the theory and practice of RCM in industries other than aviation.

It is intended for maintenance, production and operations managers who wish to learn what RCM is, what it achieves and how it is applied. It will also provide students on business or management studies courses with a comprehensive introduction to the physical (as opposed to financial) management of physical assets. Finally, the book will be invaluable for any students of any branch of engineering who seek a thorough understanding of the state-of-the-art in modern maintenance. It is designed to be read at three levels:

- Chapter 1 is written for those who only wish to review the key elements of Reliability-centred Maintenance.

- Chapters 3 to 7 describe the main elements of the RCM process itself, and will be of most value to those who seek no more than a reasonable technical grasp of the subject.

- The remaining chapters are for those who wish to explore RCM in more detail. Chapters 2 and 8 provide a brief summary of the link between RCM and traditional maintenance planning and control systems. Chapter 9 takes an in-depth look at the subject of failure – both the processes by which failures develop and the increasingly contentious subject of the relationship between age and failure. Chapter 10 considers the implementation of RCM with emphasis on the role of the people involved. Chapters 11 describes what RCM achieves and Chapter 12 provides a brief history of RCM.

JOHN MOUBRAY

Lutterworth
Leicestershire
July 1991

Acknowledgements

It has only been possible to write this book with the assistance of a great many people around the world. In particular, I would like to record my heartfelt gratitude to every one of the hundreds of people with whom I have been privileged to work over last five years, each of whom has contributed something to the material in these pages.

In addition, I would like to pay special tribute to a number of people without whose help, advice or support at crucial moments the book might not have been written at all.

Firstly, special thanks are due to Stan Nowlan for laying the foundations for this book so thoroughly, both through his own writings and in person, and to all his colleagues in the civil aviation industry for their pioneering work in this field.

Among the many clients who have made it possible to prove that RCM is a viable force in industry, I am especially indebted to the following for their support:

John Cook, Mike Hopcraft, Terry Belton and Dave Elsom of Ford of Europe

Joe Campbell of the British Steel Corporation

Dick Kemp and Brian Davies of the Scott Paper Company

Vincent Ryan of the Irish Electricity Supply Board

Brian Freeman and Don Turner of the China Light & Power Company

John Chatfield and Trevor Foltynie of the Wellcome Foundation

Godfrey Rowland, Richard Hall and Alan Owen of Rowntree Mackintosh

Ulrich Abromeit and Marie Tellessen of BP Oil

Ray Bates and K S Ying of the Hong Kong Housing Authority.

The roles played by the late Joe Versteeg, Don Humphrey, Denis Hoare and David Willson in helping me to develop or to propagate the concepts discussed in this book are also acknowledged with gratitude.

I am also indebted to all my associates for their help in applying the concepts and for their continuous feedback about what works and what doesn't work, much of which is also reflected in these pages. A special word of thanks in this respect to my colleagues Joel Black, Hugh Colman, Tony Landi and Ian Hipkin.

I would also like to thank Tony Bell for his advice and guidance over the years, and Jim Todd for his generous assistance when the book was still in its very early stages.

Finally, a special word of thanks to my family for creating an environment in which it was possible to write the book, and to Aladon Ltd for permission to reproduce the RCM Information and Decision Worksheets and the RCM 2 Decision Diagram.

1 Introduction to Reliability-centred Maintenance

1.1 The Changing World of Maintenance

Over the past fifteen years, maintenance has changed, perhaps more so than any other management discipline. The changes are due to a huge increase in the number and variety of physical assets (plant, equipment and buildings) which must be maintained throughout the world, much more complex designs, new maintenance techniques and changing views on maintenance organisation and responsibilities.

Maintenance is also responding to changing expectations. These include a rapidly growing awareness of the extent to which equipment failure affects safety and the environment, a growing awareness of the connection between maintenance and product quality, and increasing pressure to achieve high plant availability and to contain costs.

The changes are testing attitudes and skills in all branches of industry to the limit. Maintenance people are having to adopt completely new ways of thinking and acting, as engineers and as managers. At the same time the limitations of maintenance systems are becoming increasingly apparent, no matter how much they are computerised.

In the face of this avalanche of change, managers everywhere are looking for a new approach to maintenance. They want to avoid the false starts and dead ends which always accompany major upheavals. *Instead they seek a strategic framework which synthesises the new developments into a coherent pattern, so that they can evaluate them sensibly and apply those likely to be of most value to them and their companies.*

This book describes a philosophy which provides just such a framework. It is called Reliability-centred Maintenance, or RCM.

If it is applied correctly, RCM transforms the relationships between the undertakings which use it, their existing physical assets and the people who operate and maintain those assets. It also enables new assets to be put into effective service with great speed, confidence and precision.

This chapter provides a brief introduction to RCM, starting with a look at how maintenance has evolved over the past fifty years.

Since the 1930's, the evolution of maintenance can be traced through three generations. RCM is rapidly becoming a cornerstone of the Third Generation, but this generation can only be viewed in perspective in the light of the First and Second Generations.

The First Generation

The First Generation covers the period up to World War II. In those days industry was not very highly mechanised, so downtime did not matter much. This meant that the prevention of equipment failure was not a very high priority in the minds of most managers. At the same time, most equipment was simple and much of it was over-designed. This made it reliable and easy to repair. As a result, there was no need for systematic maintenance of any sort beyond simple cleaning, servicing and lubrication routines. The need for skills was also lower than it is today.

The Second Generation

Things changed dramatically during World War II. Wartime pressures increased the demand for goods of all kinds while the supply of industrial manpower dropped sharply. This led to increased mechanisation. By the 1950's machines of all types were more numerous and more complex. Industry was beginning to depend on them.

As this dependence grew, downtime came into sharper focus. This led to the idea that equipment failures could and should be prevented, which led in turn to the concept of *preventive maintenance*. In the 1960's, this consisted mainly of equipment overhauls done at fixed intervals.

The cost of maintenance also started to rise sharply relative to other operating costs. This led to the growth of *maintenance planning and control systems*. These have helped greatly to bring maintenance under control, and are now an established part of the practice of maintenance.

Finally, the amount of capital tied up in fixed assets together with a sharp increase in the cost of that capital led people to start seeking ways in which they could maximise the life of the assets.

The Third Generation

Since the mid-seventies, the process of change in industry has gathered even greater momentum. The changes can be classified under the headings of *new expectations*, *new research* and *new techniques*.

New expectations

Figure 1.1 shows how expectations of maintenance have evolved.

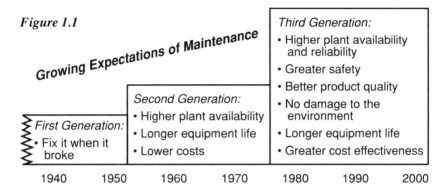

Figure 1.1

Growing Expectations of Maintenance

First Generation:	Second Generation:	Third Generation:
• Fix it when it broke	• Higher plant availability	• Higher plant availability and reliability
	• Longer equipment life	• Greater safety
	• Lower costs	• Better product quality
		• No damage to the environment
		• Longer equipment life
		• Greater cost effectiveness

| 1940 | 1950 | 1960 | 1970 | 1980 | 1990 | 2000 |

Downtime has always affected the productive capability of physical assets by reducing output, increasing operating costs and interfering with customer service. By the 1960's and 1970's, this was already a major concern in the mining, manufacturing and transport sectors. In manufacturing, the effects of downtime are being aggravated by the worldwide move towards just-in-time systems, where reduced stocks of work-in-progress mean that quite small breakdowns are now much more likely to stop a whole plant. In recent times, the growth of mechanisation and automation has meant that *reliability* and *availability* have now also become key issues in sectors as diverse as health care, data processing, telecommunications and building management.

Greater automation also means that more and more failures affect our ability to sustain satisfactory *quality standards*. This applies as much to standards of service as it does to product quality. For instance, equipment failures can affect climate control in buildings and the punctuality of transport networks as much as they can interfere with the consistent achievement of specified tolerances in manufacturing.

More and more failures have serious *safety* or *environmental* consequences, at a time when standards in these areas are rising rapidly. In some parts of the world, the point is approaching where organisations either conform to society's safety and environmental expectations, or they cease to operate. This adds an order of magnitude to our dependence on the integrity of our physical assets – one which goes beyond cost and which becomes a simple matter of organisational survival.

At the same time as our dependence on physical assets is growing, so too is their *cost – to operate* and *to own*. To secure the maximum return on the investment which they represent, they must be kept working efficiently for as long as we want them to.

Finally, the *cost of maintenance* itself is still rising, in absolute terms and as a proportion of total expenditure. In some industries, it is now the second highest or even the highest element of operating costs. As a result, in only thirty years it has moved from almost nowhere to the top of the league as a cost control priority.

New research

Quite apart from greater expectations, new research is changing many of our most basic beliefs about age and failure. In particular, it is apparent that there is less and less connection between the operating age of most assets and how likely they are to fail.

Figure 1.2 shows how the earliest view of failure was simply that as things got older, they were more likely to fail. A growing awareness of "burn-in" led to the widespread Second Generation belief in the "bath-tub" curve.

Figure 1.2

Changing Views on Equipment Failure

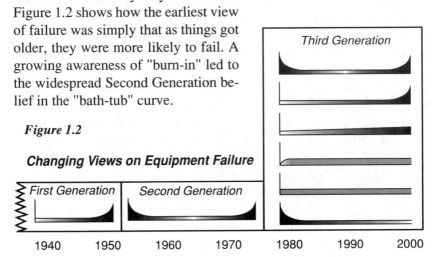

However, Third Generation research has revealed that not one or two but *six* failure patterns actually occur in practice. This is discussed in detail later, but it too is having a profound effect on maintenance.

New techniques

There has been explosive growth in new maintenance concepts and techniques. Hundreds have been developed over the past fifteen years, and more are emerging every week.

Figure 1.3 shows how the classical emphasis on overhauls and administrative systems has grown to include many new developments in a number of different fields.

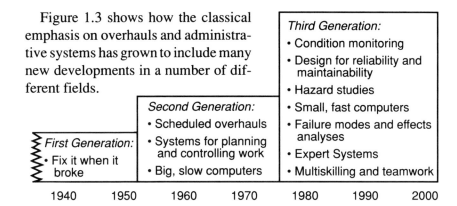

Figure 1.3:   *Changing maintenance techniques*

The new developments include:

- *decision support tools,* such as hazard studies, failure modes and effects analyses and expert systems
- *new maintenance techniques,* such as condition monitoring
- *designing equipment* with a much greater emphasis on reliability and maintainability
- *a major shift in organisational thinking* towards participation, teamworking and flexibility.

A major challenge facing maintenance people nowadays is not only to learn what these techniques are, but to decide which are worthwhile and which are not in their own organisations. If we make the right choices, it is possible to improve asset performance and *at the same time* contain and even reduce the cost of maintenance. If we make the wrong choices, new problems are created while existing problems only get worse.

The challenges facing maintenance

In a nutshell, the key challenges facing modern maintenance managers can be summarised as follows:
- to select the most appropriate techniques
- to deal with each type of failure process
- in order to fulfil all the expectations of the owners of the assets, the users of the assets and of society as a whole
- in the most cost-effective and enduring fashion
- with the active support and co-operation of all the people involved.

RCM provides a framework which enables users to respond to these challenges, quickly and simply. It does so because it never loses sight of the fact that maintenance is about physical assets. If these assets did not exist, the maintenance function itself would not exist. So RCM starts with a comprehensive, zero-based review of the maintenance requirements of each asset in its operating context.

All too often, these requirements are taken for granted. This results in the development of organisation structures, the deployment of resources and the implementation of systems on the basis of incomplete or incorrect assumptions about the real needs of the assets. On the other hand, if these requirements are defined correctly in the light of modern thinking, it is possible to achieve quite remarkable step changes in maintenance efficiency and effectiveness.

The rest of this chapter introduces RCM in more detail. It begins by exploring the meaning of "maintenance" itself. It goes on to define RCM and to describe the seven key steps involved in applying this process.

1.2 Maintenance and RCM

From the engineering viewpoint, there are two elements to the management of any physical asset. It must be maintained and from time to time it may also need to be modified.

The major dictionaries define *maintain* as *cause to continue* (Oxford) or *keep in an existing state* (Webster). This suggests that maintenance means preserving something. On the other hand, they agree that to *modify* something means to *change* it in some way. This distinction between maintain and modify has profound implications which are discussed at length in later chapters. However, we focus on maintenance at this point.

When we set out to maintain something, what is it that we wish to *cause to continue?* What is the *existing state* that we wish to preserve?

The answer to these questions can be found in the fact that every physical asset is put into service to fulfil a specific function or functions. So it follows that when we maintain an asset, the state which we wish to preserve must be one in which it continues to fulfil its intended functions.

Maintenance: Ensuring that physical assets
continue to fulfil their intended functions

Clearly, for this to be possible, the equipment must be capable of fulfilling its intended function to start with. This is because maintenance – the process of "causing to continue" – can only deliver the built-in capability (or inherent reliability) of any item. It cannot increase it.

In practice, most equipment *is* fundamentally capable of delivering the desired performance, so in most cases this is not an issue.

However, some assets are simply incapable of delivering the desired performance to start with. In these cases, maintenance on its own will not enable them do so, so the items must either be modified so that they *can* deliver the desired performance, or we must lower our expectations.

(RCM is called *Reliability-centred* Maintenance because it recognises that maintenance can do no more than ensure that physical assets continue to achieve their built in capability or *inherent reliability*.)

The "intended function" of any asset can be defined in a number of ways, depending on exactly where and how it is being used (the operating context). The term "intended function" also implies specific performance expectations. This leads to the following formal definition of Reliability-centred Maintenance:

> ***Reliability-centred Maintenance: a process***
> ***used to determine the maintenance requirements***
> ***of any physical asset in its operating context***

In the light of the earlier definition of maintenance, a fuller definition of RCM could be "a process used to determine *what must be done to ensure that any physical asset continues to fulfil its intended functions* in its present operating context".

1.3 RCM: The seven basic questions

Before setting out to analyse the maintenance requirements of the assets in any organisation, we need to know what these assets are and to decide which of them are to be subjected to the RCM review process. In most cases, this means that a comprehensive plant register must be prepared if one does not exist already, as discussed in Chapter 2.

Thereafter, the RCM process entails asking seven questions about each of the selected assets, as follows:

- *what are the functions and associated performance standards of the asset in its present operating context?*
- *in what ways does it fail to fulfil its functions?*
- *what causes each functional failure?*
- *what happens when each failure occurs?*
- *in what way does each failure matter?*
- *what can be done to prevent each failure?*
- *what should be done if a suitable preventive task cannot be found?*

These questions are introduced briefly in the following paragraphs, and then considered in detail in the remaining chapters of this book.

Functions and Performance Standards

If maintenance means ensuring that assets continue to fulfil their intended functions, then the maintenance objectives for any asset can only be established by defining what these functions are, together with the desired levels of performance.

> *The objectives of maintenance with respect to any asset are defined by the functions of the asset and its associated desired standards of performance*

For this reason, the RCM process starts by defining the *functions* and performance standards of each asset in its operating context. It also places great emphasis on the need to *quantify* performance standards where possible. These standards cover output, product quality, customer service, environmental issues, operating costs and safety.

Done properly, this step alone usually takes up about a third of the time involved in an entire RCM analysis. It also usually causes the team doing the analysis to learn a remarkable amount – often a frightening amount – about how the equipment actually works.

Functional Failures

The objectives of maintenance are defined by the functions and associated performance expectations of the asset under consideration. But how does maintenance achieve these objectives?

If the asset has been adequately designed, the only occurrence which is likely to stop it performing as it should is some kind of failure. This suggests that maintenance achieves its objectives by adopting a suitable approach to the management of failure. However, before we can apply a suitable blend of failure management tools, we need to identify what failures can occur. The RCM process does this at two levels:

• firstly, by asking how the item can fail to fulfil its functions

• then by asking what can cause each possible loss of function.

The ways in which an item can fail to fulfil its intended functions are known as *functional failures*, which are defined as *the inability of an asset to meet a desired standard of performance*. Clearly these can only be identified after the functions and performance standards of the asset have been defined.

Failure Modes

As indicated in the previous paragraph, once each functional failure has been identified, the next step is to try to identify the *failure modes* which are reasonably likely to cause each loss of function. This enables us to understand exactly what we might be seeking to prevent.

When carrying out this step, it is important to identify the cause of each failure in enough detail to ensure that time and effort are not wasted trying to treat symptoms instead of causes. On the other hand, it is equally important to ensure that time is not wasted on the analysis itself by going into too much detail.

Failure Effects

When identifying each failure mode, the *failure effects* are also recorded. These describe what would happen if the failure mode did occur, and cover such issues as downtime, effects on product quality, evidence that the failure has occurred, probable corrective action, and threats to safety or the environment. This step makes it possible to decide how much each failure matters, and so what level of preventive maintenance (if any) is needed.

The process of identifying functions, functional failures, failure modes and failure effects yields surprising and often very exciting opportunities for improving performance and safety, and also for eliminating waste. These first four steps are discussed at greater length in Chapter 3.

Failure Consequences

A detailed analysis of an average industrial undertaking is likely to yield between three and ten thousand possible failure modes. Each of these failures affects the organisation in some way, but in each case, the effects are different. They may affect operations. They may also affect product quality, customer service, safety or the environment. They will all take time and cost money to repair.

It is these consequences which most strongly influence the extent to which we try to prevent each failure. In other words, if a failure has serious consequences, we are likely to go to great lengths to try to prevent it. On the other hand, if it has little or no effect, then we may decide to undertake no preventive action beyond basic cleaning and lubrication routines.

A great strength of RCM is that it recognises that the consequences of failures are far more important than their technical characteristics. In fact, it recognises that the only reason for doing any kind of preventive maintenance is not to prevent failures *per se*, but to avoid or at least to mitigate the *consequences* of failure.

The RCM process not only recognises the importance of failure consequences in maintenance decision-making – it also classifies these consequences into four groups, as follows:

- *Hidden failure consequences:* Hidden failures have no direct impact, but they expose the organisation to other failures with serious, often catastrophic, consequences. (Most of these failures are associated with protective devices which are not fail-safe.) A great strength of RCM is the way it treats hidden failures, firstly by recognising them as such, secondly by according them a high priority and finally by adopting a simple, practical and coherent approach to maintaining them.

- *Safety and environmental consequences:* A failure has safety consequences if it could hurt or kill someone. It has environmental consequences if it could lead to a breach of any corporate, regional or national environmental standard. It is a fundamental principle of RCM that the risk of failures in these two categories should be reduced to a very low level indeed, if not eliminated altogether.

- *Operational consequences:* A failure has operational consequences if it affects production (output, product quality, customer service or operating costs in addition to the direct cost of repair). These consequences cost money, and how much they cost suggests how much needs to be spent on trying to prevent them.

• *Non-operational consequences:* Evident failures which fall into this category affect neither safety nor production, so they involve only the direct cost of repair.

We will see later how the RCM process uses these categories as the basis of a strategic framework for maintenance decision-making. By forcing a structured review of the consequences of each failure mode in terms of the above categories, it integrates the operational, environmental and safety objectives of the maintenance function. This helps to bring safety into the mainstream of engineering management.

Secondly, it focuses attention on the maintenance activities which have most effect on the performance of the organisation, and diverts energy away from those which have little or no effect. This helps to ensure that everything spent on maintenance is spent where it will do the most good.

The consequence evaluation process is discussed again later in this chapter, and in much more detail in Chapter 4.

In essence, this part of the RCM process asks whether each failure has significant consequences. If it does not, the usual default decision is no preventive maintenance. If it does, the next step is to ask what preventive tasks (if any) should be done. However, the task selection process cannot be reviewed meaningfully without first considering failure patterns and their effect on the selection of different methods of prevention.

Preventive Tasks

Many people believe that the best way to optimise plant availability is to do some kind of preventive maintenance on a routine basis. Second Generation wisdom suggests that this preventive action should consist of overhauls or component replacements at fixed intervals.

Figure 1.4 illustrates the fixed interval view of failure. It assumes that most items operate reliably for a period 'X', and then wear out. Classical thinking suggests that extensive records about equipment failure will enable us to determine this life, so that plans can be made to take preventive action shortly before the item is due to fail in future.

Figure 1.4:
The traditional
view of failure

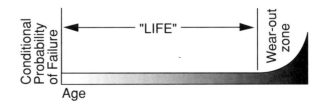

This is true for certain types of simple equipment, and for some complex items with dominant failure modes. In particular, wear-out characteristics are often found where equipment comes into direct contact with the product. Examples include crusher or hopper liners, screw conveyors, machine tooling, pump impellers, furnace refractories and so on. Age-related failures are also often associated with fatigue and corrosion.

However, equipment in general is much more complex than it was even fifteen years ago. This has led to startling changes in the patterns of equipment failure, as shown in Figure 1.5. The graphs show conditional probability of failure against operating age for a wide variety of electrical and mechanical items.

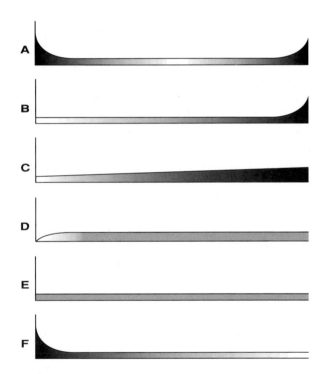

Figure 1.5:
Six patterns
of failure

Pattern A is the well-known bathtub curve. It begins with a high incidence of failure (known as *infant mortality* or *burn-in*) followed by a constant or gradually increasing failure rate, then by a wear-out zone. Pattern B shows constant or slowly increasing failure probability, ending in a wear-out zone (the same pattern as Figure 1.4).

Pattern C shows slowly increasing probability of failure, but there is no identifiable wear-out age. Pattern D shows low failure probability when the item is new or just out of the shop, then a rapid increase to a constant level, while pattern E shows a constant probability of failure at all ages (random failure). Pattern F starts with high infant mortality, which drops eventually to a constant or very slowly increasing failure probability.

Studies done on civil aircraft showed that 4% of the items conform to pattern A, 2% to B, 5% to C, 7% to D, 14% to E and no fewer than *68% to pattern F*. (The number of times these patterns occur in aircraft is not necessarily the same as in industry. But there is no doubt that as equipment grows more complex, we see more and more of patterns E and F. All six patterns are discussed at greater length in Chapters 5 and 9.)

These findings contradict the belief that there is always a connection between reliability and operating age. This belief led to the idea that the more often an item is overhauled, the less likely it is to fail. Nowadays, this is seldom true. Unless there is a dominant age-related failure mode, age limits do little or nothing to improve the reliability of complex items. In fact scheduled overhauls can actually *increase* overall failure rates by introducing infant mortality into otherwise stable systems.

An awareness of these facts has led some organisations to abandon the idea of preventive maintenance altogether. In fact, this can be the right thing to do for failures with minor consequences. But when the failure consequences are significant, *something* must be done to prevent the failures, or at least to reduce the consequences.

This brings us back to the question of preventive tasks. RCM recognises all three major categories of preventive task, as follows:
• scheduled on-condition tasks
• scheduled restoration tasks
• scheduled discard tasks.

On-condition tasks

The continuing need to prevent certain types of failure, and the growing inability of classical techniques to do so, are behind the growth of new types of failure prevention. The majority of these new techniques rely on the fact that most failures give some warning of the fact that they are about to occur. These warnings are known as ***potential failures***, and are defined as *identifiable physical conditions which indicate that a functional failure is about to occur or is in the process of occurring.*

These new techniques are used to detect potential failures so that action can be taken to avoid the consequences which could occur if they degenerate into functional failures. They are called *on-condition* tasks because items are left in service *on the condition* that they continue to meet desired performance standards. (On-condition maintenance includes *predictive maintenance, condition-based maintenance* and *condition monitoring*.)

The amount of warning given by different potential failures varies from microseconds to decades. Longer intervals mean lower inspection frequencies and more time to prevent functional failures (or at least to avoid their consequences), so a great deal of energy is being devoted to developing on-condition techniques which give as much warning as possible of imminent functional failures.

Used appropriately, on-condition tasks are a very good way of anticipating functional failures, but they can also be an expensive waste of time. RCM enables decisions in this area to be made with particular confidence.

Scheduled restoration and scheduled discard tasks

Scheduled restoration entails remanufacturing a component or overhauling an assembly at or before a specified age limit, regardless of its condition at the time. Similarly, scheduled discard entails discarding an item at or before a specified life limit, regardless of its condition at the time.

A great strength of RCM is the way it provides simple, precise and easily understood criteria for deciding which (if any) of the preventive tasks is technically feasible in any context, and if so for deciding how often they should be done and who should do them. These criteria are discussed in more detail in Chapter 5. RCM also ranks the tasks in descending order of desirability.

Default Tasks

Whether or not a preventive task is *technically feasible* is governed by the *technical characteristics* of the task and of the failure which it is meant to prevent. Whether it is *worth doing* is governed by how well it deals with the *consequences* of the failure.

If a preventive task cannot be found which is both technically feasible and worth doing, then suitable default action must be taken. The nature of this action depends on the consequences of the failure, as follows:

- a task meant to prevent the failure of a *hidden function* is worth doing if it reduces the risk of the multiple failure associated with that function to an acceptably low level. If a suitable preventive task cannot be found then a periodic ***failure-finding task*** must be performed. Failure-finding tasks entail checking hidden functions periodically to determine whether they have failed. If such a task cannot be found which reduces the risk of the multiple failure to a low enough level, then the secondary default decision is that the item may have to be redesigned (depending on the consequences of the multiple failure).

- a task meant to prevent a failure which has *safety* or *environmental* consequences is only worth doing if it reduces the risk of that failure on its own to a very low level indeed, if it does not eliminate it altogether. If a task cannot be found which reduces the risk of the failure to an acceptably low level, ***the item must be redesigned or the process must be changed.***

- if the failure has *operational* consequences, a preventive task is only worth doing if the total cost of doing it *over a period of time* is less than the cost of the operational consequences and the cost of repair over the same period. In other words, the task must be *justified on economic grounds.* If it is not justified, the initial default decision is ***no scheduled maintenance***. (If this occurs and the operational consequences are still unacceptable then the secondary default decision is again redesign).

- if a failure has *non-operational* consequences a preventive task is only worth doing if the cost of the task over a period of time is less than the cost of repair over the same period. So these tasks must also be *justified on economic grounds*. If it is not justified, the initial default decision is again ***no scheduled maintenance***, and if the repair costs are too high, the secondary default decision is once again redesign.

This approach means that preventive tasks are only specified for failures which really need them, which in turn leads to substantial reductions in routine workloads. Less routine work also means that the remaining tasks are more likely to be done properly. This together with the elimination of counter-productive tasks leads to more effective maintenance.

Compare this with the traditional approach to the development of maintenance policies. Traditionally, the maintenance requirements of each item are assessed in terms of its real or assumed technical characteristics, without considering the consequences of failure. The resulting schedules are used for all similar assets, again without considering that different consequences apply in different operating contexts. This results in large numbers of schedules which are wasted, not because they are "wrong" in the technical sense, but because they achieve nothing.

Note also that the RCM process considers the maintenance requirements of each item before asking whether it is necessary to reconsider the design. This is simply because the maintenance engineer who is on duty *today* has to maintain the equipment as it exists *today*, not what should be there or what might be there at some stage in the future.

Default tasks are considered at length in Chapter 6, and an integrated approach to consequence evaluation and task selection in Chapter 7.

1.4 Implementing RCM

We have seen how the RCM process embodies seven basic questions. In practice, maintenance people simply cannot answer all these questions on their own. This is because many (if not most) of the answers can only be supplied by production or operations people. This applies especially to questions concerning functions, desired performance, failure effects and failure consequences.

For this reason, a review of the maintenance requirements of any asset should be done by small teams which include *at least* one person from the maintenance function and one from the operations function. The seniority of the group members is less important than the fact that they should have a thorough knowledge of the asset under review. Each group member should also have been trained in RCM.

The make-up of a typical RCM review group is shown in Figure 1.6:

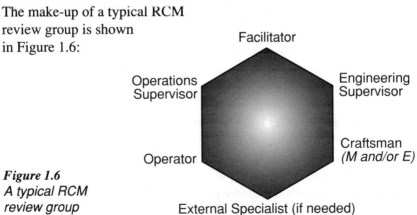

Facilitator

Operations Supervisor

Engineering Supervisor

Craftsman (M and/or E)

Operator

External Specialist (if needed) (Technical or Process)

Figure 1.6
A typical RCM review group

The use of these groups not only enables management to gain access to the knowledge and expertise of each member of the group on a systematic basis, but the group members themselves gain a greatly enhanced understanding of the asset in its operating context.

Facilitators

RCM review groups work under the guidance of highly trained specialists in RCM, known as facilitators. The facilitators are the most important people in the RCM review process. Their role is to ensure that:

- RCM is applied correctly *(in other words, that the questions are asked correctly in the right sequence, and are correctly understood by each group member)*

- the group members (especially operations and maintenance people) achieve reasonable consensus about the answers to the questions

- no significant equipment or component is overlooked

- the review meetings progress reasonably quickly

- all the RCM documents are completed correctly.

Auditors

Immediately after the review has been completed for each major piece of equipment, the senior managers with overall responsibility for the equipment need to satisfy themselves that the review has been done correctly and that they agree with the assessment of failure consequences and the selection of tasks. These managers do not have to do the audits themselves, but may delegate them to anyone in whose judgement they have sufficient confidence.

1.5 What RCM Achieves

The outcomes of an RCM analysis

If it is implemented in the manner suggested above, an RCM review yields four principal outcomes, as follows:

- greatly ***enhanced understanding of how the asset works***, together with a clear understanding of what it can and cannot achieve

- *a better understanding of how the asset can fail* together with *the root causes of each failure.* This means that maintenance energy is correctly focused on trying to solve the right problems. Not only does this help to prevent failures which occur of their own accord, but it also leads people to stop doing things which cause failures.

- lists of *proposed tasks* designed to ensure that the asset continues to operate at the desired level of performance. These take three forms:
  - maintenance schedules to be done by the maintenance department
  - revised operating procedures for the operators of the asset
  - a list of areas where changes (usually design changes) must be made to deal with situations where maintenance cannot help the asset to deliver the desired performance in its current configuration.

- greatly improved *teamworking*.

How RCM benefits organisations which use it

Desirable as they are, these outcomes should only be seen as a means to an end. Specifically, they should enable the maintenance function to fulfil all the expectations listed in Figure 1.1 at the beginning of this chapter. How they do so is summarised in the following paragraphs, and discussed again in more detail in Chapter 11.

- *Greater safety* and *environmental protection:* RCM considers the safety and environmental implications of every failure mode before considering its effect on operations. This means that steps are taken to minimise all identifiable equipment-related safety and environmental hazards, if not eliminate them altogether. By integrating safety into the mainstream of maintenance decision-making, RCM also improves attitudes to safety.

- *Improved operating performance (output, product quality and customer service):* RCM recognises that *all* types of maintenance have some value, and provides rules for deciding which is most suitable in every situation. By doing so, it helps to ensure that only the most effective forms of maintenance are chosen for each machine, and that suitable action is taken in cases where maintenance cannot help. This much more tightly focused maintenance effort leads to quantum jumps in the performance of *existing assets* where these are sought.

RCM was developed to help airlines draw up maintenance programmes for new types of aircraft *before* they enter service. As a result, it is an ideal way to develop such programmes for *new assets*, especially complex equipment for which little historical information is available. This saves much of the trial and error which is so often part of the development of new maintenance programmes – trial which is frustrating and time-consuming and error which can be very costly.

- *Greater maintenance cost-effectiveness:* RCM continually focuses attention on the maintenance activities which have most effect on the performance of the plant. This helps to ensure that everything spent on maintenance is spent where it will do the most good.

  In addition, if RCM is correctly applied to existing maintenance systems, it reduces the amount of *routine* work (in other words, proactive maintenance tasks undertaken on a *cyclic* basis) issued in each period, usually by 40% to 70%. On the other hand, if RCM is used to develop a new maintenance system, the resulting scheduled workload is much lower than it would be if the system was developed by traditional methods.

- *Longer useful life of expensive items,* due to a carefully focused emphasis on the use of on-condition maintenance techniques.

- A *comprehensive maintenance database:* An RCM review ends with a comprehensive, reliable and fully documented record of the maintenance requirements of all the significant assets used by the organisation. This makes it possible *to adapt to changing circumstances* (such as changing shift patterns or new technology) without having to reconsider all maintenance policies from scratch. It also *reduces the effects of staff turnover* with its attendant loss of experience and expertise.

  An RCM review of the maintenance requirements of each asset also provides a much clearer view of the *skills required to maintain each asset*, and for deciding *what spares should be held in stock*. A valuable by-product is also *improved drawings and manuals.*

- *Greater motivation of individuals,* especially people who are involved in the review process. This leads to greatly improved general understanding of the equipment in its operating context, together with wider "ownership" of maintenance problems and their solutions. It also means that solutions are more likely to endure.

- ***Better teamwork:*** RCM provides a common, easily understood technical language for everyone who has anything to do with maintenance.
  This gives maintenance and operations people a better understanding
  of what maintenance can (and cannot) achieve and what must be done
  to achieve it.

All of these issues are part of the mainstream of maintenance management, and many are already the target of improvement programmes. The
point about RCM is that it provides an effective step-by-step framework
for tackling *all* of them at once, and for involving everyone who has
anything to do with the equipment in the process.

   If it is applied correctly, RCM yields results very quickly. In fact, most
organisations can complete an RCM review in less than a year using their
existing staff. The review leads to a transformation in both the perceived
maintenance requirements of the physical assets used by the organisation
and in the way the maintenance function as a whole is perceived. The result is more effective, more harmonious and much cheaper maintenance.

2   The Plant Register

Most organisations own, or at least use, hundreds if not thousands of physical assets. The assets range in size from small pumps to steel rolling mills, aircraft carriers or office blocks. They may be concentrated on one small site, or spread over thousands of square kilometres. The assets could all be mobile, or they could all be fixed - in most cases, they will be a combination of the two.

The number and variety of items means that we need to draw up a comprehensive list of these assets and develop suitable numbering systems before attempting to assess maintenance requirements. This list forms the basis of management information systems used to report asset performance and maintenance costs. The list is known as the *plant register* or *plant inventory*. This chapter answers the following questions:
• what is the plant register?
• what is a "machine"?
• how should assets be numbered?
• what information should be recorded?
• how should the register be prepared?

2.1 What is the Plant Register?

The plant register is a list of all the plant, equipment and buildings owned or used by the organisation, and which require maintenance of any sort (even if some of the maintenance is sub-contracted).

The register should include all these items. Later chapters reveal how different levels of importance (or *criticality*) are attached to different items when their routine maintenance requirements are assessed. Although some items may be scheduled for no *routine* attention, every item is likely to need some kind of engineering attention during its life. As a result, every item should be listed and the register compiled accordingly.

There is a temptation to use any reasonably comprehensive-looking list as a basis for the plant register. The two which are often used in this way are the asset register kept by the accountants, and the plant list used by the contractors when the plant was built. In most cases, these lists should be approached with caution, because:

- their numbering systems are seldom suitable for maintenance management purposes
- they list items which do not concern maintenance
- they are often out of date, which means that large numbers of key items are often missing
- they are prepared by people whose objectives are different from those of the maintenance function, so equipment descriptions and groupings are often unsuitable.

So if a good one does not exist already, a special register should be prepared, together with a suitable numbering system. This comprehensive new register can be used to correct or modify other plant lists. (In fact, many maintenance departments nowadays look after the *content* of the asset register, while the accountants manage financial aspects such as depreciation. As a result, the asset register and the plant register contain the same information, with obvious benefits to the organisation.)

Finally, the plant register must be kept up to date. It is the foundation of all other maintenance systems, so if it is out of date, the other systems are out of date. The records department must always be advised of *all* new installations, plant movements, modifications and replacements and they must revise the plant register accordingly.

2.2 What is a "Machine"?

An issue which needs to be approached with care when compiling plant registers is deciding what constitutes a "machine". For instance in a plant such as a paper mill or an oil refinery, or on a naval vessel such as a nuclear submarine, most of the equipment is interconnected in some way. The plant or vessel in its entirety could be regarded as a "machine". But in each case one could also regard a single pump or turbine as a "machine".

On the other hand in a typical engineering works, lathes, shapers, drill presses and other items of equipment are seldom interconnected. The same applies to vehicles. In these cases, defining a "machine" is simple, and so the plant register can be kept correspondingly simple.

Machine definition is important because it is difficult to analyse failure possibilities and failure consequences if the "machine" concerned is too large or too complex, or if it has been subdivided illogically. The levels at which RCM analyses should be carried out are discussed in more detail in Chapter 4, but decisions in this area are much easier to make if the plant register is divided into sensible units. In most cases, this requires a structured (or *hierarchical*) approach to asset definition.

In practice, such a structure is not only essential for the preparation of maintenance schedules. It simplifies many other aspects of maintenance management, such as planning routine and non-routine work, costing and preparing management information.

The structure of the plant register depends mainly on the degree of interdependence between different assets, which in turn is closely related to the functions of the equipment. Other factors which affect it are:

- *the size of the register*: if the register consists of very few items (not more than one or two hundred), a simple structure and numbering system will suffice

- *physical area:* if the plant is very small (say less than 2500 sq m), the structure can again be kept very simple

- *the mix between static, moveable and mobile items:* for fixed plant, location usually plays a part in the structure of the register. For moveable or mobile items, function becomes more important.

It is possible to develop very complex hierarchies indeed. For instance, a large fighting ship might start with the category *vessel* which could be divided into *system* and *sub-systems* then (say) *assemblies, sub-assemblies, units* and *items*. However, most companies usually find that a two or three level hierarchy is enough.

Cost Centres, Units, Items and Components

Before considering how to develop an equipment hierarchy, it is important to define five terms which are used in this chapter. They are *cost centre, unit, item, component* and *spare*. (Any terms can be used in practice. The key is to be absolutely consistent in how they are applied.)

- *Cost Centre:* Cost centres can be defined as follows:
  "A location, person or item of equipment (or group of these), in relation to which costs may be ascertained. A cost centre may be:

* *impersonal:* a geographic location or type of equipment (or group of these)
* *personal:* a person or a group of people
* *operation:* machines and/or people which perform the same operation
* *process:* a continuous sequence of operations."

The *impersonal*, *operation* and *process* cost centre definitions refer to machines which are connected in some way. Most factories and mines are divided into production cost centres on this basis, and each cost centre usually represents a single production department. The associated numbers or codes are usually well publicised, and well understood by all employees. For these reasons, cost centre numbers are usually an ideal starting point for a plant numbering system.

* *Unit:* A unit is a collection of plant items which are interdependent upon and adjacent to each other. A key characteristic of a unit is that most of its items are mechanically or electrically interconnected, and the failure of any one of these items will directly affect the mechanical or electrical performance (or performance potential) of the unit as a whole.

* *Item:* An item is a distinct part of a unit, and is usually the smallest discrete piece of equipment that is considered from an operational point of view. For instance, a pump referred to as an item means everything which is normally found on the baseplate of the pump.

* *Component:* A component is a distinct and usually replaceable part of an item. Individual gearboxes, motors, couplings and pumps are classified as components, unless they are unusually large or complex.

* *Spare:* a spare is what the name implies - a spare part in the universally accepted sense.

Having defined the main terms which are used to describe plant groupings and individual pieces of equipment, we can now establish a plant register structure. The first example shows a three level hierarchy, and the second a two level hierarchy.

A Three level Structure

A three level structure is used for large or complex registers. The plant is divided into cost centres, units and items.

For example, consider a boiler house attached to a small factory. It contains four small boilers, a coal handling plant and other equipment. The whole steam raising facility would almost certainly be regarded as a separate cost centre so this register could be structured as shown in Figure 2.1.

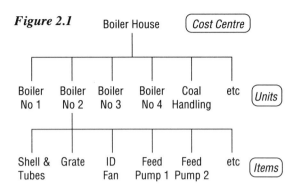

Figure 2.1

A Two level Structure

A two level structure can be used for smaller and simpler registers. The plant is divided into cost centres and items, without using units.

Consider the engineering works mentioned earlier. It might only consist of three production cost centres - a machine shop, a press shop and an assembly area. The machine shop contains (say) a milling machine,

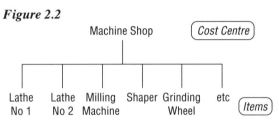

Figure 2.2

two lathes, a shaper, a grinding wheel and a drill press. Each machine would be regarded as an item, and the register structured as shown in Figure 2.2.

2.3 How should Assets be Numbered?

The most important factor affecting the development of an asset numbering system is the structure of the register. In fact, structure and numbering are inseparable. For the two and three level hierarchies described above, numbering is a simple matter. We will consider how this is done, and then review other issues affecting asset numbering.

Numbering a Three level Plant Register

For a three level plant hierarchy, the plant number contains three sets of digits. The first set is the cost centre number, the second is the unit number and the third is the item number.

For example, assume that the boiler house in Figure 2.1 has been given cost centre number (*cost code*) 256. The units associated with the boiler house might be numbered as follows:
256-01 Boiler No 1
256-02 Boiler No 2
256-03 Boiler No 3
256-04 Boiler No 4
256-05 Coal Handling Plant
256-06 Steam Mains
256-07 Boiler House Building etc.

The items associated with Boiler No 3 might be numbered as follows:
256-03-01 Shell and Tubes
256-03-02 Chain Grate Stoker
256-03-03 Feed Pump No 1
256-03-04 Feed Pump No 2
256-03-05 F D Fan
256-03-06 Rear Sootblowers etc

(If your present cost centre numbering system uses a different number of digits, the first set of digits in the plant number will vary accordingly.)

The boiler used in this example is small enough to be regarded as a unit. In other plants, the boilers might be so big that they should be treated as separate cost centres. This might for instance apply to a coal-fired boiler driving a 660 MW turbo-generator set in a power station. In this case, all the sootblowers might be regarded as one unit, and each sootblower given a separate item number.

Numbering a Two level Plant Register

For a two level hierarchy, the plant number will consist of two sets of digits. The first is the cost centre number, and the second the item number.
Taking the engineering works in Figure 2.2 as an example, the machine shop might have cost code MS. Individual items could be numbered as follows:
MS-01 Lathe No 1
MS-02 Lathe No 2
MS-03 Milling Machine
MS-04 Shaper
MS-05 Grinding Wheel etc

As this book progresses, the advantages of multi-level plant numbering systems will become increasingly apparent. However, let us now consider other plant numbering systems used in practice, their advantages and disadvantages, and some of the other issues affecting this subject.

Serial Numbering

A surprising number of organisations start at the beginning of the plant or process, give the first machine the number 1, the second machine the number 2, and so on through the plant. This type of serial numbering appears to be very simple. However, its main drawback is that it does not allow for additions to the register (which are likely to occur in the middle of the plant). As a result, the numbers allocated to additions have to be given all kinds of prefixes and suffixes. Such registers eventually become very difficult to understand and to use.

Other problems of serial numbering are that it does not distinguish between units and items, and it does not permit sensible machine groupings. This is why serial numbering should only be used for very small, simple registers.

Item vs Component Numbers

Component numbering is one of the most controversial aspects of plant numbering. As we have seen, hierarchical systems focus on units and items. However, many people believe that components should also be numbered. Some registers are even based solely on component numbers.

In essence, component numbering means that each component is given its own number which remains with it throughout its life. This number does not change if the component moves to a different location

For example, where a pump is driven by a motor through a gearbox, the pump is given a number, the motor another number and the gearbox yet another number. The component numbers are fixed directly to the components, so if a pump fails, it is replaced by a pump with a different number. This is shown in Fig 2.3. (Note that this entire assembly is seen as one item in a hierarchical numbering system.)

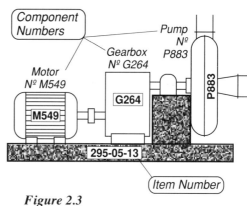

Figure 2.3

The biggest problem associated with component numbering is keeping track of components as they move from one location to another. This is not a problem from a systems design point of view. In practice, however, it is exceptionally difficult to ensure that the records department is always informed every time a component is removed and replaced, or moved from one location to another. It only requires a few cases of forgetfulness (which usually occur under emergency conditions in the middle of the night) for the component register to become hopelessly confused and out of date. Remember too that when a "remove and replace" situation arises, not one but two components are affected, so the problem is doubled.

For this reason alone, it is unwise to develop a register based solely on component numbering. However a case can sometimes be made for keeping a component register *in addition to* a unit/item register. This is often done for electric motors, but even here thought is needed.

Most plants possess a large number of electric motors, and many of them are identical. This leads to the belief that a formal system should be developed to keep track of each motor, so that "if the motor on a critical piece of equipment fails suddenly, we can find a replacement quickly". In practice, nearly all electrical supervisors keep a full set of records on the size, type and location of all the motors under their control, and their electricians usually have unlimited access to these records. This is often a "little black book" system which is handed down from one supervisor to the next, and is usually completely effective. If the electricians in your plant keep such records and their informal system works, it is a waste of time to create a parallel formal system which the electricians will probably ignore anyway. On the other hand, if motors are a problem, something must be done about it.

In general it is only worth keeping a separate formal component register under the following conditions:

- the components are subject to reworking (such as rewinding in the case of motors, or retreading in the case of tyres). If they are not subject to reworking, they are really spares and should be treated as such

- the components are sufficiently expensive and/or complex and/or critical to make it worth developing special systems to track them

- a large number of identical components are in use in different places at any one time

- there is more than one source of supply for each component

- the components have much shorter lives than the items of which they form part

- no effective informal tracking system is in operation already

- you are sure that all component movements *will* be reported quickly and accurately to the records office.

These conditions mean that it is seldom worth developing a component register, especially for fixed plant.

Vehicle Numbering

In terms of our earlier definitions, most vehicles are items. As a result the problem is not one of machine definition or register structure, but simply a matter of selecting the most appropriate numbering system. The two key issues are the size of the vehicle fleet, and whether the fleet is associated with or part of a larger register. This means that there are many different ways of numbering vehicles, and some alternatives are discussed below:

- for a small independent fleet, serial numbering is usually adequate. The numbers issued by the vehicle registering authorities may even be sufficient (provided that they do not change).

- for a large independent fleet, a two level structure can be used. The register is based on operation-type cost centres, with different cost centre numbers for (say) light passenger vehicles, light delivery vehicles, bulldozers, heavy trucks, and so on. Each vehicle has an item number attached to its cost centre number.

- when vehicles are used by a factory or mine, the entire fleet is often covered by one or two "transport" cost codes. Here a three level hierarchy can be used. The first set of digits is the cost code, the second set classifies vehicle types and the third identifies each vehicle. (If a three level hierarchy is used for the rest of the register, it should also be used for vehicles for consistency.)

There is a strong case for keeping records of vehicle components, especially engines, transmissions and tyres. This is because they meet nearly all the general requirements for a component recording system. In particular, there is usually a wide variety of sources for each component, so it is possible to compare the performance of many different makes.

These factors make it worthwhile to seek small savings on any one component, because they quickly multiply into major savings across a large fleet.

Function Codes

There is often a temptation to insert a code which indicates the equipment function into the item number. For example, a pump installation might qualify for the item number 256-03-04 in a three level hierarchy. Instead it is given the number 256-03-P-04 in order to show that it is a pump. Similarly one might use "F" for fan, "C" for compressor, "H" for hoist and so on. These codes are seldom necessary, for three reasons:

- whenever the item number occurs in a recording system or report, it is nearly always followed by a verbal description. This makes a function code superfluous.

- as far as the physical item itself is concerned, one can *see* what it is (with very few exceptions), so a function code is again superfluous.

- no matter how comprehensive the function coding system, some items always either fall outside the coding system, or serve a dual purpose. This calls for compromises which complicate the system further, and eventually make nonsense of the whole idea of function codes.

One reason given for using function codes is that they facilitate the analysis and interpretation of technical history records. This is discussed further in Chapter 9.

Generally function codes in *item* numbers achieve little, so they should be avoided. On the other hand, it sometimes makes sense to preface *component* numbers with function codes.

Composite Codes

It is surprising how often numbering systems are used which carry too much information. For instance, systems have been used which show machine location, function, category of work, trade or craft doing the work, unit and item. Such a number might look like this:

256-P-07-F-04-03

256 might show the location, *P* the function as discussed above, *07* might be a code representing (say) a breakdown, *F* the fact that a plant fitter did the job and *04* and *03* a unit and item in the conventional sense.

Numbers like this should be avoided because they are very difficult to use in practice. (In fact, the number shown is not really a plant number at all, but a mixture of plant numbers and cost categories.)

The acid test which this type of number fails is that it cannot be displayed on the machine. This is because some of the codes change according to the type of work and who is doing it. As a general rule, if a number cannot be attached physically to an asset because part of it is variable, then the coding system should be changed to eliminate the variable portion.

This does *not* mean that we ignore the category of work done and who does it. This information can be captured in other ways. It *does* mean that the relevant codes should not appear in the plant numbers.

Physical Numbering

Once the numbering system has been designed, the number allocated to each item should appear directly on or next to the asset itself. This removes any doubt about which number belongs to which asset, and so simplifies maintenance organisation and control. It also removes the most common excuse for not recording these numbers on maintenance documents. The following methods can be used to number machines:

- *painting:* Painting numbers onto machines is quick and cheap. However it is not very effective, because painted numbers are soon painted over or rubbed off.

- *punching onto casing:* This is also quick and cheap, but the numbers are difficult to read, and they often disappear under many coats of paint.

- *fixing tags:* Tags fall off very easily, so they should only be regarded as temporary if they are used at all.

- *"writing" with welding rods:* Welding affects the structural integrity of certain items, so it should not be used for numbering equipment such as pressure vessels. On the other hand, it is a good technique for large and robust machinery like earthmoving equipment.

- *number plates:* In nearly all cases, the most effective way of numbering is to fix large vehicle-type plastic or metal number plates with raised lettering onto or next to the item, using screws, rivets or epoxy paint. Unfortunately this technique is also the most expensive.

If the numbering system is designed carefully enough and the numbers displayed clearly enough, operations people often become interested in using the numbers for their own purposes. They sometimes even ask for number plates which carry both the number *and* the name of the item (all in large raised lettering) to help train staff, especially in process plants.

2.4 What Information should be Recorded?

Every item in the plant register has a great deal of "fixed" information associated with it. This information defines what the machine is and what it does. It changes seldom or never during the life of the machine, unless the machine is modified. We refer to this information as *plant data*, and it includes the following:

- an *item number*, as described earlier
- a *description* of what the item is and what it does
- *manufacturer's details,* such as brand name, model, model number and serial number
- *local supplier and/or agent,* including addresses and phone numbers
- *technical details,* such as rated speeds, rated power, capacities, frame sizes, mass, etc.
- purchase *price and date*
- *manuals and drawings,* especially operating manuals, spares lists and technical manuals.

(Note that plant data as defined above has nothing to do with technical history, which records maintenance and other work done on a machine throughout its life. Technical history is discussed in Chapter 9.)

This plant data often turns out to be one of the costliest distractions in the whole field of maintenance management. This is because it seems to be sensible to gather all the data about each item from the outset. An appropriate manual or computerised recording system is acquired, and the apparently simple task of gathering the information commenced with great enthusiasm.

The problem is that collecting all this information can take an average of one man day *per item*. In older plants, it can take considerably longer. For a plant consisting of 2000 items, this means that it can take ten man years or more to collect all the data. If it is given a high priority, the development of the rest of the maintenance management system can be paralysed sometimes for years, while planning staff hunt for all the details about each plant item.

Sadly, this happens all too often in practice.

Remember that this information is basically passive. Having it on record does not improve maintenance performance directly. It is held in the belief that it might be useful at some (unspecified) time in the future.

On the other hand, real improvements in maintenance effectiveness come from properly defined maintenance requirements and careful management of the resources needed to fulfil them. As a result, the formal gathering of fixed plant data should be given a low priority. It should really only be done when the rest of the system has been developed (if anyone feels that it is still necessary).

The whole problem of storing plant data can usually be solved by other means, such as a comprehensive technical library. These libraries contain equipment manuals, handbooks, parts catalogues and drawings, and they are usually controlled by drawing offices, because they are geared to storing large quantities of information (drawings) on a systematic basis. Draughtsmen also spend more time than most in their offices, so they are able to control the library properly. In this way, most of the information which anyone is likely to need can be made available readily, without summarising and recording it in an expensive formal system.

The idea of a technical library is of course based on the assumption that most of the technical literature can still be found. In older plants, this is seldom the case. However, older plants also benefit most quickly from the active aspects of maintenance management. As a result, it is especially in these plants that resources should not be devoted to preparing meticulous fixed records before getting on with the rest of the work.

In new plants, technical literature is usually less of a problem. In fact, many companies make it a condition of contract that they will not make the final payments for new equipment until a comprehensive (usually specified) set of technical literature has been provided. This greatly simplifies the task of setting up a technical library.

It should be clear by now that the most important aspects of a plant register are the numbering systems and the allocation of numbers to each item. Once a master list has been published and the numbers displayed on the machines, the rest can usually wait.

However, it may still be felt that fixed plant data is worth summarising and recording on a formal basis. This can be done manually, or a computer can be used. These alternatives are discussed below.

Manual Recording Systems

A manual data recording system is split into three parts: a *master list,* an *item data file* and (if required) a *component data file.* The relationship between them is illustrated in Figure 2.4.

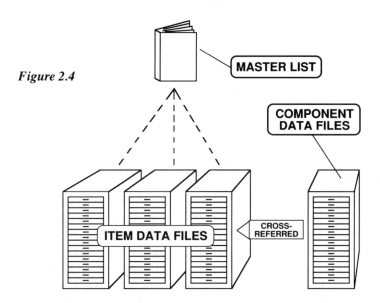

Figure 2.4

The *master list* summarises the entire register. It shows only unit and item numbers with brief descriptions. It is usually prepared in book form, and circulated throughout the organisation. This list is one of the most important documents associated with the maintenance system, so it is worth making it as presentable as possible.

The *item data file* contains separate information sheets for each item. The sheets can be stored in Kardex-type trays, or in loose leaf binders. They can even be printed on stiff board and kept in boxes. A wide range of suitable forms are available from stationery suppliers.

A *component data file* should be established only if you are going to record information about components. This file should always be cross-referred with the item data file (this can be done by indicating the item on which the component is located). Like the item data file, this file contains separate information sheets for each component, and they are stored in similar fashion. Different documents can be designed for different types of components.

Computerised Recording Systems

Fixed plant register data is usually one of the first issues to arise when computers are being considered for planned maintenance systems. In practice, this issue should only be considered *after* it has been decided whether or not this data will be stored at all.

Under no circumstances should the capabilities of computers be allowed to influence this decision. The key issue is not one of system design. It is not a matter of what the computer can or cannot do. The real question is whether the time, effort and money involved in *collecting the data* is justified by the value of having it summarised in a comprehensive recording system. As discussed at length earlier, the answer is almost always no. The same answer should apply to the development of computerised data recording systems.

If the answer is yes, then the question of computerisation does arise legitimately. In practice, it is easy to develop computerised versions of the manual systems described above, especially if the register is logical and sensibly structured. So again it is not a question of whether we *can* develop suitable systems – we can very easily – the question is whether we *need* to. In answering this question, some of the most important considerations are as follows:

- will the register be as *accessible* as it would in a manual system? Access to a manual system is a matter of opening a drawer or book and leafing through a few pages – something which requires no special training, which can be done at any time, and which never necessitates waiting while somebody finishes doing something else. A computerised system can only equal this specification if it is permanently on-line and accessible to the maintenance staff. A computer can only *improve* access via a network of terminals – this requires careful cost-justification (for a data bank whose cost-benefits are doubtful in the first place).

- will it be easy *to change* and *to add information?* Again, the criterion is that it should be at least as easy as with a manual system.

- what is involved in *transferring data* from existing manual recording systems? If you already have comprehensive manual records, do not underestimate the cost and time involved in transferring them to a new system (and the potential for introducing errors). Because these records consist largely of data which changes very little over time, it may make sense to leave existing records on the manual system, and use the new system only for new equipment.

2.5 How should the Plant Register be Compiled?

The only way to compile a truly reliable plant register, or to upgrade an existing one, is by physical observation on site. This should be done as follows:

• draw up a flow chart for each plant section. Indicate the position of each piece of equipment, taking care to include equipment in the workshops, stand-by equipment and equipment on order. Show which items are moveable and which are static, and indicate which are inter-dependent and interchangeable.

• if you are going to use a three level hierarchy, decide how the equipment should be divided into units and items within each cost centre. Take special care over this step, because it defines the structure of the whole register, and ultimately profoundly influences the rest of the maintenance system. If your organisation does not use cost centre numbers suitable for your purposes, then develop your own machine groupings and give them your own codes, or approach your financial people with a view to changing the existing cost centres.

• allocate numbers to specific units and items, taking care to allow for expansion. When this is complete, prepare and distribute the master list, and initiate a physical numbering programme.

• if it is to be included, collect the information for the fixed data records. (This step should usually be left until the rest of the maintenance system has been completed.)

3 Functions and Failures

The first step in a comprehensive review of maintenance requirements is to establish a suitable plant register, as explained in the previous chapter. The next step is to decide which assets are to be reviewed and the levels at which this is to be done. These issues are discussed in more detail in Chapter 10 and Appendix II respectively. Once they have been settled, a team of RCM analysts reviews each asset in its operating context by asking the following questions:

- what are the functions and associated performance standards of the asset in its present operating context?
- in what ways does it fail to fulfil its functions?
- what causes each functional failure?
- what happens when each failure occurs?
- in what way does each failure matter?
- what can be done to prevent each failure?
- what if a suitable preventive task cannot be found?

This chapter considers the first four of these questions. The answers are recorded on an "RCM Information Worksheet", which is shown in Figure 3.1 overleaf.

3.1 Functions and Performance Standards

Chapter 1 explained that when we maintain an asset, the state we wish to preserve is one in which it continues to fulfil its intended *functions*. This means that the maintenance requirements of any item can only be determined if these *functions* are clearly understood. Key issues in this area are discussed below under the following headings:
- different types of functions
- performance standards
- functions and the operating context
- how functions should be recorded.

RCM II INFORMATION WORKSHEET © 1990 ALADON LTD	UNIT or ITEM	5 MW Gas Turbine		Facilitator: N Smith	Date 07 - 07 - 1991	Sheet Nº 1
				Unit or Item Nº 216 - 05		
	ITEM or COMPONENT	Exhaust System		Item or Component Nº 216 - 05 - 11	Auditor: P Jones	Date 07 - 08 - 1991	of 3

FUNCTION	FUNCTIONAL FAILURE (Loss of function)		FAILURE MODE (Cause of failure)		FAILURE EFFECT (What happens when it fails)
1 To provide an unrestricted passage for all the hot turbine gases to an outlet 10m above the roof of the turbine hall	A	Passage totally blocked	1	Silencer collapses	Back pressure causes the turbine to surge violently and shut down on high exhaust temperature. Downtime to replace the silencer up to four weeks
	B	Passage partially blocked	1	Part of silencer falls off	Depending on the nature of the blockage, exhaust temperature rises possibly but not necessarily to the point where it shuts down the turbine. It is also possible that debris could damage parts of the turbine. Downtime to repair the silencer 3 - 4 weeks.
	C	Fails to contain the gas	1	Hole in flexible joint	The flexible joint is located inside the turbine hood, so most of the leaking exhaust gases would be extracted by the hood extraction system. Existing fire and gas detection equipment inside the hood is unlikely to detect an exhaust gas leak, and temperatures are unlikely to rise high enough to trigger the fire wire. A severe leak may cause the gas demister to overheat, and may also melt control wires near the leak with unpredictable effects. Pressure balances inside the hood are such that little or no gas is likely to escape from a small leak, so a small leak is unlikely to be detected by smell or hearing. Downtime to replace the flexible joint up to 3 days
			2	Lower bellows cracked	Gas escapes into the turbine hall and the ambient temperature rises. The turbine hall ventilation system would expel the gases through the louvres to atmosphere, so it is felt that the concentration of exhaust gases is unlikely to reach noxious levels. A small leak at this point may be audible. Downtime to repair up to 4 days
			3	Upper bellows cracked	The upper bellows are outside the turbine hall, so a leak here discharges to atmosphere. Ambient noise levels may rise. Downtime to repair up to 1 week.
	D	Fails to convey gas to a point 10 m above the roof	1	Exhaust stack structure fails	This failure is likely to be caused by corrosion and/or temperature-related stress cycles, which are likely to cause cracks. It is likely that the exhaust stack would start leaning long before it collapsed. Downtime to repair a few days to several weeks.
2 To reduce exhaust noise level to ISO Noise Rating 30 at 150 metres	A	Noise level exceeds ISO Noise Rating 30 at 150 m	1	Silencer material retaining mesh fails	Most of the material would be blown out, but some might fall to the bottom of the stack and obstruct the turbine outlet, with same effects as 1 - B - 1 above. Noise levels would rise gradually. Downtime to repair about 2 weeks.
...etc			2	Ducting leaks outside turbine hall	As for 1 - C - 3 above

Figure 3.1: The RCM Information Worksheet

Different Types of Functions

Every item of equipment usually has more than one – often several – functions. They can be divided into four categories:
• primary functions
• secondary functions
• protective devices
• superfluous functions.
Each of these categories is considered in more detail below.

Primary functions

Every asset is put into service to fulfil a specific function or functions. These are known as its **primary functions**. They are the reason why the asset exists at all, and so are of special interest to anyone who wishes to develop a maintenance programme. As a result, care should be taken to define them as precisely as possible.

The primary function is usually given by the name of the item. For instance, the primary function of a pump is to pump something, of a grinding machine to grind something and so on.

For example, one function of a chemical reactor in a batch-type chemical plant might be listed as:
• To heat up to 500 kg of product X from ambient temperature to boiling point (125°C) in one hour.
The primary function of a conveyor might be listed as:
• To transfer rock from hopper to crusher at a minimum rate of 15 tonnes per hour.

Secondary functions

In addition to its primary functions, nearly every item has a number of secondary functions. They are usually less obvious than the primary functions, but their failure can still have serious consequences – sometimes more serious than the failure of a primary function. This means that the need to preserve these functions can often absorb as much time and effort as primary functions, so they too need to be clearly identified.

For example, the primary function of the braking system on an aircraft is to stop the plane. If we were to leave it at that, then only one functional failure is possible - inability to stop the plane. However, this system is also meant to provide modulated stopping capability, to provide differential braking for manoeuvring on the ground, to provide anti-skid capability and so on. These additional functions mean that the braking system is subject to a large number of different functional failures, each with different consequences.

Typical secondary functions include:

- *containment:* every device whose primary function is to transfer material of any sort (especially fluids) also has to contain the materials. This includes pumps, pipes, conveyors, chutes, hoppers and pneumatic and hydraulic systems. This function should be listed in addition to the primary function, in order to ensure that the associated failures (leaks or spillages) are not overlooked.

- *support:* many items have a structural secondary function. For example, the primary function of the wall of a building might be to protect people and equipment from the weather, but it might also be expected to support the roof (and bear the weight of shelves and pictures).

- *appearance:* the appearance of many items embodies a specific secondary function. For instance, the primary function of the paintwork on most industrial equipment is to protect it from corrosion, but a bright colour might be used to enhance its visibility for safety reasons (especially in the case of mobile equipment). Similarly, the main function of a sign outside a factory is to show the name of the company which occupies the premises, but a secondary function is to project an image.

- *hygiene:* whatever its primary function, a secondary function of most equipment found in the food and pharmaceutical industries is not to contaminate the product. The associated performance standards are usually very tightly specified, and lead to rigorous and comprehensive preventive routines (cleaning and testing).

- *gauges:* fixed gauges are an important group of secondary functions. They indicate variables such as pressure, temperature, speed, flow rate, and fluid levels to within a specified percentage of the actual situation.

It is possible for one item to have as many as twenty secondary functions. In general, the more complex the item, the more functions it will have.

Protective devices

As equipment becomes more complex, the number of ways in which it can fail is growing almost exponentially. This has led to corresponding growth in the variety and severity of failure consequences.

To try to eliminate (or at least to reduce) these consequences, increasing use is being made of automatic protective devices. These work in one of five ways:

- to draw the attention of the operators to abnormal conditions *(warning lights and audible alarms which respond to failure effects. The effects are monitored by a variety of sensors including level switches, load cells, overload or overspeed devices, vibration or proximity sensors, temperature or pressure switches, etc)*
- to shut down the equipment in the event of a failure *(these devices also respond to failure effects, using the same types of sensors and often the same circuits as alarms, but with different settings)*
- to eliminate or relieve abnormal conditions which follow a failure and which might otherwise cause much more serious damage *(fire-fighting equipment, safety valves, rupture discs or bursting discs, emergency medical equipment)*
- to take over from a function which has failed *(stand-by plant of any sort, redundant structural components)*
- to prevent dangerous situations from arising in the first place *(guards).*

In some cases, the purpose of these devices is to protect people from failures, and in others to protect machines – often both. Sometimes their function is evident (so-called fail-safe protective devices), and sometimes it is hidden.

Protective devices ensure that the consequences of the failure of the function being protected are much less serious than they would be if there were no protection. As a result, the presence of a protective device usually means that the maintenance requirements of the protected function are much less stringent than they would be otherwise.

Consider a milling machine whose milling cutter is driven by a toothed belt. If the belt were to break in the absence of any protection, the feed mechanism would drive the stationary cutter into the workpiece (or vice versa) and cause serious secondary damage. This can be avoided in two ways:
- by implementing a comprehensive preventive maintenance routine designed to prevent the failure of the belt
- by providing protection such as a broken belt detector to shut down the machine as soon as the belt breaks. In this case, the only consequence of a broken belt is a brief stoppage while it is replaced, so the most cost-effective maintenance policy might simply be to let the belt fail. But *this policy is only valid if the broken belt detector is working*, and steps must be taken to ensure that this is so.

The maintenance of protective devices – especially devices which are not fail-safe – is discussed in much more detail in Chapters 4 and 6. However, this example demonstrates two fundamental points:

- that protective devices often need more routine maintenance attention than the devices they are protecting
- that we cannot sensibly consider the maintenance requirements of a protected function without considering the maintenance requirements of the protective device.

However, it is only possible to consider the maintenance requirements of protective devices if we understand their functions. So when listing the functions of any item, we must list the functions of all protective devices.

List the functions of all protective devices

A final point about protective devices concerns the way their functions should be described. Most of these devices act by exception (in other words, when something else goes wrong), so it is important to describe them correctly to avoid creating the wrong impression.

For instance, if we were to describe the function of a trip-wire as being "to stop the machine", anyone reading this description could be forgiven for thinking that the tripwire is the normal stop/start device. To remove any ambiguity, the function of a tripwire should be described as follows:
- *to be capable of* stopping the machine in an emergency from any point along its length

(The reference to "any point along its length" specifies the performance standard in this case.)

The function of a safety valve may be described as follows:
- *to be capable of* relieving the pressure in the boiler if it exceeds 250 psi

Polling systems are an increasingly common but somewhat more complex class of protective devices. For reasons which will become apparent later, more care than usual has to be taken when defining their functions.

A typical example is given by three pressure sensors installed in a hydraulic system and designed to respond if the system pressure falls below (say) 500 psi. They may be wired in such a way that if any one of the three sensors detects a pressure below 500 psi, then an alarm annunciates in the control room. If any two sensors detect a pressure below 500 psi, the machine shuts down. The functions of the associated control loops could be described as follows:
- to be capable of annunciating an alarm if any one sensor detects a pressure below 500 psi
- to be capable of shutting down the machine if any two sensors detect a pressure below 500 psi.

The function of the third switch is summarised by the following statement:
- to be capable of sending a shut down signal if one of the three switches is incapable of sending a signal and the pressure drops below 500 psi.

Superfluous Functions

Items or components are sometimes encountered which are completely superfluous. This usually happens when equipment has been modified frequently over a period of years, or when new equipment has been over-specified. (These comments do not apply to redundant components built in for safety reasons, but to items which serve no purpose at all in the context under consideration.)

For example, a steam trap was built into a steam supply line in days when the steam supply was wet. The supply system was later modified to provide clean, dry steam, so the steam trap became superfluous.

Another example is a pressure reducing valve built into the supply line between a gas manifold and a gas turbine. The original function of the valve was to reduce the gas pressure from 120 psi to 80 psi. The system was later modified to reduce the manifold pressure to 80 psi, after which the valve served no useful purpose.

It is sometimes argued that items like these do no harm and it costs money to remove them, so the simplest solution may be to leave them alone until the whole plant is decommissioned. Unfortunately, this is seldom true in practice. Although these items have no positive function, they can still fail and so reduce the overall system reliability. To avoid this, they still need maintenance, which means that they still consume resources.

It is not unusual to find that between 5% and 20% of the components of complex systems are superfluous in the sense described above. If they are eliminated, it stands to reason that the same percentage of maintenance problems and costs will also be eliminated. However, before this can be done with confidence, the functions of these components first need to be identified and clearly understood.

For all these reasons, it is essential to record all the functions of significant equipment, be they primary, secondary, protective or superfluous.

> ### *It is essential to record all the functions of significant equipment*

Performance Standards

Maintenance ensures that physical assets continue to fulfil their intended functions by anticipating, preventing or correcting situations where the assets can no longer fulfil their intended functions – in other words, situations where the equipment has "failed".

Failure is defined later in this chapter as the inability of an item to meet a desired standard of performance. This suggests that the standards used to define failure form the basis of the whole of the rest of the maintenance decision-making process. As a result, performance standards need to be clearly defined and where possible they should be quantified. This issue is complicated by the fact that every function has not one but *two* perform-ance standards associated with it, as explained below.

Inherent Reliability vs Desired Performance

The two performance standards associated with every function are the de-sired performance *(what we want to achieve)* and the inherent reliability or built-in capability of the asset with respect to that function *(what it is capable of achieving)*. With regard to the latter, RCM recognises that

- the inherent reliability of any item is established by its design and by how it is made
- maintenance cannot yield reliabi-lity beyond this inherent level.

This is shown in Figure 3.2.

In other words, if the performance which we want any asset to deliver is within its inherent capabilities, then

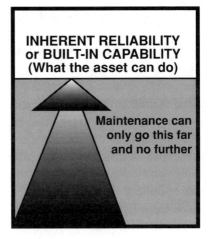

Figure 3.2:
What maintenance can achieve

Figure 3.3:
A maintainable situation

maintenance can help to achieve the desired performance. Most items *are* adequately specified, designed and built, so it is usually possible to develop maintenance programmes which ensure that they continue to deliver the desired performance. In other words, such assets are main-tainable, as shown in Figure 3.3.

On the other hand, if the desired performance exceeds the built-in capability, no amount of maintenance can deliver the desired performance. In other words, in the long term such assets are not maintainable, as illustrated in Figure 3.4.

The distinction between what we want an item to do and what it can do lies at the heart of many disputes between maintenance and production people. For instance, it is surprising how many serious reliability problems occur because desired performance exceeds built-in capability

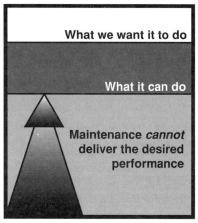

Figure 3.4:
A non-maintainable situation

(especially in the case of problems which affect product quality). Yet it is equally surprising how often production people jump to the conclusion that "there must be something wrong with the way we are maintaining it", while maintenance accuses operations of "flogging it to death".

This happens because operations people tend to think in terms of what they want out of each asset, while maintenance people tend to concentrate on what it can do. Neither of them are "wrong" – they are simply considering the question from two different points of view.

For instance, if an electric motor is too small for the job we want it to do, it will keep tripping out and will eventually burn out prematurely. No amount of maintenance will make this motor big enough. It may be perfectly adequately designed and built in its own right - it simply cannot deliver the desired performance in this context.

In these cases, implementing "better" maintenance procedures does little or nothing to solve the problem. In fact, maintaining a machine which cannot deliver the desired performance has been likened to rearranging the deck chairs on the *Titanic*. Clearly, in such cases we need to look beyond maintenance for solutions. The two main options are to modify the asset to improve its inherent reliability, or to lower our expectations and operate the machine within its capabilities.

(Note that this incapability problem seldom affects an entire asset. It often affects just one or two functions of one or two components – or even a single failure mode – but these weak links interfere with the operation of the whole chain. The process described in the rest of this book helps to identify such weak links quickly and accurately.)

Which performance standard should be listed

The fact that every function has two performance standards associated with it raises the next question: Which one should be listed when describing the function?

The answer can be found by returning to the fact that every asset is put into service to fulfil a specific function or functions - in other words, because somebody wanted it to do something. So from the viewpoint of the organisation as a whole, the *desired performance* is the starting point, because it is why the asset was acquired in the first place. In other words, specify *what we want the item to achieve* in its present operating context when listing functions and performance standards.

For example, the operators of the pump in Figure 3.5 would expect it to fill tank Y faster than water is being withdrawn from the tank. So although it can pump 1000 litres per minute, its function and the associated *desired performance* standard would be listed as follows:

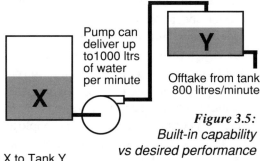

Pump can deliver up to 1000 ltrs of water per minute

Offtake from tank 800 litres/minute

Figure 3.5:
Built-in capability
vs desired performance

• to transfer water from Tank X to Tank Y at not less than 800 litres per minute.

List the desired performance (what we want the asset to achieve) when recording functions and performance standards

Other performance standards

The performance standards in the examples given so far focus on output. Other standards include *product quality, safety, energy efficiency* and the *environment*. Two of these are discussed in more detail below.

Product Quality: Greater automation means that our ability to *achieve* satisfactory product quality standards depends increasingly on the capability of the machines which produce the goods. Similarly, our ability to *sustain* high standards depends on the condition of the machines. As a result, asset performance standards must include product quality criteria where appropriate. These include *purity standards* for food, chemicals, pharmaceuticals, etc, *dimensions* for machining, filling *levels* or *weights* for packaging, *hardness* in the case of heat treatment, and so on.

For instance the main function of a milling station on a transfer machine might be
• To mill the workpiece in a cycle time of 2.25 ±0.03 minutes to a depth of 11.8 ±0.1 mm with a flatness tolerance of 0.1 and a surface finish of Ra 5.0√0.8mm.

The primary function of a sweet-packing machine might be listed as follows:
• To pack 250±1 gm of sweets into bags at a minimum rate of 75 bags per minute.

The Environment: All over the world, more and more incidents which seriously affect the environment occur because some item of equipment did not behave as it should – in other words, because something failed. At the same time, environmental standards are being steadily tightened, and the penalties for breaching them are becoming very harsh indeed.

This means that anyone involved in developing a maintenance programme for any item should find out exactly how that item might affect the environment if it fails. This in turn requires a detailed understanding of relevant corporate, municipal, regional and national environmental standards. Most of these standards will apply to the release of chemicals or particles, but some concern phenomena such as noise, light or heat.

For instance, one function of an effluent treatment plant might be listed as follows:
• To discharge not more than 200 gm per year of chemical X in waste water at a concentration not exceeding one part per million.

Functions and The Operating Context

RCM is defined as "a technique used to determine the maintenance requirements of any physical asset *in its operating context*". As this book progresses, we see how this context affects every aspect of maintenance policy-making, from the definition of functions to the selection of preventive tasks. However, perhaps the most important is the relationship between *functions* and the operating context.

For example, consider a truck which is normally used on a trip from Startsville to Endburg and back. Before the functions and the associated performance expectations of this vehicle can be defined, we need a thorough understanding of its operating context.

For instance, how far is Startsville from Endburg? Over what sort of road and what sort of terrain? What will be the "typical worst case" weather and traffic conditions on this route? What load will the truck normally be expected to carry? Are there any other ways of getting the load from Startsville to Endburg? What speed limits and fuel facilities are there along the way?

The answers to these questions might lead us to define the primary function of this vehicle as follows: *" To transport up to 40 tonnes at speeds of up to 75 mph (average 60 mph) from Startsville to Endburg on one tank of fuel."*

The context would also help to define its other functions and desired standards of performance, such as acceleration, braking, comfort, lighting and so on.

The importance of the operating context is illustrated in a slightly different way by the three identical pumps shown in Figure 3.6. The context of pump A does not include a stand-by, while the context of pump B does include one.

Stand Alone   **Duty**   **Stand-by**

Figure 3.6:
Different operating contexts

This means that the primary function of pump A is to transfer liquid from one point to another *on its own*, and that of pump B to do it *in the presence of a stand-by*. This difference means that the maintenance requirements of these pumps will be different (just how different we see later), even though the pumps are identical. So the presence of redundancy – or alternative means of production – is a feature of the operating context which must be considered in detail when defining the functions of any asset.

Quality standards and standards of customer service are other aspects of the operating context which can lead to differences between the descriptions of the functions of otherwise identical machines.

For example, identical milling stations on two transfer machines might have the same basic function – to mill a workpiece. However, depth of cut, cycle time, flatness tolerance and surface finish specifications can all be different. This could lead to quite different conclusions about their maintenance requirements.

Figure 3.7:
Describing functions

| RCM II INFORMATION WORKSHEET © 1990 ALADON LTD | UNIT |
| | ITEM |

FUNCTION	
1	To provide an unrestricted passage for all the hot turbine exhaust gas to a fixed point 10 metres above the roof of the turbine hall
2	To reduce the exhaust noise levels to ISO Noise Rating 30 at 150 metres
3	To ensure that the surface temperature of the ducting inside the turbine hall does not exceed 60°C
4	To transmit a warning signal to the turbine control system if the exhaust gas temperature exceeds 475°C and a shutdown signal if it exceeds 500°C at a point 4 metres from the turbine
5	To allow free movement of the ducting in response to temperature changes

How Functions should be Listed

Functions are listed in the extreme left hand column of the RCM Information Worksheet. Primary functions are listed first, and the functions are numbered numerically, as shown in Figure 3.7. (The functions listed apply to the exhaust system of a five megawatt gas turbine.)

3.2 Functional Failures

The first part of this chapter explained how each item of equipment fulfils a specific function or functions. The next step in the information gathering process is to determine how these functions can be lost. The loss of a function is known as a *functional failure*.

Functional failures are considered in detail in this part of this chapter, starting with a definition of the term "failure". Thereafter, we review the following issues:
- the relationship between performance standards and functional failures
- the implications of the fact that one function can have a number of different functional failures
- the impact of the operating context on the definition of failure
- how functional failures should be listed.

Defining Failure

In days gone by, it was easy to decide whether or not a piece of equipment was functioning. From a maintenance viewpoint, this was usually a go/no go decision - the item was working, or it had broken down. But things have changed as equipment has become more complex.

For example, most people would agree that an automobile engine, a slurry pump or a tyre has failed if it can no longer perform its primary function. But there are times when an item still functions, but not at the intended level. The engine might run powerfully and smoothly, but its fuel consumption is excessive. The pump may pump slurry, but very slowly. The tyre may hold air, but its tread may be worn beyond legally acceptable limits.

Have these items failed? If not, how bad must their condition be before we say that they have failed? To answer these questions, let us begin by defining failure in broad terms as an unsatisfactory condition.

How unsatisfactory it is depends on the failure consequences, which in turn depend on the operating context of the equipment. For example high oil consumption in an aircraft engine may be no problem on a short-range flight, but the same rate of consumption may exhaust the oil on a long-range flight. The failure of a pump might have little effect if a stand-by is present, but may be highly unsatisfactory if there is no stand-by.

So the boundary between satisfactory and unsatisfactory conditions depends on the function of the item in its operating context. As discussed at length in the first part of this chapter, this boundary is specified by a performance standard. As a result, a functional failure is defined as the inability of any physical asset to meet a desired standard of performance.

> *A functional failure is defined as the*
> *inability of any physical asset to meet*
> *a desired standard of performance*

Failures and Performance Standards

The above definition of functional failure covers the complete loss of function. It also covers situations where the performance falls outside acceptable limits.

For example, the primary function of a sweet-packing machine was listed earlier as being "To pack 250±1 gm of sweets into bags at a minimum rate of 75 bags per minute." This machine has failed:
• if it stops altogether
• if it packs more than 251 gm of sweets into any bags
• if it packs less than 249 gm into any bags
• if it packs at a rate of less than 75 bags per minute.

In situations like these, the performance standards and the associated functional failures are fairly easy to define. However, things are not quite so simple if the point where "failure" occurs involves a lot of judgement.

For example, one function of a hydraulic system is to contain oil. How well it should fulfil this function can be subject to widely differing points of view. There are production managers who believe that a hydraulic leak only amounts to a functional failure if it is so bad that the equipment stops working altogether. On the other hand, an engineer or materials manager might suggest that a functional failure has occurred if the leak causes excessive consumption of hydraulic oil over a long period of time. Then again, a safety officer might say that a functional failure has occurred if the leak creates a pool of oil on the floor in which people could slip and fall or which might create a fire hazard. This is illustrated in Figure 3.8.

Figure 3.8:
Different views
about failure

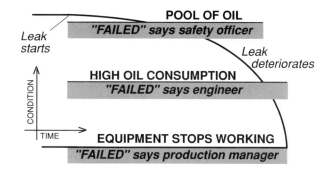

It is beyond the scope of this chapter to suggest who is right. The point to note here is that the performance standard used to define functional failure – in other words, the point where we say "so far and no further" – defines the level of preventive maintenance needed to avoid that failure (in other words, to sustain the required level of performance). In the example given, more intensive maintenance will be needed to avoid high oil consumption than to avoid seizure of the gearbox, while an even higher level will be needed to prevent the pool of oil.

In practice, a great deal of time and energy is saved if the performance standard is agreed before the failure occurs, and if everyone acts on the basis of that standard when it does occur. This is why these standards must be defined clearly for each item of equipment in its operating context, and also why they should be set by (maintenance and design) engineers and operations people working together.

> **Performance standards should be set by operations and engineering people working together**

Different Functional Failures

The above discussion suggests that as any item can have more than one function, so any function can suffer from a number of different functional failures, as explained in the following paragraphs.

Total and partial loss of function

Different functional failures which can apply to a single function include total and partial loss of function. Total loss of function occurs when an item stops working altogether and partial loss when it fails to achieve a specified performance standard.

For example, the primary function of the pump shown in Figure 3.5 is listed as being "to pump water from tank X to Tank Y at not less than 800 litres/minute". This function could suffer from two functional failures, as follows:
• fails to pump any water at all
• pumps water at less than 800 litres per minute.

This shows that partial loss of function occurs when an item operates inefficiently. It also occurs when an item operates outside specific tolerance limits, as for the sweet packing machine or in the example below:

The function of a temperature gauge could be listed as "to display the temperature of process X to within *(say)* 2% of the actual process temperature". This gauge can suffer from three functional failures, as follows:
• fails altogether to display process temperature
• displays a temperature more than 2% higher than the actual temperature
• displays a temperature more than 2% lower than the actual temperature.

Partial loss of function is nearly always caused by different failure modes from total loss, and the consequences are different. This is why *all* the functional failures which could affect each function should be recorded.

Record all the functional failures associated with each function.

Multiple performance standards

Partial loss of function is one reason why a function can have more than one functional failure. Another is that one function can embody several performance standards, and failure to achieve any one of them amounts to a functional failure.

For example, consider the milling station mentioned earlier, whose primary function was defined as follows:
• To mill the workpiece in a cycle time of 2.25 ±0.03 minutes to a depth of 11.8 ±0.1 mm with a flatness tolerance of 0.1 and a surface finish of Ra5.0√0.8mm.
The functional failures associated with this function could be listed as follows:
• Completely unable to mill workpiece
• Mills workpiece in a cycle time longer than 2.28 minutes
• Mills workpiece in a cycle time less than 2.22 minutes
• Cuts deeper than 11.9 mm
• Cuts shallower than 11.7 mm
• Mills out of flatness specification
• Surface finish too rough.

Note that over half of the functional failures in this example deal with the failure of the machine to achieve given quality standards. This underlines the extent to which product quality is becoming a key maintenance issue.

Functional failures and the operating context

In the same way that identical items can have different functions in different situations, so their functional failures can differ in different situations.

For example, we saw how the pump shown in Figure 3.5 fails if it is completely unable to pump water, and if it pumps less than 800 litres/minute. If the same pump is used to fill a tank from which water is drawn at 900 litres/minute, it fails at the point where the throughput of the pump drops below 900 litres/minute.

For pumps B and C in Figure 3.6, the duty/stand-by relationship means that functional failure is defined somewhat differently. If the system as a whole is considered (in other words, the pair of pumps), three different functional failures could be defined as shown overleaf:

RCM II INFORMATION WORKSHEET © 1990 ALADON LTD		UNIT or ITEM	*5 MW Turbine*
		ITEM or COMPONENT	*Exhaust System*

	FUNCTION		FUNCTIONAL FAILURE
1	To provide an unrestricted passage for all the hot turbine exhaust gas to an outlet 10 metres above the roof of the turbine hall	A	Passage completely blocked
		B	Passage partially blocked
		C	Fails to contain the gas
		D	Fails to convey gas to a point 10 m above the roof
2	To reduce the exhaust noise levels to ISO Noise Rating 30 at 150 metres	A	Noise level exceeds ISO Noise Rating 30 at 150 metres
3	To ensure that the surface temperature of the ducting inside the turbine hall does not exceed 60°C	A	Duct surface temperature exceeds 60°C
4	To transmit a warning signal to the turbine control system if the exhaust gas temperature exceeds 475°C and a shutdown signal if it exceeds 500°C at a point 4 metres from the turbine	A	Incapable of sending warning signal if exhaust temperature exceeds 475°C
		B	Incapable of sending shutdown signal if exhaust temperature exceeds 500°C
5	To allow the ducting to move freely in response to temperature changes	A	Does not allow free movement of ducting

Figure 3.9: Describing functional failures

• Fails altogether to pump *(i.e. both pumps fail)*
• Duty pump fails *(this covers the situation in which the duty pump fails and the stand-by pump takes over)*
• Incapable of providing a pumping capability if the duty pump fails *(this covers failure of the stand-by pump while the duty pump is still working).*

For all three pumps, failure to contain the liquid is also a functional failure, as discussed earlier. The points to note at this stage are that the precise definition of failure for any item depends very much on its operating context, and that identical items can suffer from different functional failures if the operating context is different.

> ***Identical items can suffer from different functional failures if the operating context is different***

How Functional Failures should be Listed

Functional failures are listed in the second column of the RCM Information Worksheet. They are coded alphabetically, as shown in Figure 3.9.

3.3 Failure Modes

We have seen that by defining the functions and desired standards of performance of any asset, we are defining the objectives of maintenance with respect to that asset. We have also seen that defining functional failures enables us to spell out exactly we mean by "failed".

However, the process of anticipating, preventing, detecting or correcting failures is applied to individual *failure modes*. In other words, *we really manage maintenance at the failure mode level*. Why this is so is illustrated in the following example:

The function of the pump in Figure 3.5 is "To transfer water from Tank X to Tank Y at 800 litres/minute". The functional failures and some of the failure modes associated with this function appear on the RCM Information Worksheet shown in Figure 3.10. Figure 3.11 shows that the pump is a single-stage end-suction volute pump sealed by a stuffing box with an independent supply of sealing water.

In this example, we look more closely at the three failure modes which are thought to be likely to affect the impeller only. These are discussed in some detail below and summarised in Figure 3.11:

• *Impeller wear* is likely to be an age-related phenomenon. As shown in Figure 3.11, this means that it is likely to conform to the second of the six failure patterns introduced in Figure 5.5 on Page 12 (Failure Pattern B). So if we know

RCM II INFORMATION WORKSHEET ⓒ 1990 ALADON LTD	UNIT or ITEM *Cooling Water Pumping Systen*	
	ITEM or COMPONENT	

	FUNCTION		FUNCTIONAL FAILURE *(Loss of Function)*		FAILURE MODE *(Cause of Failure)*
1	To transfer water from tank X to tank Y at not less than 800 litres/minute	A	Unable to transfer any water at all	1 2 3 4 5 6	Bearing seizes **Impeller falls off shaft** **Impeller smashed by foreign object** Coupling shears Motor burns out Suction line completely blocked ... etc
		B	Transfers less than 800 litres per minute	1 2	**Impeller worn** Partially blocked suction line ... etc

Figure 3.10: Failure modes of a pump

roughly what the useful life of the impeller is, and if the consequences of the failure are serious enough, then we may decide to *prevent this failure* by changing the impeller just before the end of the useful life.

- *Impeller smashed by foreign object:* The likelihood of a foreign object appearing in the suction line will almost certainly have nothing to do with how long the impeller has been in service. As a result, it stands to reason that this failure mode will occur on a random basis (Pattern E in Figure 1.5). There would also be no warning of the fact that the failure is about to occur. So if the consequences were serious enough, and the failure happened often enough, we would be likely to consider *modifying the system*, perhaps by installing some sort of filter or screen in the suction line.

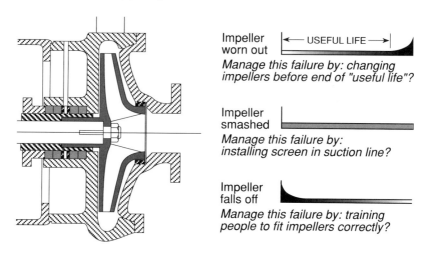

Impeller worn out
|←— USEFUL LIFE —→|
Manage this failure by: changing impellers before end of "useful life"?

Impeller smashed
Manage this failure by: installing screen in suction line?

Impeller falls off
Manage this failure by: training people to fit impellers correctly?

Figure 3.11: Failures of the impeller of a centrifugal pump

- *Impeller falls off:* If the impeller fastening mechanism is adequately designed and it still keeps falling off, this would almost certainly be because it wasn't put on properly in the first place. (If we knew that this was so, then perhaps the failure mode should actually be described as " Impeller incorrectly mounted on shaft".) This in turn means that the failure mode is most likely to occur soon after start up, as shown in Figure 3.11 (Pattern F in Figure 5.5), and we would probably deal with it by improving the relevant *training or procedures.*

These examples illustrate two crucial points:

- the level at which we manage the maintenance of any item is not at the level of the item as a whole (in this case, the pump), and not even at the level of any component (in this case, the impeller), but at the level of each failure mode. So before we can proceed with the development of a system to manage the maintenance of the item, *we need to identify what these failure modes are* (or could be)

- in the example, it was suggested that one of the failure modes could be eliminated by a design change and another by improving training or procedures. So *not every failure mode is dealt with by scheduled maintenance.* Chapters 4 to 6 describe an orderly approach to deciding what *is* likely to be the most suitable way of dealing with each failure.

(Note also that the solutions proposed in Figure 3.11 represent only one of several possibilities in each case.

For instance we could monitor impeller wear by monitoring the pump performance and only change the impeller when it needs it. We also need to bear in mind that adding a screen to the suction line adds three more failure possibilities, which need to be analysed in turn (it could block up, it could be holed and therefore cease to screen, and it could disintegrate and damage the impeller.)

Chapters 5 and 6 in particular examine the implications of these alternatives in more detail).

These points all indicate that the identification of failure modes is one of the most important steps in the development of any programme intended to ensure that any asset continues to fulfil its intended functions. In practice, depending on the complexity of the item and the level at which it is being analysed, between one and thirty failure modes can be listed per functional failure. The rest of this section of this chapter considers some of the key issues in this area, under the following headings:

- root causes
- what failure modes should be listed
- failure modes and the operating context
- how failure modes should be listed.

Root Causes of Failure

If we are serious about preventing failures, we need to identify the *root* causes of each functional failure. In other words, when listing failure modes, we need to identify all the likely reasons why any asset could fail or does fail to reach its desired standard of performance, and not the effects of other failures (except when deliberately "black-boxing" failure modes, as discussed in Appendix II).

For example, one plant had some 200 gearboxes, all of the same design and all performing more or less the same function on the same type of equipment. Initially, the following failure modes were recorded for one of these gearboxes:
• Gearbox bearings seize
• Gear teeth stripped.
These failure modes were listed to begin with because the people carrying out the review recalled that each failure had happened in the past to their knowledge (some of the gearboxes were twenty years old). The failures did not affect safety but they had serious operational consequences. So the implication at this stage was that it might be worth doing preventive tasks like "check gear teeth for wear" or "check gearbox for backlash", and "check gearbox bearings for vibration".

After further discussion, however, it emerged that both failures had occurred because the oil level had not been checked when it should have been, and the gearboxes had actually failed due to lack of oil. What is more, no-one could recall that any of the gearboxes had failed if they had been properly lubricated. As a result, the failure mode was eventually recorded as:
• Gearbox fails due to lack of oil.
This underlined the importance of the obvious preventive task, which was to check the oil level periodically. (This is not to suggest that all gearboxes should be treated in this way. Some are much more complex or much more heavily loaded, and so are subject to a wider variety of failure modes. In other cases, the failure consequences may be much more severe, which would call for a more defensive view of failure possibilities.)

This example indicates that a fair amount of lateral thinking is needed when considering failure modes. In particular, do not fall into the trap of concentrating *only* on failure mechanisms which are commonly regarded as "normal wear and tear" (most of which are ultimately attributable to fatigue, oxidation, corrosion, erosion and wear).

Other important categories of root causes are summarised in the following paragraphs. Many of them are failures caused by people, which means that they should be treated with some sensitivity as explained later. However, where they occur, they should still be listed so that the right preventive or corrective action can be taken, and time and energy are not wasted trying to "solve" the wrong problem.

Dirt

Dirt or dust is a very common cause of failure. It interferes directly with machines by causing them to block, stick or jam. It is also a principal cause of the failure of functions which deal with the appearance of the asset (things which should look clean look dirty). Dirt can also cause product quality problems, either by getting into the clamping mechanisms of machine tools and causing misalignment, or by getting directly into products such as food, pharmaceuticals or the oilways of engines. As a result, this failure mode in particular should be identified whenever it is likely to interfere with a significant function of the asset.

Inadequate lubrication

Lubrication is associated with two types of failure modes. The first is seizure or excessive wear caused by lack of lubrication, as discussed in the above example. The second concerns failure of the lubricant itself, due to shearing of the oil molecules, oxidation, and additive depletion.

As explained in Chapter 6, it is not necessary to use RCM to develop lubrication routines for simple total loss lubrication systems, but it is worth using this process to review the failure modes which can affect totally enclosed or centralised lubrication systems.

Disassembly (or misassembly)

If whole machines come adrift, assemblies fall apart or components fall off, the consequences are usually very serious so the relevant failure modes should be listed. These are usually the failure of welds or rivets due to cracking or corrosion, or threaded components which come undone (such as bolts or pipefittings).

Also take care to record the functions and associated failure modes of locking mechanisms such as split pins and lock nuts when considering the integrity of assemblies.

Incorrect set-up or operation

Many functional failures are caused when machines are operated incorrectly. Typical failure modes include operating at the wrong speed or in the wrong sequence, using the wrong tools or materials, starting up or shutting down too quickly, ramming fixed plant with mobile equipment and using emergency stopping devices inappropriately.

Similarly, many machines fail to function correctly because they are set up incorrectly. This applies both to the primary functions of the equipment and to the setting or calibration of instrumentation.

These failure modes should all be listed where they are known to occur, so that appropriate corrective action can be taken. (This usually consists of training and/or improved operating procedures.)

When listing failure modes caused by people rather than machines, take care simply to record *what* went wrong and not *who* caused it. If too much emphasis is placed on who at this stage, the analysis could become unnecessarily adversarial, and people begin to lose sight of the fact that it is an exercise in avoiding or solving problems, not attaching blame. For instance, it is enough to say "control valve set too high", not "control valve incorrectly set by instrument technician".

Incorrect process or packaging materials

Major headaches in many packaging plants are caused by erratic, inadequate or incompatible packaging materials. Similarly, manufacturing processes often suffer functional failures caused by process materials which are out of spec (in terms of such variables as consistency, hardness or pH). These too should be listed where they are known to occur.

What Failure Modes should be Listed

Only failure modes which might reasonably be expected to occur in the context in question should be recorded. In other words, do not try to list every single failure possibility regardless of its likelihood.

When listing failure modes, do not try to list every single failure possibility regardless of its likelihood

"Reasonably likely" failure modes include the following:

- failures which have occurred before on the same or similar assets (unless the item has been modified so that the failure cannot occur again)
- failure modes which are already the subject of preventive maintenance routines, and so which would occur if no preventive maintenance was being done
- any other failure modes which have not yet occurred but which are considered to be real possibilities.

In most cases, a failure mode which has never occurred before and which is considered to be extremely unlikely should not be listed. However, the decision not to list a failure mode should be tempered by careful consideration of the failure consequences.

If the consequences are likely to be very severe indeed, then less likely failure possibilities *should* be listed and subjected to further analysis. For instance, a failure mode which might be dismissed as laughably unlikely in the relatively safe environment of a vehicle assembly plant may be taken very seriously in a nuclear power plant, even though the probability of the failure may be the same in both cases.

Conversely, the analysis should *not* be restricted *only* to failures which have occurred in the past. This is often done in the belief that we can only really decide how to deal with failures after they have occurred. In fact, this belief is not only invalid, but if the failure has serious consequences, it can be very dangerous. As explained in Chapter 9, it is also contrary to the whole idea of prevention.

Sources of Information about Failure Modes

In practice, information about failure modes which have occurred or which might reasonably be expected to occur can be obtained from:

- operators, craftsmen or foremen who have had a long association with the equipment
- the manufacturer or vendor of the equipment
- other users of the same equipment
- technical history records
- data banks.

Of these, the best source of information is usually people who know the equipment well. Although comprehensive history records and data banks can also be a valuable source of information, they should be treated with caution for the following reasons:

- they are often incomplete
- they seldom describe the full context in which the failure took place
- by their very nature, they cannot describe failures which have not yet occurred
- they often describe failure modes which are really the effect of some other failure (as explained earlier in this chapter).

Failure Modes and the Operating Context

We have seen how the functions and functional failures of any item are influenced by its operating context. This is also true of failure modes.

For example, a vehicle operating in the Arctic would be subject to different failure modes from the same make of vehicle operating in the Sahara desert.

Similarly, a gas turbine powering a jet aircraft would have different failure modes from the same type of turbine acting as a prime mover on an oil platform.

This also applies to the three pumps shown in Figure 3.6. The failure modes which are likely to affect the stand-by pump (such as brinelling of the bearings, stagnation of water in the pump casing and even the "borrowing" of key components to use elsewhere in an emergency) are different from those which affect the duty pump, as set out in Figure 3.10.

This illustrates the point that if the operating context is different, items which are technically identical can have different failure modes.

How Failure Modes should be Listed

The failure modes which cause each functional failure are listed in the third column of the RCM Information Worksheet. They are coded numerically, as shown in Figures 3.1 and 3.10.

The description of failure effects and the analysis of failure consequences are greatly simplified if failure modes are described as clearly as possible. The best way to do this is to avoid using the word "fails", and to find some other verb to describe the failure mode.

For example, it is clearer to say "coupling hub shears" instead of "coupling fails". "Feed hopper fails" could mean anything from a small leak to total collapse of the hopper, but if the right verb is used, there is no doubt. Note also the comments made on page 58 about failures caused by people.

In the case of valves or switches, indicate whether the loss of function is caused by the item failing in the open or closed position – "valve jams in open position" is more descriptive than "valve fails". In the interests of complete clarity, it may even be necessary to describe a failure mode at two levels:

For instance, "valve jams in open position due to rust on lead screw" is clearer than "valve jams". Similarly, it might be appropriate to distinguish between a bearing which "seizes due to normal wear and tear" and one which "seizes due to lack of lubrication".

(In the first case, the rust on the lead screw is really the failure mode or root cause of the failure, and the jammed valve is actually a failure effect.)

3.4 Failure Effects

The fourth step in the review process entails listing what actually happens when each failure mode occurs. These are known as *failure effects*. The description of these effects should include all the information needed to support the evaluation of the consequences of the failure. Specifically, when describing the effects of a failure, the following should be recorded:

- what evidence (if any) that the failure has occurred
- in what ways (if any) it poses a threat to safety or the environment
- in what ways (if any) it affects production or operations
- what physical damage (if any) is caused by the failure
- what must be done to repair the failure.

These issues are reviewed in the following paragraphs. Note that one of the main objectives of this entire exercise is to establish whether preventive maintenance is necessary. If we are to do this correctly, we cannot start by assuming that some sort of preventive maintenance is being done already, so the effects of a failure should be described as if nothing was being done to prevent it.

> ***The effects of a failure should be described***
> ***as if nothing was being done to prevent it***

Evidence of Failure

Failure effects should be described in a way which enables the RCM analysts to decide whether the failure will become evident to the operating crew under normal circumstances. For instance, the description should state whether the failure causes warning lights to come on or alarms to sound (or both), and whether the warning is given on a local panel or in a central control room (or both).

Similarly, the description should state whether the failure is accompanied (or preceded) by obvious physical effects such as loud noises, fire, smoke, escaping steam, unusual smells, or pools of liquid on the floor. It should also state whether the machine shuts down as a result of the failure.

For example, if we are considering the seizure of the bearings of the pump illustrated in Figure 3.5, the failure effects might be described as follows (the italics describe what would make it evident to the operators that a failure has occurred):

• Motor trips out and *trip alarm sounds in the control room.* Tank Y *low level alarm sounds after 20 minutes,* and *tank runs dry after 30 minutes.* Downtime required to replace the bearings 4 hours.

In the case of a stationary gas turbine, a failure mode that occurred in practice was the gradual build up of combustion deposits on the compressor blades. These deposits could be partially removed by the periodic injection of special materials into the air stream, a process known as "jet blasting". The failure effects were described accordingly as follows:

• Compressor efficiency declines and governor compensates to sustain power output, causing exhaust temperature to rise. Exhaust temperature is displayed on the local control panel and in the central control room. If no action is taken, exhaust gas temperature rises above 475°C under full power. *A high exhaust gas temperature alarm annunciates on the local control panel and a warning light comes on in the central control room.* Above 500°C, *the control system shuts down the turbine.* (Running at temperatures above 475°C shortens the creep life of the turbine blades.) The blades can be partially cleaned by jet blasting, and jet blasting takes about 30 minutes.

This is an unusually complex failure mode, so the description of the failure effects is somewhat longer than usual. (The average description of a failure effect usually amounts to between twenty and forty words.)

When dealing with protective devices, the description should state briefly what would happen if the protected device were to fail while the protective device was unserviceable. It should also make it clear whether the failure of the protective device on its own would be evident to the operating crew, and if so, how it would be evident.

Safety and Environmental Hazards

Modern industrial plant design has evolved to the point that only a small proportion of failure modes present a direct threat to safety or the environment. However, if there is a possibility that someone could get hurt or killed as a direct result of the failure, or an environmental standard or regulation could be breached, the failure effect should describe how this could happen. Examples include:

• increased risk of fire or explosions
• the escape of hazardous chemicals (gases, liquids or solids)
• electrocution
• falling objects
• pressure bursts (especially pressure vessels and hydraulic systems)
• exposure to very hot or molten materials
• the disintegration of large rotating components

- vehicle accidents or derailments
- exposure to sharp edges or moving machinery
- increased noise levels
- the collapse of structures
- the growth of bacteria
- ingress of dirt into food or pharmaceutical products
- flooding.

When listing these effects, do not prejudge the evaluation of the failure consequences by making statements like "this failure has safety consequences" or "this failure affects the environment". Simply state what happens, and leave the evaluation of the consequences to the next stage of the RCM process.

Note also that we are not only concerned about possible threats to our own staff (production and maintenance), but also about threats to the safety of customers and the community as a whole. As mentioned earlier in this chapter, this requires a detailed knowledge of all the safety and environmental standards which govern the operation, which in turn may call for considerable research by the team doing the analysis.

Secondary Damage and Production Effects

Failure effect descriptions should also help with decisions about operational and non-operational failure consequences. To do so, they should indicate how production is affected (if at all), and for how long. This is usually given by the amount of downtime associated with each failure. In this context, downtime means the total amount of time the asset would normally be out of service owing to this failure, from the moment it fails until the moment it is fully operational again. As indicated in Figure 3.12, this is usually much longer than the repair time.

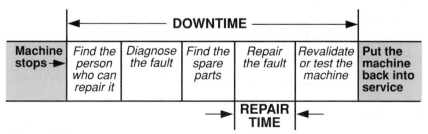

Figure 3.12:
Downtime vs repair time

Downtime as defined above can vary greatly for different occurrences of the same failure, and the most serious consequences are usually caused by the longer outages. Since it is consequences which are of most interest to us, the downtime recorded on the information worksheet should be based on the "typical worst case".

For instance, if the downtime caused by a failure which occurs late on a weekend night shift is usually much longer than it is when the failure occurs on a normal day shift, and if such night shifts are a regular occurrence, we list the former.

It is of course possible to moderate the consequences of failure by taking steps to shorten the downtime, most often by reducing the amount of time it takes to get hold of a spare part. However, as we are still in the process of defining the problem at this stage in the analysis, we only record the situation as it exists now.

Note also that if the failure affects operations, we record downtime and not the "mean time to repair" the failure (MTTR), for two reasons:

- we are dealing with the typical worst case and not the "mean" time, and
- in many people's minds, the word "repair time" has the meaning shown in Figure 3.12, which can cause unnecessary confusion.

If the failure does not cause any process stoppages, then we do record the average amount of time it takes to repair the failure. Other effects which should be listed where relevant include:

- whether and how product quality or customer service is affected, and if so whether any financial penalties are involved
- whether the failure leads to an increase in overall operating costs in addition to the direct cost of repair (such as higher energy costs)
- whether any other equipment or activity also has to stop (or slow down)
- what secondary damage (if any) is caused by the failure.

Failure effects should also state what must be done to repair the failure. This can be included in the statement about downtime, as shown in italics in the following examples:

- Downtime *to replace bearings* about four hours
- Downtime *to clear the blockage and reset the trip switch* about 30 minutes
- Downtime to *strip the turbine and replace the disc* about 2 weeks.

How Failure Effects should be Listed

Failure effects are listed in the last column of the Information Worksheet alongside the relevant failure mode, as shown in Figure 3.1.

4 Failure Consequences

Previous chapters have explained how the RCM process asks the following seven questions about each asset:

- what are the functions and associated performance standards of the asset in its present operating context?
- in what ways does it fail to fulfil its functions?
- what causes each functional failure?
- what happens when each failure occurs?
- in what way does each failure matter?
- what can be done to prevent each failure?
- what if a suitable preventive task cannot be found?

The answers to the first four questions were discussed at length in Chapter 3. This showed how RCM Information Worksheets are used to record the functions of the asset under review, and to list all the associated functional failures, failure modes and failure effects.

The last three questions are asked about each individual failure mode. This chapter considers the fifth question:

- *in what way does each failure matter?*

Technically Feasible and Worth Doing

Every time a failure mode occurs, the organisation which uses the asset is affected in some way. Some failure modes affect output, product quality or customer service. Others threaten safety or the environment. Some lead to an increase in operating costs, for instance by increasing energy consumption, while a few have an impact in four, five or even all six of these areas. Still others may appear to have no effect at all if they occur on their own, but may expose the organisation to the risk of much more serious failures.

If any of these failures are not prevented, time and effort need to be spent correcting them. This also affects the organisation, because repairing failures consumes resources which might be better used elsewhere.

The nature and severity of these consequences govern the way in which the failure is viewed by the organisation. If they are very serious, then we are likely to go to considerable lengths to prevent the failure, or at least to anticipate it in time to reduce or eliminate the consequences. This is especially true if the failure could hurt or kill someone, or if it is likely to have a serious effect on the environment. We also tend to take a dim view of failures which interfere with production or operations, or which cause significant secondary damage.

On the other hand, if the consequences of the failure are trivial, it is possible that we may decide to take no preventive action and simply take appropriate corrective action when the failure does occur.

This suggests that the consequences of failures are far more important than their technical characteristics. It also suggests that the whole idea of failure prevention is not so much about preventing the failures themselves, but about avoiding or reducing the *consequences* of failure.

> ***Failure prevention has much more to do with***
> ***avoiding or reducing the consequences of failure***
> ***than it has to do with preventing the failures themselves***

If this is accepted, then it stands to reason that any preventive action is only *worth doing* if it deals successfully with the consequences of the failure which it is meant to prevent.

> ***A preventive task is worth doing if it deals***
> ***successfully with the consequences of the***
> ***failure which it is meant to prevent***

(This of course presupposes that it is technically possible to prevent the failure in the first place. Whether or not a preventive task is *technically feasible* depends on the technical characteristics of the task and of the failure which it meant to prevent. The criteria governing technical feasibility are discussed in more detail in Chapter 5.

If it is not possible to find a suitable preventive task, the nature of the failure consequences also indicate what default action should be taken. Default tasks are reviewed in Chapter 6.)

However, the remainder of this chapter considers the criteria used to evaluate the consequences of failure, and hence to decide whether any form of preventive task is *worth doing*.

Categories of Failure Consequences

The impact which any failure has on the organisation – in other words, the extent to which each failure *matters* – depends on the *operating context* of the asset, the *performance standards* which apply to each function, and the *physical effects* of each failure mode. This combination of context, standards and effects means that every failure has a specific set of consequences associated with it.

The RCM process groups failure consequences into four categories, and it does so in two stages. The first stage separates hidden functions from evident functions. As explained in the next part of this chapter, a **hidden function** is one whose failure will not become evident to the operating crew under normal circumstances. These functions are separated from evident functions because they need special handling. (We will see that they are usually associated with protective devices which are not fail safe. Since these failures account for *up to half the failure modes which can affect modern, complex equipment,* they could well become *the* dominant issue in maintenance over the next twenty years.)

The next stage is to classify evident failures into three further categories in descending order of importance, as follows:

- *safety* and *environmental consequences.* A failure has safety consequences if it could hurt or kill someone. It has environmental consequences if it could lead to a breach of any corporate, regional or national environmental standard

- *operational consequences.* A failure has operational consequences if it affects production or operations (output, product quality, customer service or operating costs in addition to the direct cost of repair)

- *non-operational consequences.* Evident failures that fall into this category affect neither safety nor production, so they involve only the direct cost of repair.

By ranking evident failures in this order, RCM ensures that the safety and environmental implications of *every* evident failure mode are considered. This approach unequivocally puts people ahead of production. It also means that the safety, environmental and economic consequences of each failure are assessed in one exercise, which is much more cost-effective than considering them separately.

The next four sections of this chapter consider each of these categories in detail, starting with hidden failures.

4.1 Hidden Failure Consequences

We have seen that nearly every item of equipment has more than one and sometimes dozens of functions. When most of these functions fail, it will inevitably become apparent to someone that the failure has occurred.

For instance, some failures cause warning lights to flash or alarms to sound, or both. Others cause machines to shut down or some other part of the process to be interrupted. Others lead to product quality problems or increased use of energy, and yet others are accompanied by obvious physical effects such as loud noises, escaping steam, unusual smells or pools of liquid on the floor.

For example, Figure 3.6 in the previous chapter showed three pumps which are shown again in Figure 4.1 below. If a bearing on Pump A seizes, pumping capability is lost. This failure on its own will inevitably become apparent to the operators, either as soon as it happened or when some downstream part of the process is interrupted. (The operators might not know immediately that the problem was caused by the bearing, but they would know something unusual had happened.)

Figure 4.1: *Different operating contexts*

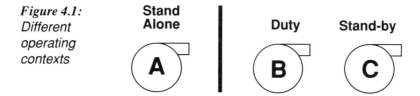

Failures of this kind are classed as evident because someone will eventually find out about it when they occur on their own. However, some failures occur in such a way that nobody knows that the item is in a failed state unless or until some other failure also occurs.

For instance, if Pump C in Figure 4.1 failed, no-one would be aware of the fact because under normal circumstances Pump B would still be working. In other words, the failure of pump C on its own has no direct impact unless or until Pump B also failed (an abnormal circumstance).

Pump C exhibits the two chief characteristics of a hidden function. The first and most important is that the failure of this pump *on its own* is not evident to the operating crew under normal circumstances. This leads to the following definition of a hidden function:

> *A hidden function is one whose failure will*
> *not become evident to the operating crew under*
> *normal circumstances if it occurs on its own.*

The second point about the failure of Pump C is that it will not become evident to the operating crew unless some other failure also occurs, or someone makes a point of checking periodically whether Pump C is still in working order.

In other words, the failure of Pump C only has any consequences if another failure – in this case, the failure of Pump B – also occurs. The failure of pump B while pump C is in a failed state is known as a *multiple failure*. This phenomenon is illustrated in Figure 4.2.

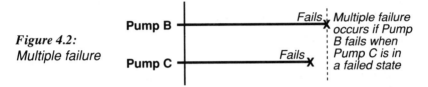

Figure 4.2: Multiple failure

This illustrates the fact that a hidden failure *on its own* has no *direct* consequences, but it does have an indirect consequence in that it increases the risk of a multiple failure.

The only consequence of a hidden failure is increased risk of a multiple failure

Given that failure prevention is mainly about avoiding the consequences of failure, this example also suggests that when we develop maintenance programmes for hidden failures, our main objective is actually to prevent – or at least to reduce the risk of – the associated multiple failure.

The main objective of a maintenance programme for a hidden function is to prevent – or at least to reduce the risk of – the associated multiple failure

So *how hard we try* to prevent the hidden failure depends on the consequences of the multiple failure.

How hard we try to prevent a hidden failure depends on the consequences of the multiple failure

For example, Pumps B and C might be pumping cooling water to a nuclear reactor. In this case, if the reactor could not be shut down fast enough, the ultimate consequences of the multiple failure could be a melt-down, with horrific safety, environmental and operational consequences.

On the other hand, the two pumps might be pumping water into a tank which has enough capacity to supply a downstream process for two hours. In this case, the consequence of the multiple failure would be that production stops after two hours, and then only if neither of the pumps could be repaired before the tank ran dry. Further analysis might suggest that at worst, this multiple failure might cost the organisation (say) £2 000 in lost production.

In the first of these examples, the consequences of the multiple failure are very serious indeed, so we would go to great lengths to preserve the integrity of the hidden function (which in this case is the stand-by pump). In the second case, the consequences of the multiple failure are purely economic, and how much it costs would influence how hard we would try to prevent the hidden failure.

Identifying Hidden Failures

The above discussion suggests that hidden failures can be separated from evident failures by asking the following question:

> ***Will the loss of function caused by this failure mode on its own become evident to the operating crew under normal circumstances?***

If the answer to this question is no, the failure mode is hidden, and if the answer is yes, it is evident.

The following paragraphs will show how this question adds a whole new dimension to the management of failure. However, it can cause time-consuming and even dangerous misunderstandings if it is not thoroughly understood. The following issues need special attention:
• the distinction between functional failures and failure modes
• the question of time
• what exactly is meant by "the operating crew"
• what are "normal circumstances" in this context.
These issues are reviewed in more detail later in this chapter. Before doing so, we consider where hidden functions are usually found in real life, and what implications this has from the maintenance viewpoint. In particular, it will become apparent that the vast majority of hidden functions are protective devices which are not fail-safe.

> ***The vast majority of hidden functions are protective devices which are not fail-safe***

Hidden Failures and Protective Devices

Chapter 3 mentioned that the growth in the number of ways in which equipment can fail has led to corresponding growth in the variety and severity of failure consequences which fall into the evident categories. It also mentioned that protective devices are being used increasingly in an attempt to eliminate (or at least reduce) these consequences, and explained how these devices work in one of five ways:

- to alert operators to abnormal conditions
- to shut down the equipment in the event of a failure
- to eliminate or relieve abnormal conditions which follow a failure and which might otherwise cause much more serious damage
- to take over from a function which has failed
- to prevent dangerous situations from arising.

In essence, the function of these devices is to ensure that the consequences of the failure of the protected function are much less serious than they would be if there were no protection. So any protective device is in fact part of a system with at least two components:

- the protective device
- the protected function.

For example, Pump C in Figure 4.1 can be regarded as a protective device, because it "protects" the pumping function if pump B should fail. Pump B is of course the protected function.

The existence of such a system creates two parallel sets of failure possibilities, depending on whether the protective device is fail-safe or not. We consider the implications of each in the following paragraphs, starting with devices which are fail-safe.

Fail-safe protective devices

In this context, *fail-safe* means that the failure of the device on its own will become evident to the operating crew under normal circumstances.

> ***In the context of this book, a "fail-safe" device is
> one whose failure on its own will become evident
> to the operating crew under normal circumstances***

This means that in a system which includes a fail-safe protective device, there are three failure possibilities in any period, as follows.

The first possibility is that *neither device fails*. In this case everything proceeds normally.

The second possibility is that the *protected function fails before the protective device*. In this case the protective device carries out its intended function and, depending on the nature of the protection, the consequences of failure of the protected function are reduced or eliminated.

The third possibility is that the *protective device fails before the protected function*. This would be evident because if it were not, the device would not be fail-safe in the sense defined above. If normal good practice is followed, the failure is reported and rectified quickly, so the chance of the protected device failing while the protective device is in a failed state is very low indeed

If the multiple failure could affect safety or the environment, the possibility of these consequences is virtually eliminated if the protected function is shut down while the protective device is being repaired. This means that the consequences of the failure of a fail-safe protective device usually fall into the "operational" or "non-operational" categories. (In many cases, it may be practical to avoid even these consequences by providing alternative protection while the failed protective device is being rectified. For instance, an operator could be asked to keep an eye on a pressure gauge – and his finger by a stop button – while a pressure switch is being replaced.)

Protective devices which are not fail-safe

In a system which contains a protective device which is not fail-safe, the fact that the device is unable to fulfil its intended function is *not* evident under normal circumstances. This creates four failure possibilities in any given period, two of which are the same as those which apply to a fail-safe device. The first is where *neither device fails*, in which case everything proceeds normally as before.

The second possibility is that the *protected function fails at a time when the protective device is still functional*. In this case the protective device also carries out its intended function, so the consequences of the failure of the protected device are again reduced or eliminated altogether.

For example, consider a situation where a pressure relief valve (the protective device) is mounted on a pressure vessel (the protected function). If the pressure rises above acceptable limits, the valve would relieve and so reduce or eliminate the consequences of over-pressurisation.

The third possibility is that the *protective device fails while the protected function* is still working. In this case, the failure has no direct consequences. In fact no-one even knows that the protective device is in a failed state, because it is a hidden function as explained earlier.

For example, if the pressure relief valve was jammed shut, no-one would be aware of the fact as long as the pressure in the vessel remained within normal operating limits (unless someone made a point of checking periodically whether the valve was still functioning. However, as discussed later we assume *at this point in the analysis* that no scheduled maintenance is being done, because the whole purpose of the analysis is to find out whether such routines are necessary). In other words, this failure – the inability of the valve to fulfil its intended function – *on its own* has no direct consequences.

The fourth possibility during any one cycle is that *the protective device fails, then the protected function fails* while the protective device is in a failed state. As mentioned earlier, this situation is known as a *multiple failure*. (This is a real possibility simply because the failure of the protective device is not evident, and so no-one would be aware of the need to take corrective – or alternative – action to avoid the multiple failure.)

> ***In the case of protective devices, a multiple failure***
> ***only occurs if the protected function fails while***
> ***the protective device is in a failed state***

In the case of the relief valve, if the pressure in the vessel rose excessively while the valve was jammed, the vessel would probably explode (unless someone acted very quickly or unless there was other protection in the system).

Further examples of hidden failures and the multiple failures which could follow if they are not detected are:

- *vibration switches:* A vibration switch designed to shut down a large fan might be configured in such a way that its failure is hidden. However, this only matters if the fan vibration rises above acceptable limits (*a second failure*), causing the fan bearings and possibly the fan itself to disintegrate (*the consequences of the multiple failure*).

- *ultimate level switches: Ultimate* level switches are designed to activate an alarm or shut down equipment if a primary level switch fails to operate. In other words, if an ultimate low level switch jams, there are no consequences unless the primary switch also fails (*the second failure*), in which case the vessel or tank would run dry (*the consequences of the multiple failure*).

- *fire hoses:* The failure of a fire hose has no direct consequences. It only matters if there is a fire (*a second failure*), when the failed hose may result in the place burning down and people being killed (*the consequence of the multiple failure*).

Other typical hidden functions include emergency medical equipment, most types of fire detection, fire warning and fire fighting equipment, overload or overspeed protection devices, redundant structural components, parachutes, inflatable life rafts, nearly all forms of stand-by plant and most emergency power generation systems.

Performance Standards and Hidden Failures

So far, this part of this chapter has defined hidden failures, explained how they are identified and described the relationship between protective devices and hidden functions. The next question concerns the performance standards which apply to hidden functions.

One of the most important conclusions which has been drawn so far is that the only direct consequence of a hidden failure is increased exposure to the risk of a multiple failure. Since it is the latter which we most wish to avoid, the performance standard which applies to a hidden failure must be connected with the risk of the associated multiple failure.

We have seen that where a system is protected by a device which is not fail-safe, a multiple failure can only occur if the protected device fails while the protective device is in a failed state. This was illustrated in Figure 4.2 for the pump with the stand-by.

So the *probability* of a multiple failure in any period must be given by the probability that the protected function will fail while the protective device is in a failed state during the same period. A rigorous approach to this issue is illustrated in Figure 4.3 overleaf. It shows that the probability of a multiple failure in any period is calculated as follows:

Probability of a multiple failure	=	Probability of failure of the protected function	x	Average downtime of the protective device

This equation indicates that the rigorous approach to establishing the performance standard for a hidden function entails three steps:

- first establish what level of probability the organisation is prepared to accept for the multiple failure
- then determine the probability that the protected function will fail in the period under consideration

Figure 4.3:
CALCULATING THE PROBABILITY OF A MULTIPLE FAILURE

The probability that a *protected function will fail* in any period is the inverse of its mean time between failures, as illustrated in Figure 4.3a below:

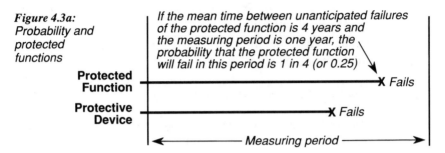

Figure 4.3a:
Probability and protected functions

If the mean time between unanticipated failures of the protected function is 4 years and the measuring period is one year, the probability that the protected function will fail in this period is 1 in 4 (or 0.25)

Protected Function — X Fails
Protective Device — X Fails
Measuring period

The probability that the *protective device will be in a failed state* in any period is given by the percentage of time which it is in a failed state during that period. This is of course measured by its downtime, as shown in Figure 4.3b below:

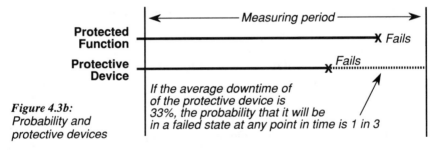

Measuring period
Protected Function — X Fails
Protective Device — X Fails

If the average downtime of of the protective device is 33%, the probability that it will be in a failed state at any point in time is 1 in 3

Figure 4.3b:
Probability and protective devices

The *probability of the multiple failure* is calculated by multiplying the probability of failure of the protected function by the average downtime of the protective device. For the case described in Figure 4.3(a) and (b) above, the probability of a multiple failure would be as indicated in Figure 4.3(c) below:

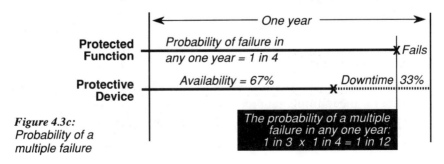

One year
Protected Function — Probability of failure in any one year = 1 in 4 — X Fails
Protective Device — Availability = 67% — X Downtime 33%

Figure 4.3c:
Probability of a multiple failure

The probability of a multiple failure in any one year: 1 in 3 x 1 in 4 = 1 in 12

- finally, determine what availability the hidden function must achieve to reduce the risk of the multiple failure to the required level.

This means that the performance standard for a hidden function can be expressed as the level of availability needed to reduce the risk of the associated multiple failure to an acceptable level.

> ***The performance standard for a hidden function is the availability needed to reduce the risk of the associated multiple failure to an acceptable level.***

When calculating the risks associated with protected systems, there is often a tendency to regard the probability of failure of the protected and protective devices as fixed. This leads to the belief that the only way to change the probability of the multiple failure is to change the hardware (in other words, to modify the system), perhaps by adding more protective devices or by replacing existing components with ones which are thought to be more reliable.

In fact, this belief is incorrect, because *it is usually possible to vary both the probability of failure of the protected function and (especially) the downtime of the protective device* by adopting suitable maintenance and operating policies. As a result, *it is also possible to reduce the probability of the multiple failure to almost any **desired** level within reason* by adopting such policies. (Zero is of course an unattainable ideal.)

For example, the consequences of both pumps in Figure 4.3 being in a failed state may be such that the users *want* the risk of the multiple failure to be less than 1 in 1 000 in any one year (or 10^{-3}). Assume that it has also been estimated that if the duty pump is suitably maintained, the mean time between unanticipated failures of the duty pump can be increased to ten years, which corresponds to a probability of failure in any one year of one in ten, or 10^{-1}.

So to reduce the probability of the multiple failure to less than 10^{-3}, the downtime of the stand-by pump must not exceed 10^{-2}, or 1%. In other words it must be maintained in such a way that its availability exceeds 99%. This is illustrated in Figure 4.4 below.

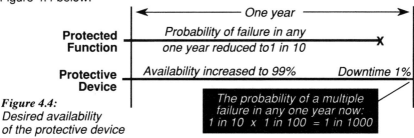

Figure 4.4:
Desired availability
of the protective device

In practice, the probability which is considered to be acceptable for any multiple failure depends on its consequences. In a few cases levels of acceptability are specified by regulatory authorities, but in the vast majority of cases *the assessment has to be made by the users of the asset.* Since these consequences vary hugely from system to system, what is deemed to be acceptable varies equally widely. To illustrate this point, four possible such assessments are given below for four different systems:

Failure of Protected Function	Failed State of Protective Device	Multiple Failure	Acceptable Probability of Multiple Failure
Spelling error	Spell-checker in a word-processing programme unable to check spelling	Spelling mistake undetected	10 per year?
10kW motor on pump B overloaded	Trip switch jammed in closed position	Motor burns out: £300 to rewind	1 in 50 years?
Duty pump B fails	Stand-by pump C failed	Total loss of pumping capability: £200 000 in lost production	1 in 10 000 years?
Boiler over-pressurised	Relief valves jammed shut	Boiler blows up: 12 people die	1 in 100 000 000 years?

These levels of acceptability are not meant to be prescriptive and do not necessarily reflect the views of the author. They are meant to demonstrate that in any protected system, *someone* must decide what is acceptable before it is possible to decide on the level of protection required, and that this assessment will differ for different systems. (Who this "someone" might be is discussed in more detail in Part 4.2 of this chapter.)

In practice, it is seldom necessary – indeed it is often impossible – to perform a rigorous quantitative analysis of the probability of multiple failure in the manner described above. It is usually adequate to make a judgment about the required availability of the protective device based on a qualitative assessment of the reliability of the protected function and the possible consequences of the multiple failure. This is discussed further in Chapter 6. However, if the multiple failure is particularly serious, then a rigorous analysis *should* be performed.

The following paragraphs consider how it is possible to influence:
- the rate at which protected functions fail
- the availability of protected devices.

Routine Maintenance and Hidden Functions

In a system which incorporates a non-fail-safe protective device, the probability of a multiple failure can be reduced as follows:

- reduce the probability of the *protected* function failing by:
  * doing some sort of preventive maintenance
  * changing the way in which the protected function is operated
  * changing the design of the protected function.

- increase the availability of the *protective* device by
  * doing some sort of preventive maintenance
  * checking periodically if the protective device has failed
  * modifying the protective device.

Prevent the failure of the protected function

We have seen that the probability of a multiple failure is partly based on the probability of failure of the protected function. This could almost certainly be reduced by improving the maintenance or operation of the protected device, or even (as a last resort) by changing its design.

Specifically, if the failures of a protected function can be anticipated or prevented, the mean time between (unanticipated) failures of this function would be increased. This in turn would reduce the probability of the multiple failure.

For example, one way to prevent the simultaneous failure of pumps B and C is to try to prevent unanticipated failures of pump B. By reducing the number of these failures, the mean time between failures of pump B would be increased and so the probability of the multiple failure would be correspondingly reduced, as shown in Figure 4.4.

However, bear in mind that the reason for installing a protective device is that the protected function is vulnerable to unanticipated failures with serious consequences.

Secondly, if no action is taken to prevent the failure of the protective device, it will inevitably fail at some stage and hence cease to provide any protection. *After this point, the probability of the multiple failure is equal to the probability of the protected device failing on its own.*

This situation must be unacceptable, or a protective device would not have been installed to begin with. This suggests that we must at least try to find a practical way of preventing the failure of protective devices which are not fail safe.

Prevent the hidden failure

In order to prevent a multiple failure, we must try to ensure that the hidden function is not in a failed state if and when the protected function fails. If a preventive task could be found which was good enough to ensure 100% availability of the protective device, then a multiple failure is theoretically almost impossible.

For example, if a preventive task could be found which could ensure 100% availability of Pump C while it is in the stand-by state, then we can be sure that C would always take over if B failed.

(In this case a multiple failure is only possible if the users operate Pump C while B is being repaired or replaced. However, even then the risk of the multiple failure is low, because B should be repaired quickly and so the amount of time the organisation is at risk is fairly short. Whether or not the organisation is prepared to take the risk of running Pump C while Pump B is down depends on the consequences of the multiple failure and on whether it is possible to arrange other forms of protection, as discussed earlier.)

In practice, it is most unlikely that any preventive task would cause any function, hidden or otherwise, to achieve an availability of 100% indefinitely. What it must do, however, is deliver the availability needed to reduce the probability of the multiple failure to an acceptable level.

For example, assume that a preventive task is found which enables Pump C to achieve an availability of 99%. If the mean time between unanticipated failures of Pump B is 10 years, then the risk of the multiple failure would be 10^{-3} (1 in 1000), as discussed earlier.

If the availability of Pump C could be increased to 99.9% then the probability of the multiple failure would be reduced to 10^{-4} (1 in 10 000), and so on.

So for a hidden failure, a preventive task is only worth doing if it secures the availability needed to reduce the probability of the multiple failure to an acceptable level.

> ***For hidden failures, a preventive task is worth doing
> if it secures the availability needed to reduce the
> probability of a multiple failure to an acceptable level***

The ways in which failures can be prevented are discussed in Chapter 5. However, Chapter 5 also explains that it is often impossible to find a preventive task which secures the required availability. This applies especially to the type of equipment which suffers from hidden failures. So if we cannot find a way to *prevent* a hidden failure, we need to find some other way of improving the availability of the hidden function.

Detect the hidden failure

If it is not possible to find a suitable way of *preventing* a hidden failure, it is still possible to reduce the risk of the multiple failure by checking the hidden function periodically to find out if it is still working. If this check (called a "failure-finding" task) is carried out at a suitable frequency and if the function is rectified as soon as it is found to be faulty, it is still possible to secure high levels of availability. Scheduled failure-finding is discussed in detail in Chapter 6.

Modify the equipment

In a very small number of cases , it is either impossible to find any kind of routine task which secures the desired level of availability, or it is impractical to do it at the required frequency. However, something must still be done to reduce the risk of the multiple failure to an acceptable level, so in these cases, it is usually necessary to "go back to the drawing board" and reconsider the design.

If the multiple failure could affect safety or the environment, redesign is compulsory. If the multiple failure only has economic consequences, the need for redesign is assessed on economic grounds.

Redesign can be used to reduce the risk or to change the consequences of a multiple failure in the following ways:

- *substitute an evident function for the hidden function.*
- *duplicate the hidden function* (but if we duplicate – or even triplicate – a hidden function, it remains hidden and so it still needs to be treated accordingly. All that changes is the probability of the multiple failure.)
- *make the hidden function evident with another device* (bearing in mind that if more functions are added, then more functional failures need to be analysed. Many of them will also be hidden.)

The question of redesign is also considered in more detail in Chapter 6.

Hidden Functions: The Decision Process

All the points made thus far about the development of a maintenance strategy for hidden failures can be summarised as shown in Figure 4.5 overleaf:

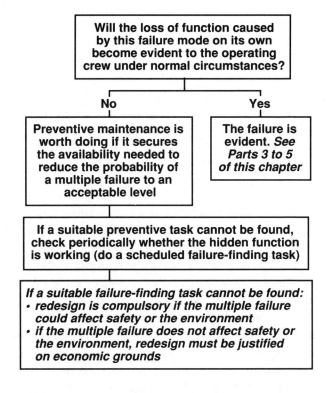

Figure 4.5:
Identifying and
developing a
maintenance
strategy for a
hidden failure

Will the loss of function caused by this failure mode on its own become evident to the operating crew under normal circumstances?

No

Preventive maintenance is worth doing if it secures the availability needed to reduce the probability of a multiple failure to an acceptable level

Yes

The failure is evident. *See Parts 3 to 5 of this chapter*

If a suitable preventive task cannot be found, check periodically whether the hidden function is working (do a scheduled failure-finding task)

If a suitable failure-finding task cannot be found:
- *redesign is compulsory if the multiple failure could affect safety or the environment*
- *if the multiple failure does not affect safety or the environment, redesign must be justified on economic grounds*

Further Points about Hidden Functions

Earlier in this chapter, it was mentioned that four issues need special care when asking the first question in Figure 4.5. These are:
- the distinction between functional failures and failure modes
- the question of time
- what exactly is meant by "the operating crew"
- what are "normal circumstances" in this context.

Two further issues also need careful consideration:
- the primary and secondary functions of protective devices
- "fail-safe" devices.

These are all discussed in more detail in the following paragraphs.

Functional failure and failure mode

At this stage in the RCM process, every failure mode which is reasonably likely to cause each functional failure will already have been identified on the RCM Information Worksheet. This has two key implications:

- firstly, we are *not* asking what failures could occur. All we are trying to establish is whether each failure mode *which has already been identified as a possibility* would be hidden or evident if it did occur.

- secondly, we are *not* asking whether the operating crew can diagnose the failure mode itself. We are asking if the *loss of function* caused by the failure mode will be evident under normal circumstances. (In other words, we are asking if the failure mode has any effects or symptoms which under normal circumstances, would lead the observer to believe that the item is no longer capable of fulfilling its intended function.)

For example, consider the case of a motor vehicle which suffers from a blocked fuel line. The average driver (in other words, the average "operator") would not be able to diagnose this failure mode without expert assistance, so there might be a temptation to call this a hidden failure. However, the *loss of the function* caused by this failure mode *is* evident, because the car stops working. Note also that it does so as a direct and inevitable consequence of the blocked fuel line on its own.

The question of time

There is often a temptation to describe a failure as "hidden" if a considerable period of time elapses between the moment the failure occurs and the moment it is discovered. In fact, this is not the case. If the loss of function eventually becomes apparent to the operators, and it does so as a direct and inevitable result of this failure *on its own*, then the failure is treated as evident, no matter how much time elapses between the failure in question and its discovery.

For example, a tank fed by Pump A in Figure 4.1 may take weeks to empty, so the failure of this pump might not be apparent as soon as it occurs. This might lead to the temptation to describe the failure as hidden. However, this is not so because the tank runs dry as a direct and inevitable result of the failure of Pump A *on its own.* Therefore the fact that Pump A is in a failed state *will* inevitably become evident to the operating crew.

Conversely, the failure of Pump C will only become evident if Pump B also fails (unless someone makes a point of checking Pump C from time to time.) If pump B were to be operated and maintained in such a way that it is never necessary to switch on Pump C, it is possible that the failure of Pump C *on its own* would never be discovered.

This example demonstrates that time is not an issue when considering hidden failures. We are simply asking whether anyone will be aware of the fact that the failure has occurred *on its own*, and *not* if they will be aware *when* it occurs.

The operating crew

When asking whether a failure is evident, the term *operating crew* refers to anyone who has occasion to observe the equipment or what it is doing at any time in the course of their normal daily activities, and who can be relied upon to report that it has failed.

Failures can be observed by people with many different points of view. They include operators, drivers, quality inspectors, craftsmen, supervisors, and even the tenants of buildings. However, whether any of these people can be relied upon to detect and report a failure depends on four critical elements:

- the observer must be in a position either to detect the failure mode itself or to detect the loss of function caused by the failure mode. This may be a physical location or access to equipment or information (including management information) which will reveal the failure condition.

- the observer must be able to recognise the condition as a failure.

- the observer must understand and accept that it is part of his or her job to report failures.

- the observer must have unrestricted access to a simple and reliable procedure for reporting failures.

Normal circumstances

Careful analysis of the duties of certain operators reveals that many of these duties are actually maintenance tasks. It is wise to start from a zero base when considering these tasks, because it may transpire that many of them and (in particular) the frequencies with which they are done need to be radically revised.

In other words, when asking if a failure will become evident to the operating crew under "normal" circumstances, the word *normal* should be given the following meanings:

- that nothing is being done to *prevent* the failure. If a preventive task is currently successfully preventing the failure, it could be argued that the failure is "hidden" because it does not occur. However in Chapter 3 it was pointed out that failure modes and effects should be listed and the rest of the RCM process applied as if no preventive tasks are being done, because one of the main purposes of the exercise is to review what maintenance we should be doing in the first place.

- that no specific task is being done to *detect* the failure. A surprising number of tasks which already form part of an operator's normal duties are in fact routines designed to check if hidden functions are working.

For example, pressing a button on a control panel every day to check if all the alarm lights on the panel are working is in fact a failure-finding task.

We shall see later that failure-finding tasks are covered by the RCM task selection process, so once again it should be assumed at this stage in the analysis that this task is not being done (even though the task is currently genuinely part of the operator's normal duties). This is because the RCM process might reveal a more effective task, or the need to do the same task at a higher or lower frequency.

(Quite apart from the question of maintenance tasks, there is often considerable doubt about what the "normal" duties of the operating crew actually are. This occurs most often where standard operating procedures are either poorly documented or do not exist. In these cases, the RCM review process does much to help clarify what these duties should be, and can do much to help lay the foundations of a full set of operating procedures. This applies especially to high-technology plants.)

Primary and secondary functions

Thus far we have focused on the primary function of protective devices, which is to be capable of fulfilling the function they are designed to fulfil when called upon to do so. As we have seen, this is usually after the protected function has failed. However, an important secondary function of many of these devices is that they should not work when nothing is wrong.

For instance, the primary function of a pressure switch might be listed as follows:
- to be capable of transmitting a shut down signal when the system pressure falls below 250 psi
The implied secondary function of this switch is:
- to be incapable of transmitting a shutdown signal when the system pressure is above 250 psi.

The failure of the first function is hidden, but the failure of the second is evident because if it occurs, the switch transmits a spurious shut-down signal and the machine stops. If this is likely to occur in practice, it should be listed as a failure mode of the function which is interrupted (usually the primary function of the machine). As a result, there is usually no need to list the implied second *function* separately, but the failure mode should be listed under the relevant function if it is reasonably likely to occur.

"Fail-safe" devices

It often happens that a protective circuit is said to be fail-safe when it is not. This usually occurs when only part of a circuit is considered instead of the circuit as a whole.

An example is again provided by a pressure switch, this time attached to a hydro-static bearing. The switch was meant to shut down the machine if the oil pressure in the bearing fell below a certain level. It emerged during discussion that if the electrical signal from the switch to the control panel was interrupted, the machine would shut down, so the failure of the switch was initially judged to be evident.

However, further discussion revealed that a diaphragm inside the switch could deteriorate with age, so the switch could become incapable of sensing changes in the pressure. This failure was hidden, and the maintenance programme for the switch was developed accordingly.

To avoid this problem, take care to include the sensors and the actuators in the analysis of any control loop, as well as the electrical circuit itself.

4.2 Safety and Environmental Consequences

Safety First

As we have seen, the first step in the consequence evaluation process is to identify hidden failures so that they can be dealt with appropriately. All remaining failure modes – in other words, failures which are not classified as hidden – must by definition be evident.

At the start of this chapter, it was explained that evident failure modes are grouped into three categories, as follows:

- those which could affect safety
- those which affect production or operations
- those which only involve the direct cost of repair.

Of these categories, the RCM process considers the safety implications of each failure mode first, for two reasons:

- a more and more firmly held belief among employers, employees, customers and society in general that hurting or killing people in the course of business is simply not acceptable, and hence that everything possible should be done to minimise the possibility of any sort of safety-related incident or environmental excursion.

• the more pragmatic realisation that the levels of risk which are tolerated for safety-related incidents tend to be several orders of magnitude lower than those which are tolerated for failures which have operational consequences. As a result, in most of the cases where a preventive task is worth doing from the safety viewpoint, it will also be more than adequate from the operational viewpoint.

At one level, safety refers to the safety of individuals in the workplace. Specifically, RCM asks whether anyone could get hurt or killed either as a direct result of the failure mode itself or by other damage which may be caused by the failure.

> ***A failure mode has safety consequences***
> ***if it causes a loss of function or other***
> ***damage which could hurt or kill someone***

At another level, "safety" refers to the safety or well-being of society in general. Nowadays, failures which affect society tend to be classed as "environmental" issues. In fact, in many parts of the world the point is fast approaching where organisations either conform to society's environmental expectations, or they will no longer be allowed to operate. So quite apart from any personal feelings which anyone may have on the issue, environmental probity is becoming a prerequisite for corporate survival.

Chapter 3 explained how society's expectations take the form of municipal, regional and national environmental standards. Some organisations also have their own sometimes even more stringent corporate standards. A failure mode is said to have environmental consequences if it could lead to the breach of any of these standards.

> ***A failure mode has environmental consequences***
> ***if it causes a loss of function or other damage***
> ***which could lead to the breach of any known***
> ***environmental standard or regulation***

Note that when considering whether a failure mode has safety or environmental consequences, we are now considering whether one failure mode on its own could have the consequences. This is different from Part 4.1 of this chapter, in which we considered the failure of both elements of a protected system.

The Question of Risk

Much as most people would like to live in an environment where there is no possibility at all of death or injury, it is generally accepted that there is an element of risk in everything we do. In other words, absolute zero is unattainable, even though it is a worthy target to keep striving for. This immediately leads us to ask what *is* attainable.

To answer this question, we first need to consider the question of risk in more detail.

Risk assessment consists of three elements. The first asks what could happen if the event under consideration did occur. The second asks how likely it is for the event to occur at all. The combination of these two elements provides a measure of the degree of risk. The third – and often the most contentious element – asks whether this risk is acceptable.

For example, consider a failure mode which could result in death or injury to ten people *(what could happen)*. The probability that this failure mode could occur is once in every thousand years *(how likely it is to occur)*. On the basis of these figures, the risk associated with this failure is:

10 × (1 in 1000) = 1 casualty per 100 years

Now consider a second failure mode which could cause 1000 casualties, but the probability that this failure could occur is once in every 100 000 years. The risk associated with this failure is:

1000 × (1 in 100 000) = 1 casualty per 100 years.

In these examples, the risk is the same although the figures upon which it is based are quite different. Note also that these examples do not indicate whether the risk is acceptable – they merely quantify it. Whether or not the risk is acceptable is a separate and much more difficult question. (In practice, it is highly unlikely that most organisations would accept the level of risk shown for any single failure mode.)

The following paragraphs consider each of the three elements of risk in more detail.

What could happen if the failure occurred?

Two issues need to be considered when considering what could happen if a failure were to occur. These are *what actually happens* and *whether anyone is likely to be hurt or killed* as a result.

What actually happens if any failure mode occurs should be recorded on the RCM Information Worksheet as its failure effects, as explained at length in Part 3.4 of this book. This also lists a number of typical effects which pose a threat to safety or the environment.

The fact that these effects *could* hurt or kill someone does not necessarily mean that they *will* do so every time they occur. Some may even occur quite often without doing so. However, the issue is not whether such consequences are inevitable, but whether they are possible.

For example, a failure which could cause a fire is always regarded as a safety hazard because the presence of a fire-extinguishing system does not *guarantee* that the fire will be controlled and extinguished.

As a result, the RCM process always assesses safety consequences at the most conservative level. In the absence of clear evidence that a failure cannot affect safety or the environment, it is assumed that it can.

(If a number of different effects could follow a particular failure mode, some risk analysts actually try to identify them all, and then try to quantify the probability that each will occur after the failure mode in question has occurred. This leads to the somewhat macabre practice of asking whether someone is more likely to lose an arm than a leg as a result of the failure, and then whether an arm is worth more than a leg, or whether the failure could cause one person or ten people to die and then whether ten people are worth more than one. This is the currency of the insurance industry, not of managers who have a genuine concern for the wellbeing of their workforce and of the community in which they live.

In practice, RCM eliminates the need for this type of analysis by asking as realistically as possible what the worst case could be, and then develops a maintenance strategy on the basis of that scenario alone.)

How likely is the failure to occur?

Part 3.3 of this book mentions that only failure modes which are reasonably likely to occur in the context in question should be listed on the RCM Information Worksheet. As a result, if the Information Worksheet has been prepared on a realistic basis, the mere fact that the failure mode has been listed suggests that there is some likelihood that it could occur, and therefore that it should be subjected to further analysis.

Is the risk acceptable?

One of the most difficult aspects of the management of safety is the extent to which beliefs about what is acceptable vary from individual to individual and from group to group. This perception is influenced by a great many issues, among which are the following:

- *individual values:* To explore this issue in any depth is well beyond the scope of this book. Suffice it to contrast the views on acceptable risk likely to be held by a mountaineer with those of someone who suffers from vertigo, or those of an underground miner with those of someone who suffers from claustrophobia.

- *industry values:* While every industry nowadays recognises the need to operate as safely as possible, there is no escaping the fact that some are intrinsically more dangerous than others. Some even compensate for higher levels of risk with higher pay levels. The views of society as a whole on this subject are expressed in the form of the safety and environmental regulations which apply to that industry. The views of any individual who works in that industry ultimately boil down to his or her perception of whether the intrinsic risks are "worth it".

- *the degree of control which the individual has over the situation:* People are generally prepared to accept a higher level of risk when they believe that they are personally in control of the situation than when they believe that the situation is out of their control.

  For example, people tolerate much higher levels of risk when driving their own cars than they do as aircraft passengers. (The extent to which this issue influences perceptions of risk is given by the startling statistic that 1 person in 11 000 000 who travels by air between New York and Los Angeles in the USA is likely to be killed while doing so, while 1 person in 14 000 who makes the trip by road is likely to be killed. And yet some people insist on making this trip by road because they believe that they are "safer"!)

  This distinction is found on a grander scale when considering whether the risk is "natural" or "man-made". Most people seem to feel that if the problem is natural in origin, they will accept a higher level of risk than they would if it was caused by man, simply because they feel that there is not an awful lot they can do about the forces of nature.

  Consider for example the current almost indifferent attitude of society towards the risks associated with naturally-occurring radioactive radon gas versus the passions aroused by nuclear installations.

- *The effect on "future generations":* The safety of children – especially unborn children – has an especially powerful effect on peoples' views about what is acceptable. Adults frequently display a surprising and even distressing disregard for their own safety. (Witness how much time has to be spent on persuading the mavericks among the world's workers to wear protective clothing.) However, threaten their offspring and their attitude changes completely.

For example, the author worked with one group which had occasion to discuss the properties of a certain chemical. Words like "toxic" and "carcinogenic" were treated almost with a yawn, even though most of the members of this group were the people most at risk. However, as soon as it was mentioned that the chemical was also mutagenic and teratogenic, and the meaning of these words was explained to the group, the chemical was suddenly viewed with vastly greater respect. This despite the fact that the toxic risks were an order of magnitude greater than the others.

- *knowledge:* perceptions of risk are greatly influenced by how much people know about the equipment, the process of which it forms part and the failure mechanisms associated with each failure mode. The more they know, the better their judgement. (Ignorance is often a two-edged sword. In some situations people take the most appalling risks out of sheer ignorance, while in others they wildly exaggerate the risks – also out of ignorance. On the other hand, we need to remind ourselves constantly of the extent to which familiarity can breed contempt.)

A great many other factors also influence perceptions of risk, such as the value placed on human life by different cultural groups, religious values and even factors such as the age and marital status of the individual.

All of these factors mean that it is impossible to specify a standard of acceptability for any risk which is absolute and objective. This suggests that the acceptability of any risk can only be assessed on a basis which is both relative and subjective – "relative" in the sense that the risk is compared with other risks about which there is a fairly clear consensus, and "subjective" in the sense that the whole question is ultimately a matter of judgement. But *whose* judgement?

Who should evaluate risks?

The very diversity of the factors discussed above mean that it is simply not possible for any one person to assess risk in a way which will be universally acceptable. If he is too conservative, people will ignore and may even ridicule the evaluation. If he is too relaxed, he might end up being accused of playing with people's lives (if not actually killing them).

This suggests further that a satisfactory evaluation of risk can only be done by a group. As far as possible, this group should represent people who are likely to have a clear understanding of the failure mechanism, the failure effects (especially the nature of any hazards), the likelihood of the failure occurring and what possible measures can be taken to anticipate or prevent the failure.

The group should also include people who will have a legitimate view on the acceptability or otherwise of the risks. This means representatives of the likely victims (most often operators or craftsmen in the case of direct safety hazards) and management (who usually bear the responsibility if someone is hurt or an environmental standard is breached).

If it is applied in a properly focused and structured fashion, the collective wisdom of such a group will do much to ensure that the organisation does the best it can to identify and manage all the failure modes which could affect safety or the environment. (Note that the use of groups like these is in keeping with the worldwide trend towards laws which say that industrial safety is the responsibility of all employees, and not just the responsibility of management.)

Groups of this nature can usually reach consensus quite quickly when dealing with direct safety hazards, because they include the people at risk. Environmental hazards are not quite so simple, because society at large is the "likely victim" and many of the issues involved are unfamiliar. So any group which is expected to consider whether a failure could breach an environmental standard or regulation must find out beforehand which of these standards and regulations cover the process under review.

Safety and Preventive Maintenance

If a failure mode could affect safety or the environment, the RCM process stipulates that we must try to prevent it. The above discussion suggests that preventive maintenance is only worth doing if it reduces the risk of the failure to an acceptably low level.

> *For failure modes which have safety or environmental consequences, a preventive task is only worth doing if it reduces the risk of the failure to an acceptably low level*

If a suitable preventive task cannot be found, redesign is compulsory, simply because we are dealing with a recognised safety or environmental hazard which cannot be adequately prevented. In this context "redesign" means that something must be changed. This could be a modification to the equipment itself, or a change to a process or an operating procedure. As explained in more detail in Chapter 6, such changes are usually undertaken with one of two objectives:

• to reduce the risk of the failure mode occurring to an acceptable level

• to change things in such a way that the failure no longer has safety or environmental consequences.

Note that when dealing with safety and environmental issues, RCM does not raise the question of economics. If it is not safe we have an obligation either to prevent it from failing, or to make it safe. This suggests that the decision process for failure modes which have safety or environmental consequences can be summarised as shown in Figure 4.6 below:

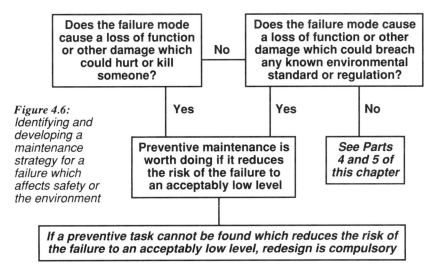

Figure 4.6:
Identifying and developing a maintenance strategy for a failure which affects safety or the environment

The basis on which we determine the technical feasibility and frequency of different types of preventive task is again discussed in Chapter 5.

RCM and Safety Legislation

A question often arises concerning the relationship between RCM and safety legislation (environmental legislation is dealt with directly). In practice, most legislation governing safety merely demands that the users of the assets do whatever is prudent to ensure that the equipment is safe, and is often couched in fairly general terms. In the vast majority of cases, the RCM process wholly satisfies this type of legislation.

However, some regulations demand that specific tasks should be done on specific types of equipment at specific frequencies. If the RCM process suggests a different task and/or a different frequency, it is wise to continue doing the task specified by the legislation and to discuss the suggested change with the appropriate regulatory authority.

4.3 Operational Consequences

How Failures Affect Operations

So far, this chapter has dealt with hidden functions (most of which are protective devices which are not fail-safe), and failures which have safety or environmental consequences.

However, the primary function of most equipment in industry is connected in some way with the need to earn revenue or to support revenue earning activities. For example, the primary function of most equipment used in manufacturing is to add value to materials, while most of the equipment in the transport sector (buses, trucks, trains or aircraft) is used to generate revenue directly.

The failure of much of this equipment affects the revenue-earning capability of the organisation. As often as not, this effect is greater – sometimes much greater – than the cost of repairing the failure. So if a failure is not hidden and does not pose a threat to safety or the environment, the RCM consequence evaluation process focuses next on the operational consequences of failure.

> ***A failure has operational consequences if it has a direct adverse effect on operational capability***

In general, failures affect operations in four ways:

- *they affect total output*. This occurs when equipment stops working altogether or when it works too slowly. As we shall see, this results either in increased production costs if the plant has to work extra time to catch up, or lost sales if the plant is already fully loaded.

- *they affect product quality*. If a machine can no longer hold manufacturing tolerances or if a failure causes materials to deteriorate, the likely result is either scrap or expensive rework.

- *they affect customer service*. Equipment failures affect customer service in many ways, ranging from the late delivery of orders to the late departure of passenger aircraft. Frequent or serious delays sometimes attract heavy penalties (as in large construction contracts), but in most cases they do not result in an *immediate* loss of revenue. However chronic service problems eventually cause customers to lose confidence and take their business elsewhere.

- *increased operating costs in addition to the direct cost of repair.* For instance, the failure might lead to the increased use of energy or it might involve switching to a more expensive alternative process.

All of these consequences are *economic*. In other words, they cost money.

Preventing Operational Failures

The overall economic effect of any failure which has operational consequences depends on two factors:

- how much the failure costs each time it occurs, in terms of its effect on output, quality, service and operating costs plus how much it costs to repair, as discussed above

- how often it happens.

Up to this point, we have not paid much attention to how often failures are likely to occur, because this has not been a primary measure of consequences. (For example, failure rates have little bearing on safety-related failures, because the objective in these cases is to avoid any failures on which to base a rate.) However, if the failure consequences are economic, the total cost *is* affected by how often the consequences are likely to occur. In other words, to assess the economic impact of these failures, we need to assess how much they are likely to cost *over a period of time*.

Consider for example the pump shown in Figure 3.5, and again in Figure 4.7. The pump is controlled by one float switch which activates the pump when the level in Tank Y drops to 120 000 litres, and another which switches the pump off when the level in Tank Y reaches 240 000 litres. A

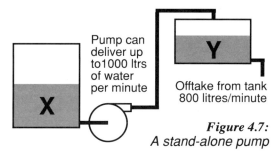

Figure 4.7:
A stand-alone pump

low level alarm is located just below the 120 000 litre level. If the tank runs dry, the downstream process has to be shut down. This costs the organisation which uses the pump £5 000 per hour.

Assume that it has already been agreed that one failure mode which can affect this pump is "Bearing seized", and that this seizure is caused by normal wear and tear. For the sake of simplicity, assume that the motor on this pump is equipped with an overload switch, but there is no trip alarm wired to the control room.

This failure mode and its effects might be described on an RCM Information Worksheet as shown in Figure 4.8:

FAILURE MODE (Cause of failure)	FAILURE EFFECT (What happens when it fails)
1 Bearing seizes	Motor trips but no alarm sounds in control room. Level in tank drops until low level alarm sounds at 120 000 litres. Downtime to replace the bearing 4 hours. *(The mean time between occurrences of this failure mode is about 3 years.)*

Figure 4.8: FMEA for bearing failure on the stand-alone pump

In this example, water is being drawn out of the tank at a rate of 800 litres per minute, so the tank runs dry 2.5 hours after the low level alarm sounds. It takes 4 hours to replace the bearing, so the downstream process stops for 1.5 hours. So this failure costs:

$$1.5 \times £5\,000 = £7\,500$$

in lost production every three years, plus the cost of replacing the bearing.

Assume for the purpose of this example that it is *technically feasible* to check the bearing for audible noise once a week (the basis upon which we make this kind of judgement is discussed at length in the next chapter). If the bearing is found to be noisy, the operational consequences of failure can be avoided by ensuring that the tank is full before starting work on the bearing. This provides five hours of storage, so the bearing can now be replaced in four hours without interfering with the downstream process.

Assume also that the pump is located in an unmanned pumping station. It has been agreed that the check should be carried out by a maintenance craftsman, and that the total time needed to do each check is twenty minutes. Assume further that the total cost of employing the craftsman is £24 per hour, in which case it costs £8 to perform each check. If the MTBF of the bearing is 3 years, he will do about 150 checks per failure. In other words, the cost of the checks is:

$$150 \times £8 = £1\,200$$

every three years, again plus the cost of replacing the bearing.

In this example, the scheduled task is clearly cost-effective relative to the cost of the operational consequences of the failure plus the cost of repair. This suggests that if a failure has operational consequences, the basis for deciding whether a preventive task is worth doing is economic, as follows:

> *For failure modes with operational consequences, a preventive task is worth doing if, over a period of time, it costs less than the cost of the operational consequences plus the cost of repairing the failure which it is meant to prevent*

Conversely, if a cost-effective preventive task cannot be found, then *it is not worth doing any scheduled maintenance* to try to anticipate or prevent the failure mode under consideration.

If a preventive task cannot be found and the failure consequences are still unacceptable, it may be desirable to change the design of the asset (or to change the process) in order to reduce total costs by:

- reducing the frequency of the failure, if not eliminating it altogether
- reducing or eliminating the consequences of the failure
- making a preventive task cost-effective.

Note that to begin with, we again only consider the desirability of making changes *after* we have established whether it is possible to extract the desired performance from the existing asset as it is currently configured. However, in this case modifications also need to be cost-justified, whereas they were the compulsory default action for failure modes with safety or environmental consequences.

In the light of these comments, the decision process for failures with operational consequences can be summarised as follows:

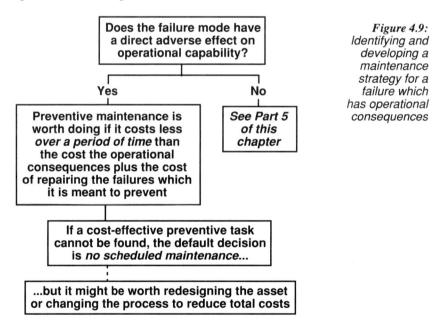

Figure 4.9:
Identifying and developing a maintenance strategy for a failure which has operational consequences

Note that this analysis is carried out for each individual failure mode, and not for the machine as a whole. This is because each preventive task is designed to prevent a specific failure mode, so the economic feasibility of each task can only be compared to the costs of the failure mode which it is meant to prevent. In each case, it is a simple go/no go decision.

In practice, when assessing individual failure modes in this way, it is very seldom necessary to do a detailed cost-benefit study based on actual downtime costs and MTBF's as shown in the example. This is because the economic desirability is usually self-evident in most cases where the failure mode has operational consequences.

Evaluating the need for preventive maintenance in this way takes a great deal of time. However, it yields a very much more precisely focused and much more cost-effective preventive maintenance programme than traditional techniques. It is also much simpler and theoretically much sounder than attempts to assess the need for preventive maintenance on the basis of some hypothetical overall optimum level of plant availability.

Factors Affecting Operational Consequences

A great many factors influence operational failure consequences. They not only vary from machine to machine, but as time passes they also change in response to changing circumstances. The following paragraphs review some of the most important issues which should be considered when assessing these consequences.

Batch and flow processes

A key factor which affects operational failure consequences is the type of production. This ranges from flow process plants where nearly all the equipment is interconnected, to jobbing operations where most of the machines are independent.

In flow processes, the failure of a single item can either stop the entire plant or significantly reduce output, unless surge capacity or stand-by plant is available. The consequences are usually so severe that special efforts are made to prevent the failures, or at least to mitigate their effects. Much of the maintenance work in these plants is done during shutdowns, and a primary maintenance objective is to keep these shutdowns as short and as far apart as possible.

In batch or jobbing plants, most functional failures only curtail the output of a single machine or line. The consequences of such failures are determined mainly by the duration of the stoppage and the amount of work-in-progress queuing in front of subsequent operations. So failure consequences in batch plants tend to be less severe than in flow processes. (Similar reasoning applies to vehicle fleets, where failure consequences are also associated with single items of equipment.)

Most machines in batch plants operate independently, so it is easier to release them one at a time for maintenance. This makes it easier to plan a steady maintenance workload through the year, and a wider variety of preventive tasks and task frequencies can also be accommodated.

Shift arrangements

Shift arrangements profoundly affect the consequences of failure. Some plants operate for eight hours per day five days a week (and even less in bad times). Others operate continuously for seven days a week. Between lie a wide range of alternatives, many of which apply differently in different parts of the same plant.

In a single shift plant, it is possible to make up for time lost due to a failure by working overtime. This leads to increased production costs, so the need for prevention must be considered in the light of these costs.

On the other hand, if the same plant is working to capacity it is not possible to make up for lost time, and so downtime causes lost sales. This costs a great deal more than extra overtime, so it is worth trying much harder to prevent the failure under these circumstances. However, it is also more difficult to make equipment available for maintenance in a fully-loaded plant, so preventive tasks must be selected with special care.

As products move through different stages in their life cycles or as economic conditions change, organisations can move from one end of this spectrum to the other surprisingly quickly. For this reason in particular, it is wise to review maintenance policies continuously in the light of changing circumstances.

Work-in-progress

Work-in-progress refers to any material which has not yet been through all the steps of the manufacturing process. It is usually stored in tanks, in hoppers, in bins on the factory floor, on conveyors or in special stores. The consequences of the failure of any machine are greatly influenced by the amount of this work-in-progress between it and the next machines in the process, and the amount of time needed to repair the failure.

Consider an example where the volume of work in the queue is sufficient to keep the next operation working for six hours and it only takes four hours to repair the failure mode under consideration. In this case, the failure has no operational consequences. Conversely, if it took eight hours to repair, it could have operational consequences because the next operation would come to a halt.

The severity of these consequences in turn depends on:

- the amount of work-in-progress between that operation and the next, and so on down the line
- whether any of the operations affected is a bottleneck operation (in other words an operation which governs the output of the whole line). If it is, the failure will cause lost output, and the consequences of failure are correspondingly severe
- whether it is possible to bypass the failed operation or to make the product on other equipment.

This is complicated by the fact that although failures with operational consequences cost money, it also costs money to hold stocks of work-in-progress. Nowadays stockholding costs of any kind are so high that reducing them to an absolute minimum is a top priority. This is a major objective of "just-in-time" systems and their derivatives.

These systems affect work-in-progress stocks as much as any other, so the cushion which these stocks used to provide against failure is rapidly disappearing. This is something of a vicious circle, because the pressure on maintenance departments to reduce failures in order to make it possible to do without the cushion is also increasing. This in turn means that from the maintenance viewpoint, we need to strike a balance between the economic implications of operational failures, and:

- the cost of holding work-in-progress stocks in order to mitigate the effects of those failures, or
- the cost of doing scheduled maintenance tasks with a view to preventing the failures.

Repair time

The faster a functional failure can be repaired, the smaller its operational consequences. Fast repair times can be achieved by increasing the *speed of response* to the failure. Ways in which this can be done include:

- ensuring that the failure is reported quickly
- ensuring that craftsmen are notified quickly
- employing enough craftsmen on shift to ensure that queues of functional failures awaiting attention do not develop (this is usually a very expensive option, and should only be considered when all other possibilities have been exhausted)

- training operators to repair the failures (response is instantaneous, because the people who would normally report the failures would now repair them).

Faster repair times can also be achieved by increasing the *speed of repair* itself. For complex equipment, this usually means improving the diagnostic ability of the person doing the repairs. In other cases, it may entail modifying the equipment to facilitate repair.

All of these options cost money. So once again, it is a matter of deciding whether to invest in one of the options, or to invest in failure prevention, or just to live with the failure consequences.

Spares

Another factor which profoundly influences the consequences of failure is the availability of spares. In fact, many people seem to have lost sight of the fact that the *only* reason for keeping a stock of spare parts is to avoid or reduce the consequences of failure.

The relationship between spares and failure consequences hinges on the time it takes to procure spares from suppliers. If it could be done instantly there would be no need to stock any spares at all. But in the real world procuring spares takes time. This is known as the lead time, and it ranges from a matter of minutes to several months or years. If the spare is not a stock item, the lead time often dictates how long it takes to repair the failure, and hence the severity of its consequences.

On the other hand, holding spares in stock also costs money. So a balance must be struck between investing in spares stocks, investing in failure prevention or just living with the consequences of failure.

Stand-by plant

The availability of stand-by plant also affects the operational consequences of failure. If no stand-by is available, a functional failure affects operating capability for as long as it takes to repair it. Preventive policies must be considered in the light of these consequences. If a stand-by *is* available it is possible to switch over immediately in the event of a failure, usually with no effect on operations. (Note that stand-by plant itself is a hidden function, and needs to be maintained accordingly.)

But stand-by plant also costs money. So again we must decide whether to invest in stand-by plant, invest in failure prevention or just live with the failure consequences.

Market demand

The operational consequences of failure are sometimes influenced by cyclic variations in demand for the products or services provided by the organisation. For example, soft drink companies experience greater demand for their products in summer than in winter, while urban transport companies experience peak demand during rush hours.

In cases like these, the operational consequences of failure are much more serious at the times of peak demand, so maintenance programmes should be designed to ensure maximum availability at these times.

Raw material supply

Sometimes the consequences of failure are influenced by cyclic fluctuations in the supply of raw materials. Food manufacturers often experience periods of intense activity during harvest times and periods of little or no activity at other times. This applies especially to fruit processors and sugar mills. During peak periods, operational failures not only affect output, but can lead to the loss of large quantities of raw materials if they cannot be processed before they deteriorate.

4.4 Non-operational Consequences

The consequences of an evident failure which has no direct adverse effect on safety, the environment or operational capability are classified as *non-operational*. The only consequences associated with these failures are the direct costs of repair, so these consequences are also *economic*.

Consider for example the pumps shown in Figure 4.10. This set-up is very similar to that shown in Figure 4.7, except that there are now two pumps (both of which are identical to the pump in Figure 4.7). The duty pump is controlled by one float switch which activates the pump when the level in Tank Y drops to 120 000 litres, and another which switches the pump off when the level reaches 240 000 litres. A second switch is located just below the low level switch of the duty pump, and this switch is designed both to sound an alarm in the control room if the water level reaches it, and to switch on the stand-by pump. If the tank runs dry, the downstream process has to be shut down. This also costs the organisation which uses the pump £5 000 per hour.

As before, assume that it has already been agreed that one failure mode which can affect the duty pump is "Bearing seized", and that this seizure is caused by normal wear and tear. Assume that the motor on the duty pump is also equipped with an overload switch, but again there is no trip alarm wired to the control room.

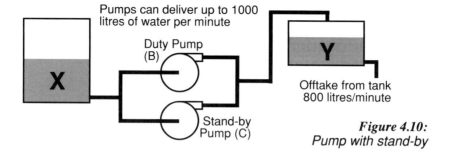

Figure 4.10:
Pump with stand-by

This failure mode and its effects might be described on an RCM Information Work-sheet as shown in Figure 4.11:

	FAILURE MODE *(Cause of failure)*	FAILURE EFFECT *(What happens when it fails)*
1	Bearing seizes	Motor trips but no alarm sounds in control room. Level in tank drops until low level alarm sounds at 120 000 litres, and stand-by pump is switched on automatically. Time required to replace the bearing 4 hours. *(The mean time between occurrences of this failure is about 3 years.)*

Figure 4.11: FMEA for failure of bearing on duty pump with stand-by

In this example, the stand-by pump is switched on when the duty pump fails, so the tank does not run dry. So the only cost associated with this failure is:

the cost of replacing the bearing.

Assume however that it is still *technically feasible* to check the bearing for audible noise once a week. If the bearing were found to be noisy, the operators would switch over manually to the stand-by pump and the bearing would be replaced.

Assume that these pumps are also located in an unmanned pumping station., and that it has again been agreed that the check – which also takes twenty minutes – should be done by a maintenance craftsman at a cost of £8 per check. So once again, he will do about 150 checks per failure. In other words, the cost of the preventive maintenance programme per failure is:

150 x £8 = £1 200 plus the cost of replacing the bearing.

In this example, the cost of doing the scheduled task is now much greater than the cost of not doing it. As a result, it is not worth doing the preventive task *even though the pump is technically identical to the pump described in Figure 4.8.*

This suggests that it is only worth trying to prevent a failure which has non-operational consequences if, over a period of time, the cost of the preventive task is less than the cost of correcting the failure. If it is not, then scheduled maintenance is not worth doing.

> ***For failure modes with non-operational consequences,***
> ***a preventive task is worth doing if over a period of time,***
> ***it costs less than the cost of repairing the failures which***
> ***it is meant to prevent***

If a preventive task is not worth doing, then in rare cases a modification might be justified for much the same reasons as those which apply to failures with operational consequences.

Further Points Concerning Non-operational Consequences

Three more points need to be considered when reviewing failures with non-operational consequences, as follows:

- *secondary damage:* Some failure modes cause considerable secondary damage if they are not anticipated or prevented, which adds to the cost of repairing them. A suitable preventive task could make it possible to prevent or anticipate the failure and avoid this damage. However, such a task is only justified if the cost of doing it is less than the cost of repairing the failure and the secondary damage.

  For example, in Figure 4.11 the description of the failure effects suggests that the seizure of the bearing causes no secondary damage. If this is so, then the analysis is valid. However, if the unanticipated failure of the bearing also causes (say) the shaft to shear, then a preventive task which detects imminent bearing failure would enable the operators to shut down the pump before the shaft is damaged. In this case the cost of the unanticipated failure of the bearing is:
  the cost of replacing the bearing and the shaft.
  On the other hand, the cost of the preventive task (per bearing failure) is still:
  £1 200 plus the cost of replacing the bearing.
  Clearly, the task is worth doing if the cost of replacing the shaft is greater than £1 200. If it costs less than £1 200 to replace the shaft, then *this task* is still not worth doing.

- *protected functions:* it is only valid to say that a failure will have non-operational consequences because a stand-by or redundant component is available if it is reasonable to assume that the protective device will be functional when the failure occurs. This of course means that a suitable maintenance programme must be applied to the protective device (the stand-by pump in the example given above).

- *serious multiple failures:* if the consequences of the multiple failure of a protected system are particularly serious, then it may be worth trying to prevent the failure of the protected function as well as the protective device, as illustrated in Figure 4.3 and 4.4.

4.5 Conclusion

This chapter has demonstrated how the RCM process provides a comprehensive strategic framework for managing failures. As summarised in Figure 4.12, this framework:

- classifies all failures on the basis of their consequences. In so doing it separates hidden failures from evident failures, and then ranks the consequences of the evident failures in descending order of importance

- provides a basis for deciding whether preventive maintenance is worth doing in each case

- suggests what action should be taken if a suitable preventive task cannot be found.

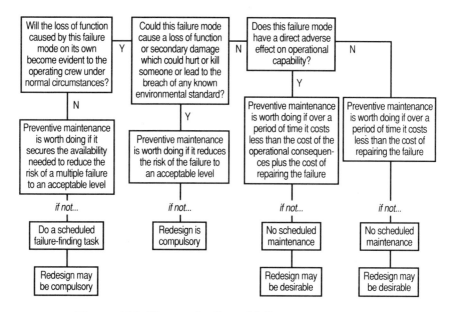

Figure 4.12: *The evaluation of failure consequences*

The different types of preventive tasks and default actions are discussed in the next three chapters, together with an integrated approach to consequence evaluation and task selection.

5 Preventive Tasks

5.1 Technical Feasibility

Chapter 4 explained that the primary objective of preventive maintenance is to avoid, or at least to reduce, the *consequences* of failure. This led to the conclusion that a preventive task is only *worth doing* if it deals successfully with the consequences of the failure mode which it is meant to prevent, as follows:

- if the failure is *hidden*, the task must secure the availability needed to reduce the risk of a multiple failure to an acceptable level. If a suitable preventive task cannot be found, the initial default action is scheduled failure-finding.

- if the failure has *safety* or *environmental consequences*, the task should reduce the risk of failure to a very low level indeed (if not eliminate it). If a suitable preventive task cannot be found, the default action is that something must be changed (the process or the design of the asset).

- if the failure has *operational* or *non-operational* consequences, the total cost of doing the preventive task over a period of time must be lower than the cost of not doing it. If a cost-effective preventive task cannot be found, the initial default action is no scheduled maintenance.

This framework suggests that the actions which can be taken to deal with failures can be divided into two groups – *preventive* tasks, and *default* tasks which must be undertaken if a suitable preventive task cannot be found. These correspond to the sixth and seventh of the seven questions which make up the basic RCM decision process, as follows:

- *what can be done to prevent each failure?*

- *what if a suitable preventive task cannot be found?*

This chapter focuses on the sixth question. Specifically, it concentrates on the criteria used to decide whether tasks are *technically feasible*, but it also looks in more detail at how we decide whether specific categories of tasks are worth doing. (Chapter 6 reviews the default tasks.)

When we ask whether a preventive task is technically feasible, we are simply asking whether it is *possible* for the task to prevent or anticipate the failure in question. This has nothing to do with economics – economics are part of the consequence evaluation process which has already been considered at length – but instead it depends on the technical characteristics of the failure mode and of the task itself.

> ***Whether or not a preventive task is technically***
> ***feasible depends on the technical characteristics***
> ***of the failure mode and of the task***

This chapter develops the criteria for technical feasibility for the three principal categories of preventive tasks, which are scheduled *on-condition* tasks, scheduled *restoration* tasks and scheduled *discard* tasks. We will also see that two issues dominate task selection from the technical viewpoint. These are:

• the relationship between the age of the item under consideration and how likely it is to fail

• what happens once a failure has started to occur.

The following paragraphs start by considering tasks which apply when there is a relationship between age (or exposure to stress) and failure, and then consider the more difficult cases where there is no such relationship.

5.2 Age-Related Failures

For centuries – certainly since machines have come into widespread use – mankind has tended to believe that as equipment gets older, it is more likely to fail. Figure 5.1 illustrates this view of failure. It assumes that similar items performing a similar duty will perform reliably for a period, perhaps with a small number of random early failures, and then most of the items "wear out" at about the same time.

Figure 5.1:
The traditional
view of failure

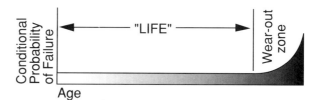

The wear-out point is known as the point at which there is a *rapid increase in the conditional probability of failure*. This is actually a somewhat simplistic view of the relationship between age and failure, because there are in fact three ways in which the probability of failure can increase as an item gets older. These are illustrated in Figure 5.2.

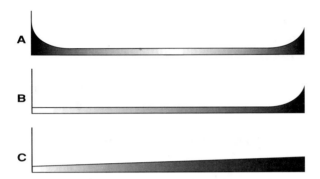

Figure 5.2:
Age-related
failure patterns

These patterns were introduced in Chapter 1 and are discussed at much greater length in Chapter 9. The characteristic shared by patterns A and B is that they both display a point at which there is a rapid increase in the conditional probability of failure. As we shall see, this makes them comparatively easy to deal with from the preventive maintenance viewpoint. Pattern C however shows a steady increase in the probability of failure, but no distinct wear-out zone.

In general, age-related failure patterns apply to items which are very simple, or to complex items which suffer from one or two dominant failure modes. In practice, they are commonly found under conditions of direct wear (typically at points where the equipment comes into direct contact with the product), and they are also associated with fatigue, corrosion and oxidation.

> ***Wear-out characteristics most often occur where equipment comes into direct contact with the product. Age-related failures also tend to be associated with fatigue, oxidation and corrosion.***

A number of examples of points where *equipment comes into contact with the product* were given on page 12.

Fatigue affects items – especially metallic items – which are subjected to reasonably high-frequency cyclic loads. The rate and extent to which *oxidation* and *corrosion* affect any item depend of course on its chemical composition, the extent to which it is protected and the environment in which it is operating.

For items which do conform to one of the failure patterns shown in Figure 5.2, classical theory suggests that it is possible to determine a point, usually referred to as a "life", at which it is possible to take some sort of action to prevent the failures from happening again in the future, or at least to reduce the consequences of the failures.

Two preventive options which are available under these circumstances are *scheduled restoration tasks* and s*cheduled discard tasks*. They are considered in more detail in the next two sections of this chapter.

5.3   Scheduled Restoration Tasks

As the name implies, scheduled restoration entails taking periodic action to restore an existing item or component to its original condition (or more accurately, to restore its original *resistance to failure*). Specifically:

> ***Scheduled restoration entails remanufacturing a single component or overhauling an entire assembly at or before a specified age limit, regardless of its condition at the time***

Scheduled restoration tasks are also known as *scheduled rework tasks*. As the above definition suggests, they include overhauls which are done at pre-set intervals.

The Frequency of Scheduled Restoration Tasks

If the failure mode under consideration conforms to Pattern A or B, it is possible to identify the age at which wear-out begins. This is commonly regarded as the "life" of the item. The scheduled restoration task is done at intervals slightly less than this life. In other words:

> ***The frequency of a scheduled restoration task is governed by the age at which the item or component shows a rapid increase in the conditional probability of failure.***

In the case of Pattern C, at least four different restoration intervals need to be analysed to determine the optimum interval (if one exists at all). This is also discussed in more detail in Chapter 9.

In practice, the frequency of a scheduled restoration task can only be determined satisfactorily on the basis of reliable historical data. This is seldom available when assets first go into service, so it is usually impossible to specify scheduled restoration tasks in prior-to-service maintenance programmes. (For example scheduled restoration tasks were only assigned to seven components in the initial programme developed for the Douglas DC 10). However, items subject to very expensive failure modes should be put into age exploration programmes as soon as possible to find out if they would benefit from scheduled restoration tasks.

The Technical Feasibility of Scheduled Restoration

The above comments indicate that for a scheduled restoration task to be technically feasible, the first criteria which must be satisfied are that

- there must be a point at which there is an increase in the conditional probability of failure (in other words, the item must have a "life")
- we must be reasonably sure what the life is.

Secondly, most of the items must survive to this age. If too many items fail before reaching it, the nett result is an increase in unanticipated failures. Not only could this have unacceptable consequences, but it means that the associated restoration tasks are done out of sequence. This in turn disrupts the entire schedule planning process.

(Note that if the failure has safety or environmental consequences, *all* the items must survive to the age at which the scheduled restoration task is to be done, because we cannot risk failures which might hurt people or damage the environment. In this context, the comments about safe-life limits which are made in the next part of this chapter apply equally to scheduled restoration tasks.)

Finally, scheduled restoration must restore the original resistance to failure of the asset, or at least something close enough to the original condition to ensure that the item continues to be able to fulfil its intended function for a reasonable period of time.

For example, no-one in his right mind would try to overhaul a domestic light bulb, simply because it is not possible to restore it to anything like its original condition (regardless of the economics of the matter). On the other hand, it could be argued that retreading a tyre restores it to something approaching its original condition.

These points lead to the following general conclusions about the technical feasibility of scheduled restoration:

> ### *Scheduled restoration tasks are technically feasible if:*
> - *there is an identifiable age at which the item shows a rapid increase in the conditional probability of failure*
> - *most of the items survive to that age (all of the items if the failure has safety or environmental consequences)*
> - *they restore the original resistance to failure of the item*

The Effectiveness of Scheduled Restoration Tasks

Even if it is technically feasible, scheduled restoration might still not be worth doing. This is because other tasks may be even more effective. Examples showing how this might occur in practice are discussed later in this paper.

If a more effective task cannot be found, there is often a temptation to select scheduled restoration tasks purely on the grounds of technical feasibility. An age limit applied to an item which behaves as shown in Figure 5.1 means that some items will receive attention before they need it while others might fail early, but the nett effect may be an overall reduction in the number of unanticipated failures. However even then scheduled restoration might not be worth doing, for the following reasons:

- as mentioned earlier, a reduction in the number of failures is not sufficient if the failure has *safety* or *environmental* consequences, because we want to eliminate these failures altogether.

- if the consequences are economic, we need to be sure that over a period of time, the cost of doing the scheduled restoration task is less than the cost of allowing the failure to occur. When comparing the two, bear in mind that an age limit lowers the service life of any item, so it increases the number of items sent to the workshop for restoration. Why this is so is shown in Figure 5.3 (which is the same as failure pattern B, except that it shows frequency of failure instead of probability of failure):

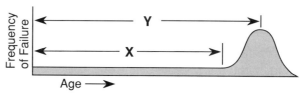

Figure 5.3:
"Useful" life (X) vs
"average" life (Y)

If no preventive maintenance is done, Y is the average age at which failures occur. (As explained in Chapter 9, this is known as the average life or the mean time between failures.) To prevent most of the failures, scheduled restoration must be done before age X, which is the age at which there is a rapid increase in the conditional probability of failure (and which we will refer to as the "useful life").

For example, consider a case where X is 18 months, and Y is 24 months. In a period of twelve years, the failure occurs *six* times if no preventive maintenance is done, while the preventive task would be done *eight* times. In other words, the preventive task has to be done 33% more often than the failure would occur on its own.

If each failure costs (say) £2000 in lost production and repair, failures would cost £12000 over a twelve year period. If each scheduled restoration task costs (say) £1200, these tasks would cost £9600 over the same period. So in this case, the task *is* cost-effective.

On the other hand, if Y is 36 months and all other figures remain the same, failures only occur four times every twelve years, and would cost £8000 over this period. The scheduled restoration task would still cost £9600 over the same period, so it would *not* be cost-effective.

When considering failures which have operational consequences, bear in mind that a scheduled restoration task may itself affect operations. In most cases, this effect is likely to be less than the consequences of the failure because:

• the scheduled restoration task would normally be done at a time when it is likely to have the least effect on production (usually during a so-called production window)

• the scheduled restoration task is likely to take less time than it would to repair the failure because it is possible to plan more thoroughly for the scheduled task.

If there are no operational consequences, scheduled restoration is only justified if it costs substantially less than the cost of repair (which may be the case if the failure causes extensive secondary damage).

5.4   Scheduled Discard Tasks

Once again as the name implies, scheduled discard means replacing an item or component with a new one at pre-set intervals. Specifically:

> ### *Scheduled discard tasks entail discarding an item or component at or before a specified age limit, regardless of its condition at the time*

These tasks are done on the understanding that replacing the old component with a new one *will* restore the original resistance to failure.

The Frequency of Scheduled Discard Tasks

Like scheduled restoration tasks, scheduled discard tasks are only technically feasible if there is a direct relationship between failure and operating age, as shown by the graphs in Figure 5.2. The frequency at which they are done is determined on the same basis, so:

> ### *The frequency of a scheduled discard task is governed by the age at which the item or component shows a rapid increase in the conditional probability of failure*

In general, there is a particularly widely held belief that all items "have a life", and that installing a new part before this "life" is reached will automatically make it "safe". This is not always true, so RCM takes special care to focus on safety when considering scheduled discard tasks.

For this reason, RCM recognises two different types of life-limits when dealing with scheduled discard tasks. The first apply to tasks meant to avoid failures which have safety consequences, and are called *safe-life* limits. Those which are intended to prevent failures which do not have safety consequences are called *economic-life* limits.

Safe-life limits

Safe-life limits only apply to failures which have safety or environmental consequences so the associated tasks must prevent all failures. In other words, no failures should occur before this limit is reached. This means that safe-life limits cannot apply to items which conform to pattern A, because infant mortality means that some items must fail prematurely. In fact, they cannot apply to *any* failure mode where the probability of failure is more than zero to begin with.

In practice, safe-life limits can only apply to failure modes which occur in such a way that *no* failures can be expected to occur before the wear-out zone is reached.

Ideally, safe-life limits should be determined before the item is put into service. It should be tested in a simulated operating environment to determine what average life is actually achieved, and a conservative fraction of this life used as the safe-life limit. This is illustrated in Figure 5.4.

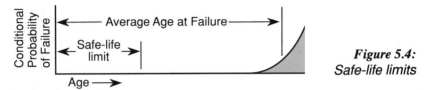

Figure 5.4:
Safe-life limits

There is never a perfect correlation between a test environment and the operating environment. Testing a long-lived part to failure is also costly and obviously takes a long time, so there is usually not enough test data for survival curves to be drawn with confidence. In these cases safe-life limits can be established by dividing the average by an arbitrary factor as large as three or four. This implies that the conditional probability of failure at the life limit would essentially be zero. In other words, the safe-life limit is based on a 100% probability of survival to that age.

The function of a safe-life limit is to avoid the occurrence of a critical failure, so the resulting discard task is *worth doing* only if it ensures that no failures occur before the safe-life limit.

Economic-life limits

Operating experience sometimes suggests that the scheduled discard of an item is desirable on economic grounds. This is known as an *economic-life limit*. It is based on the actual age-reliability relationship of the item, rather than a fraction of the average age at failure.

The only justification for an economic life limit is cost-effectiveness. In the same way that scheduled restoration increases the number of jobs passing through the workshop, so scheduled discard increases the consumption of the parts which are subject to discard. As a result, the cost-effectiveness of scheduled discard tasks is determined in the same way as it is for scheduled restoration tasks.

In general, an economic life-limit is *worth applying* if it avoids or reduces the operational consequences of an unanticipated failure, or if the failure which it prevents causes significant secondary damage.

Clearly, we must know the failure pattern before we can assess the cost effectiveness of scheduled discard tasks. For new assets, a failure mode which has major economic consequences should also be put into an age-exploration programme to find out if a life limit is applicable. However, as with scheduled restoration, there is seldom enough evidence to include this type of task in an initial scheduled maintenance programme.

The Technical Feasibility of Scheduled Discard Tasks

The above comments indicate that scheduled discard tasks are technically feasible under the following circumstances:

> *Scheduled discard tasks are technically feasible if:*
> - *there is an identifiable age at which the item shows a rapid increase in the conditional probability of failure*
> - *most of the items survive to that age (all of the items if the failure has safety or environmental consequences)*

There is no need to ask if the task will restore the original condition because the item is replaced with a new one.

5.5   Failures which are Not Age-related

We have seen that the age-related failure patterns shown in Figure 5.2 usually apply where the equipment comes into contact with the product, or where fatigue, oxidation or corrosion is present. However, as mentioned in Chapter 1, the majority of failure modes conform to one of the failure patterns shown in Figure 5.4.

Figure 5.5:
Failures which
are not
age-related

In general, the failure patterns depend on the complexity of the item. The more complex the item the more likely it is to conform to patterns E and F. These patterns are typically associated with electronic, hydraulic and pneumatic equipment. (The majority of rolling element bearings also conform to failure pattern E.)

The most important characteristic of patterns D, E and F is that after the initial period, there is little or no relationship between reliability and operating age. In these cases, unless there is a dominant age-related failure mode, age limits do little or nothing to reduce the probability of failure.

(In fact, scheduled overhauls can actually *increase* overall failure rates by introducing high infant mortality into otherwise stable systems. This is borne out by the high and rising number of nasty accidents around the world which have occurred either while maintenance is under way or immediately after a maintenance intervention. It is also borne out by the production man who says that "every time maintenance works on it over the weekend, it takes us until Wednesday to get it going again".)

As mentioned in Chapter 1, an intuitive awareness of these facts has led some people to abandon the idea of preventive maintenance altogether. Although this can be the right thing to do for failures with minor consequences, when the failure consequences are serious, *something* must be done to prevent the failures or at least to avoid the consequences.

The continuing need to prevent certain types of failure, and the growing inability of classical techniques to do so, are behind the growth of new types of failure prevention. Foremost among these are the techniques known as on-condition maintenance.

5.6   Scheduled On-condition Tasks

Potential Failures

On-condition maintenance is based on the fact that a great many failures do not occur instantaneously, but actually develop over a period of time. As we shall see, if evidence can be found that this failure process is under way, it may be possible to take action to prevent the failure and/or to avoid the consequences.

The point in the failure process at which it is possible to detect that the failure is occurring or is about to occur is known as a *potential failure*.

A potential failure is an identifiable physical condition which indicates that a functional failure is either about to occur or in the process of occurring

Examples of potential failures include
* hot spots showing deterioration of furnace refractories
* vibrations indicating imminent bearing failure
* cracks showing metal fatigue
* particles in gearbox oil showing imminent gear failure
* excessive tread wear on tyres, etc.

In practice, there are thousands of ways of finding out if failures are in the process of occurring. Figure 5.6 illustrates the general process. It is called the *P-F curve,* because it shows how a failure starts, deteriorates to the point at which it can be detected (the potential failure point "P") and then, if it is not detected and corrected, continues to deteriorate – usually at an accelerating rate – until it reaches the point of functional failure ("F").

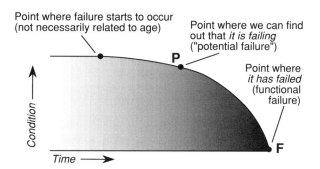

Figure 5.6:
The P-F curve

If a potential failure is detected between point P and point F, there are two possibilities:

* *to prevent the functional failure*. Depending on the nature of the failure mechanism, it is sometimes possible to intervene to repair the existing component before it fails completely. In this case, we both prevent the failure *and* avoid or reduce the consequences.

For instance, a crack in a wall is a potential failure. If it is discovered in time, it may be possible to shore up the foundations and so prevent the wall from deteriorating to the point that it falls down (the functional failure). In this case, there are likely to be operational consequences because it would probably be necessary to vacate the premises while this work is under way, but at least we avoid the safety consequences which would arise if the wall fell down.

- *to avoid the consequences of the failure.* In most cases, detecting a potential failure does not actually prevent the item from failing, but still makes it possible to avoid or reduce the consequences of the failure.

For example, the unanticipated failure of a ball bearing may have a serious effect on production. If it is found to be noisy before it seizes, it may be possible to replace it at a time when production is not affected. In this case, the failure of the bearing is not "prevented" – it is doomed whatever happens – but the operational consequences of the failure are avoided.

This leads to the concept of *on-condition maintenance*, which is defined as checking items for potential failures so that action can be taken to prevent or to avoid the consequences of the functional failure.

> ***On-condition tasks entail checking equipment for potential failures, so that action can be taken either to prevent the functional failure or to avoid the consequences of the functional failure***

On-condition tasks are so called because the items which are inspected are left in service *on the condition* that they continue to meet specified performance standards.

The Frequency of On-condition Tasks

In addition to the potential failure itself, we need to consider the amount of time (or the number of stress cycles) which elapse between the point at which a potential failure occurs – in other words, the point at which it becomes *detectable* – and the point where it deteriorates into a functional failure. As shown in Figure 5.7, this interval is known as the *P-F interval*.

> ***The P-F interval is the interval between the occurrence of a potential failure and its decay into a functional failure***

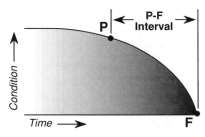

Figure 5.7: The P-F interval

The P-F interval is important because it governs the frequency at which the on-condition task must be done. The frequency of checking must be significantly less than the P-F interval if we want to detect the potential failure before it becomes a functional failure.

The frequency of on-condition tasks
must be less than the P-F interval

The P-F interval is also known as the warning period or the lead time to failure. It can be measured in any units which provide an indication of exposure to stress (running time, units of output, stop-start cycles etc), but for reasons discussed in more detail in Chapter 7, it is most often measured in terms of elapsed time. For different failure modes, it varies from fractions of a second to several decades.

Note that if an on-condition task is done at intervals which are longer than the P-F interval, there is a chance that we will miss the failure altogether. On the other hand, if we do the task at too small a percentage of the P-F interval, we will waste resources on the checking process.

For instance, if the P-F interval for a given failure mode is two weeks, we will be certain of detecting the failure if the item is checked once a week. Conversely, if it is checked once a month, it is possible to miss the whole failure process. On the other hand if the P-F interval is three months, it is a waste of resources to check the item every day.

In practice it is usually sufficient to select a task frequency equal to half the P-F interval. This ensures that the inspection will detect the potential failure before the functional failure occurs, while (in most cases) providing a reasonable amount of time to do something about it.

This leads to the concept of the *nett P-F interval*, which is the minimum interval likely to elapse between the *discovery* of a potential failure and the occurrence of the functional failure. This is illustrated in Figures 5.8 and 5.9, which both show a failure with a P-F interval of nine months.

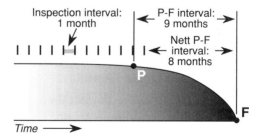

Figure 5.8:
Nett P-F interval (1)

If the item is inspected monthly as shown in Figure 5.8, the nett P-F interval is 8 months. On the other hand, if it is inspected at six monthly intervals as shown in Figure 5.9, the nett P-F interval is 3 months. This means that in the first case the minimum amount of time available to do something about the failure is five months longer than in the second, but the inspection task has to be done six times more often.

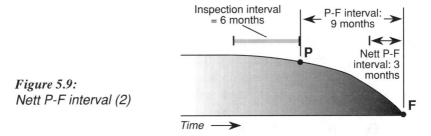

Figure 5.9:
Nett P-F interval (2)

The nett P-F interval governs the amount of time *available* to:

• take whatever action is needed to avoid the consequences of the failure

• plan corrective action so that it can be done without disrupting production and without disrupting other maintenance activities

• organise the people and materials needed to rectify the failure.

In some cases the amount of time *required* is a matter of hours (say until the end of an operating cycle or the end of a shift) or even minutes, as we will see later. In others it can be weeks or even months (say until a major shutdown). This means that the amount of time needed to do something about the potential failure must be considered within the framework of the P-F interval when setting on-condition task frequencies. If the nett P-F interval is too short for any sensible action to be taken, then the on-condition task is clearly not technically feasible.

   This leads to the general conclusion that longer P-F intervals are desirable for four reasons:

• fewer on-condition inspections are required

• there is more time to organise the people and materials needed to correct the potential failure

• it is easier to plan to correct the potential failure without disrupting operations or other maintenance activities

• it is possible to do whatever is necessary to avoid the consequences of the failure in a more considered and hence more controlled fashion.

This explains why so much energy is being devoted to finding potential failure conditions and associated on-condition techniques which give the longest possible P-F intervals.

Clearly, the P-F interval must also be fairly consistent if it is to provide a reliable basis for planning. This issue is discussed in more detail later. However, note that it is possible to make use of very short P-F intervals in certain specialised cases.

For example, failures which affect the balance of large fans cause serious problems very quickly, so on-line vibration sensors are used to shut the fans down when such failures occur. In this case, the P-F interval is very short, so monitoring is continuous. Note also that the monitoring device is being used *to avoid the consequences* of the failure.

Technical Feasibility of On-condition Tasks

The above paragraphs suggest that on-condition tasks are technically feasible if they satisfy the following criteria:

> *Scheduled on-condition tasks are technically feasible if:*
> - *it is possible to define a clear potential failure condition*
> - *the P-F interval is fairly consistent*
> - *it is practical to monitor the item at intervals less than the P-F interval*
> - *the nett P-F interval is long enough to be of some use (in other words, long enough to prevent or avoid the consequences of the functional failure)*

Categories of On-condition Techniques

The four major categories of on-condition techniques are as follows:
- *condition monitoring* techniques
- techniques based on variations in *product quality*
- *primary effects monitoring* techniques
- inspection techniques based on the *human senses.*

These are each reviewed in the following paragraphs.

Condition monitoring

The most sensitive on-condition maintenance techniques usually involve the use of some type of equipment to detect potential failures. In other words, equipment is used to monitor the condition of other equipment. These techniques are known as *condition monitoring* to distinguish them from other types of on-condition maintenance.

Condition monitoring techniques are seldom more than highly sensitive versions of the human senses. Some of them are now very sensitive indeed, and can give several months (if not several years) warning of failure. However, a major limitation of nearly every condition monitoring device is that it monitors only one condition. For instance, a vibration analyser only monitors vibration and cannot detect chemicals or temperature changes. So greater sensitivity is bought at the price of the versatility which is inherent in the human senses.

The P-F intervals associated with different monitoring techniques vary from a few minutes to several months. Different techniques also pinpoint failures with different degrees of precision. Both of these factors must be considered when assessing the *feasibility* of any technique.

The purchase price of different condition monitoring systems ranges from a few hundred to tens of thousands of pounds. Some can be applied by semi-skilled workers while others need highly skilled technicians. In many cases, monitoring devices are permanently built into the equipment. (Note that when this is done, the monitoring device comprises an additional, usually hidden, function, so its maintenance requirements must be assessed along with all the others.) Other condition monitoring services are offered by central bureaux on a fee-paying basis.

These considerations all help to decide whether condition monitoring is *worth doing,* and need to be evaluated as carefully as those which effect technical feasibility.

Condition monitoring embraces several hundred different techniques, so a detailed study of the subject is well beyond the scope of this chapter. However, Appendix I provides a brief summary of about fifty of the better known techniques. All of these techniques are designed to detect failure *effects* (or more precisely, potential failure effects, such as changes in vibration characteristics, changes in temperature, particles in lubricating oil, leaks, and so on). They are classified accordingly in Appendix I under the following headings:
• dynamic effects
• particle effects
• chemical effects
• physical effects
• temperature effects
• electrical effects.
The criteria for assessing whether on-condition tasks are technically feasible and worth doing should be applied especially rigorously to condition

monitoring techniques, because condition monitoring can be spectacularly effective when it is appropriate, but when it is inappropriate it can be a very expensive and sometimes bitterly disappointing waste of time.

Product quality variation

In some industries, an important source of data about potential failures is the quality management function. Often the emergence of a defect in an article produced by a machine is directly related to a defect in the machine itself. Many of these defects emerge gradually, and so provide timely evidence of potential failures. If the data gathering and evaluation procedures exist already, it costs very little to use them to provide warning of equipment failure.

For example Statistical Process Control (SPC) is being used increasingly widely to monitor product quality. SPC checks are usually carried out by machine operators, and the measurements recorded on an SPC chart as shown by the crosses in Figure 5.10.

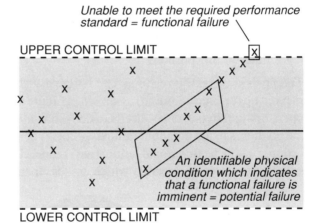

Figure 5.10:
On-condition
maintenance
and SPC

The process is considered to be "out of control" – in other words, in a functionally failed state – if the measurements fall outside the upper or lower control limits. Figure 5.10 indicates how these measurements correspond to the concepts of a potential and functional failure. It suggests that SPC can be seen as a form of on-condition maintenance, especially where deviations are associated directly with specific failure modes.

So these valuable sources of on-condition data should be incorporated into maintenance systems whenever there is an appropriate relationship between a failure mode and a product quality characteristic.

Primary effects monitoring

Primary effects (speed, flow rate, pressure, temperature, power, current, etc) are yet another source of information about equipment condition. The effects can be monitored by
• a person reading a gauge and perhaps recording the reading manually
• a computer as part of a process control system
• a traditional chart recorder.
The records of these effects or their derivatives are compared with reference information, and so provide evidence of a potential failure. However, in the case of the first option in particular, take care to ensure that:

• the person taking the reading knows what the reading should be when all is well, what reading corresponds to a potential failure and what corresponds to functional failure

• the readings are taken at a frequency which is less than the P-F interval (in other words, the frequency should be less than the time it takes the pointer on the dial to move from the potential failure level to the functional failure level when the failure mode in question is occurring)

• that the gauge itself is maintained in such a way that it is sufficiently accurate for this purpose.

The process of taking readings can be greatly simplified if gauges are marked up (or even coloured) as shown in Figure 5.11. In this case, all the operator – or anyone else – needs to do is look at the gauge and report if the pointer is in the potential failure (yellow?) zone, or take more drastic action if it is in the functional failure (red?) zone. However the gauge must still be monitored at intervals which arc less than the P-F interval.

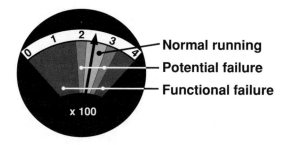

Figure 5.11:
Using gauges
for on-condition
maintenance

(For obvious reasons, this suggestion only applies to gauges which are measuring a steady state. Also take care to ensure that gauges marked up in this way are not taken off and remounted in the wrong place.)

The human senses

Perhaps the best known on-condition inspection techniques are those based on the human senses (look, listen, feel and smell). The two main disadvantages of using these senses to detect potential failures are that:

- the process is subjective, so it is difficult to develop precise inspection criteria
- by the time it is possible to detect most failures using the human senses, the process of deterioration is already quite far advanced. This means that the P-F intervals are usually short, so the checks must be done more frequently than most and response has to be rapid.

However, the advantages of using these senses are as follows:

- the average human being is highly versatile and can detect a wide variety of failure conditions, whereas any one condition monitoring technique can only be used to monitor one type of potential failure
- if extensive use is made of people who are at or near the assets anyway in the course of their normal duties, this form of monitoring can be very cost-effective.

In particular, the human senses are worth considering where failure is random or there is a high degree of infant mortality, and P-F intervals are short. In these cases, monitoring needs to be virtually continuous. While on-line monitoring techniques may be technically feasible for some of these failures, they are often too expensive to be justified by the consequences of the failures.

Maintenance craftsmen can be used to do these inspections, but this too is often impractical for the following reasons:

- if the P-F interval is short, the inspection frequency will be very high – sometimes more than once per shift. This can lead to so many high-frequency tasks that craftsmen do little more than travel from one inspection to the next. This travelling time plus the cost of planning and controlling the inspections makes the use of craftsmen for this purpose expensive, often to the point where it is simply not worth using them in this capacity.
- many skilled craftsmen find high frequency inspections boring and are often reluctant to do them at all.
- skilled craftsmen are very scarce in many parts of the world, so it is often difficult to spare them for this kind of work in the first place.

A third option is to use operators to do high frequency inspections. The main attraction of using operators in this capacity is that they are near the equipment all the time, so it is more economical and organisationally easier for them to do high frequency checks. This can have profound implications in terms of organisation, industrial relations and reporting relationships. Yet operators can do a great deal to improve the effectiveness of these inspections, subject to three conditions:

- they are properly trained in how to recognise the conditions which they are expected to diagnose
- they have access to simple and reliable procedures for reporting any problems which they do find (this is discussed in detail in Chapter 8)
- they can be reasonably sure that action will be taken on the basis of their reports, or that they will receive constructive feedback in cases of misdiagnosis.

On-condition Tasks: Some of the Pitfalls

When considering the technical feasibility of on-condition maintenance, three issues need special care. They concern:
• functional failures preceded by more than one potential failure
• the distinction between potential and functional failures
• the distinction between potential failure and age.
These issues are discussed in more detail in the following paragraphs.

Functional failures preceded by more than one potential failure

Most failure modes can be preceded by more than one – often several – different potential failures. Each one of these potential failures will have a different P-F interval, and will require different types and levels of skill to apply. It is essential to consider as many different potential failures as possible when considering each failure mode, in order to ensure that the most cost-effective maintenance programme is developed.

> ***All the potential failures and on-condition tasks which could apply to each failure mode should be considered***

For example, consider a ball bearing whose failure is described as "bearing seizes due to normal wear and tear". Figure 5.12 shows how this failure could be preceded by a variety of potential failures, each of which could be detected by a different on-condition task.

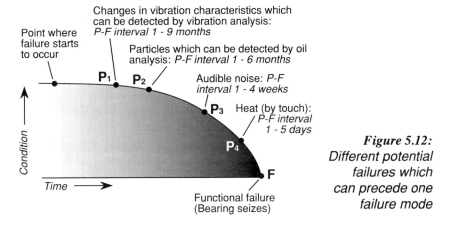

Figure 5.12:
Different potential failures which can precede one failure mode

This does not mean *all* ball bearings will exhibit these potential failures, nor will they necessarily have the same P-F intervals. The extent to which each technique is technically feasible and worth doing depends very much on the operating context of the bearing. For instance:

* the bearing may be buried so deep in the machine that it is impossible to monitor its vibration characteristics

* it is only possible to detect particles in the oil if the bearing is operating in a totally enclosed oil-lubricated system

* background noise levels may be so high that it is impossible to detect the noise made by a failing bearing

* it may not be possible to reach the bearing housing to feel how hot it is.

Potential and functional failures

In practice, confusion often arises over the distinction between potential and functional failures. This happens because certain conditions can correctly be regarded as potential failures in one context and as functional failures in another. This is especially common in the case of leaks.

For example, a minor leak in a flanged joint on a pipeline might be regarded as a potential failure if the pipeline is carrying water. In this case, the on-condition task would be "Check pipe joints for leaks". The task frequency is based on the amount of time it takes for an "acceptable" minor leak to become an "unacceptable" major leak, and suitable corrective action would be initiated whenever a minor leak was discovered.

However, if the same pipeline was carrying a toxic substance like cyanide, any leak at all would be regarded as a functional failure. In this case it is not feasible to ask anyone to check for leaks, so some other method would need to be found to prevent the failure. This would almost certainly entail some sort of modification.

This example demonstrates how important it is to agree exactly what is meant by a functional failure *before* considering what should be done to prevent it.

The P-F interval and operating age

When applying these principles for the first time, people often have difficulty in distinguishing between the "life" of a component and the P-F interval. This leads them to base on-condition task frequencies on the real or imagined "life" of the item. If it exists at all, this life is usually many times greater than the P-F interval, so the task achieves little or nothing.

In reality, we measure the life of a component forwards from the moment it enters service. On the other hand, the P-F interval is measured back from the functional failure, so the two concepts are often completely unrelated. The distinction is especially important because failures which are not related to age (in other words, random failures) are as likely to be preceded by some sort of warning as those which are not.

For example, Figure 5.13 depicts a component which conforms to a random failure pattern (pattern E). One of the components failed after five years, a second after six months and a third after two years. In each case, the functional failure was preceded by a potential failure with a P-F interval of four months.

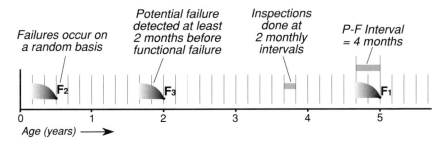

Figure 5.13: *Random failures and the P-F interval*

Figure 5.13 shows that in order to prevent the functional failure (by detecting the potential failure), we need to do an inspection task every 2 months. Because the failures occur on a random basis, we don't know when the next one is going to happen, so the cycle of inspections must begin as soon as the item is put into service. In other words, the timing of the *inspections* has nothing to do with the age or life of the component.

However, this does not mean that on-condition tasks apply *only* to items which fail on a random basis. They can also be applied to items which suffer age-related failures, as discussed overleaf and again in Chapter 9.

When On-condition Tasks are Worth Doing

On-condition tasks need to satisfy the following criteria to be considered worth doing:

- if the failure is *hidden*, it has no direct consequences. So an on-condition task intended to prevent a hidden failure should reduce the risk of the multiple failure to an acceptably low level. In practice, because the function is hidden, many of the potential failures which normally affect evident functions would also be hidden. What is more, much of this type of equipment suffers from random failures with very short or non-existent P-F intervals, so it is fairly unusual to find an on-condition task which is technically feasible and worth doing for a hidden function. But this does not mean that one should not be sought.

- if the failure has *safety* or *environmental* consequences, an on-condition task is only worth doing if it reduces the likelihood of the functional failure itself to an acceptably low level. In particular, it must be relied on to give enough warning of the failure to ensure that action can be taken in time to avoid the safety or environmental consequences.

- if the failure does not involve safety, the task must be cost-effective, so the cost of doing the on-condition task must be less than the cost of not doing it. The question of cost-effectiveness applies to failures with operational and non-operational consequences, as follows:

  * *Operational* consequences are usually expensive, so an on-condition task which reduces the failure rate – thus reducing the rate at which the operational consequences occur – is likely to be cost-effective, because the cost of inspection is usually low. This was illustrated in the example given on pages 95 and 96.

  * The only cost of a functional failure which has *non-operational* consequences is the cost of repair. Sometimes this is almost the same as the cost of correcting the potential failure which precedes it. In such cases, even though an on-condition task may be technically feasible, it would not be cost-effective, because the cost of the inspections plus the cost of correcting the potential failures would be greater than the cost of repairing the functional failure (see pages 100 and 101.) However, an on-condition task may be justified if the functional failure costs a lot more to repair than the potential failure, especially if the former causes secondary damage.

5.7 Selecting Preventive Tasks

It is seldom difficult to decide whether a preventive task is *technically feasible*. The characteristics of the failure govern this decision, and they are usually clear enough to make the decision a simple yes/no affair.

Deciding whether they are *worth doing* usually needs more judgement. For instance, Figure 5.12 indicates that it may be technically feasible for two or more tasks of the *same* category to prevent the same failure mode. They may even be so closely matched in terms of cost-effectiveness that which one is chosen becomes a matter of personal preference.

The situation is complicated further when tasks from two *different* categories are both technically feasible for the same failure mode.

For example, most countries nowadays specify a minimum legal tread depth for tyres (usually about 2 mm). Tyres which are worn below this depth must either be replaced or retreaded. In practice, truck tyres – especially tyres on similar vehicles in a single fleet working the same routes – show a fairly close relationship between age and failure. Retreading restores nearly all the original failure resistance, so they could be scheduled for restoration after they have covered a set distance. This means that all the tyres in the truck fleet would be retreaded after they had covered the specified mileage, whether or not they needed it.

Figure 5.14 shows a hypothetical example of such a fleet, where records show that most of the tyres last between 50 000 and 70 000 km. If a scheduled restoration policy were to be adopted on the basis of this information, all of the tyres would be retreaded at 50 000 km. However, if this policy were adopted many tyres would be retreaded long before it was really necessary. In some cases, tyres which could have lasted as much as 70 000 km would be retreaded at 50 000 km, so they could lose up to 20 000 km of useful life.

Figure 5.14:
Tread wear
on truck tyres

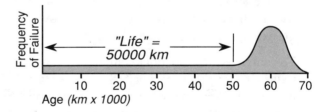

On the other hand, as discussed in Chapter 9, it is possible to define a potential failure condition for tyres related to tread depth. Checking tread depth is quick and easy, so it is a simple matter to check the tyres (say) every 2000 km and to arrange for them to be retreaded only when they need it. This would enable the fleet operator to get an average of 60 000 km out of his tyres without endangering his drivers, instead of the 50 000 km which he gets if he does the scheduled restoration task described above – an increase in useful tyre life of 20%. So in this case on-condition tasks are much more cost-effective than scheduled restoration.

This example suggests the following basic order of preference for selecting preventive tasks:

On-condition tasks

On-condition tasks are considered first in the task selection process, for the following reasons:

- they can nearly always be performed without moving the asset from its installed position and usually while it is in operation, so they seldom interfere with the production process. They are also easy to organise.

- they identify *specific* potential failure conditions so corrective action can be clearly defined before work starts. This reduces the amount of repair work to be done, and enables it to be done more quickly.

- by identifying equipment on the point of potential failure, they enable it to realise almost all of its useful life. Since the number of removals for potential failures is only slightly larger than the number which would result from functional failures, both the total repair costs and the spares needed to support the repair process can be kept to a minimum.

Scheduled restoration tasks

If a suitable on-condition task cannot be found for a particular failure, the next choice is a scheduled restoration task. It too must be technically feasible, so the failures must be concentrated about an average age. If they are, scheduled restoration prior to this age can reduce the incidence of functional failures. This may be cost-effective for failures with major economic consequences, or if the cost of doing the scheduled restoration task is significantly lower than the cost of repairing the functional failure. The disadvantages of scheduled restoration are that:

- it can only be done when items are stopped and (usually) sent to the workshop, so the tasks nearly always affect production in some way

- the age limit applies to all items, so many items or components which might have survived to higher ages will be removed

- restoration tasks involve shop work, so they generate a much higher workload than on-condition tasks.

However, scheduled restoration is nearly always preferable to scheduled discard because it involves remanufacturing things instead of throwing them away.

Figure 5.15:
The task
selection
process

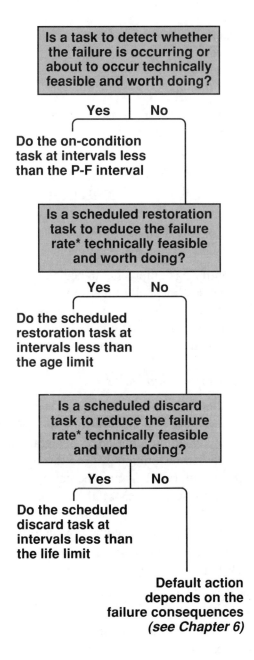

Is a task to detect whether the failure is occurring or about to occur technically feasible and worth doing?

Yes | No

Do the on-condition task at intervals less than the P-F interval

Is a scheduled restoration task to reduce the failure rate* technically feasible and worth doing?

Yes | No

Do the scheduled restoration task at intervals less than the age limit

Is a scheduled discard task to reduce the failure rate* technically feasible and worth doing?

Yes | No

Do the scheduled discard task at intervals less than the life limit

Default action
depends on the
failure consequences
(see Chapter 6)

* *"to avoid all failures"*
if the failure could affect
safety or the environment

Scheduled discard tasks

Scheduled discard is usually the least cost-effective of the three preventive tasks, but where it is technically feasible, it does have a few desirable features. Safe-life limits can prevent certain critical failures, while an economic-life limit can reduce the frequency of functional failures which have major economic consequences.

However, these tasks suffer from all the same disadvantages as scheduled restoration tasks.

Combinations of tasks

For a very small number of failure modes which have safety or environmental consequences, a task cannot be found which *on its own* reduces the risk of failure to an acceptably low level, and a suitable modification does not readily suggest itself.

In these cases, it may be possible to find a combination of tasks (usually from two different task categories, such as an on-condition task and a scheduled discard task), which reduces the risk of the failure to an acceptable level. Each task is carried out at the frequency appropriate for that task. However, it must be stressed that situations in which this is necessary are very rare, and care should be taken not to employ such tasks on a "belt and braces" basis.

The task selection process

The task selection process is summarised in Figure 5.15. Note that this basic order of preference is valid for the vast majority of failure modes, but it does not apply in every single case. If a lower order task is clearly a more cost-effective method of preventing a failure than a higher order task, then the lower order task should be selected.

6 Default Actions

Previous chapters have mentioned that if a preventive task cannot be found which is both technically feasible and worth doing for any failure mode, then the default action which must be taken is governed by the consequences of the failure, as follows:

- if a preventive task cannot be found which reduces the risk of the multiple failure associated with a *hidden function* to an acceptably low level, then a periodic *failure-finding task* must be performed. If a suitable failure-finding task cannot be found, then the secondary default decision is that the item may have to be redesigned (depending on the consequences of the multiple failure).

- if a preventive task cannot be found which reduces the risk of a failure which could affect *safety* or *the environment* to an acceptably low level, **the item must be redesigned or the process must be changed.**

- if a preventive task cannot be found which costs less over a period of time than a failure which has *operational* consequences, the initial default decision is **no scheduled maintenance**. (If this occurs and the operational consequences are still unacceptable then the secondary default decision is again redesign).

- if a preventive task cannot be found which costs less over a period of time than a failure which has *non-operational* consequences, the initial default decision is **no scheduled maintenance**, and if the repair costs are too high, the secondary default decision is once again redesign.

The location of the default actions in the RCM decision framework is shown in Figure 6.1 opposite. In essence, we are now considering the seventh of the seven questions which make up the RCM decision process:

• what should be done if a suitable preventive task cannot be found?

This chapter considers each of the default actions in some detail, starting with failure-finding. It also considers routine tasks which *fall outside the RCM decision framework*. These include certain types of lubrication, zonal inspections and walk-around checks.

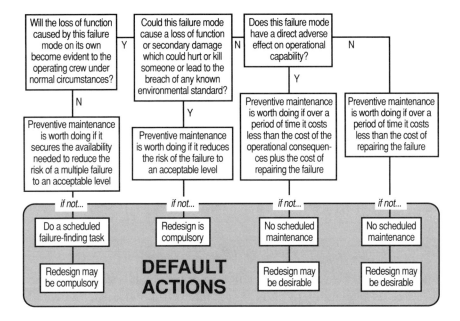

Figure 6.1: *Default actions*

6.1 Scheduled Failure-finding Tasks

Chapter 4 defines a hidden failure as one which on its own will not become evident to the operating crew under normal circumstances. It also explains that these failures have no direct consequences, but they expose the organisation to the risk of multiple failures.

One way to avoid a multiple failure is to try to prevent the failure of the hidden function. Chapter 5 explained that this can only be done if one of the three types of preventive task is suitable.

If we cannot *prevent* the failure of a hidden function, it is still essential to reduce the risk of the multiple failure. This part of this paper shows how this can be done by checking periodically whether the hidden function is still working. Such checks are known as failure-finding tasks.

> ***Scheduled failure-finding entails checking***
> ***a hidden function at regular intervals***
> ***to find out whether it has failed***

Strictly speaking, failure-finding tasks are not preventive because we are looking for failures after they have occurred. However, they *are* regarded as preventive because they aim to prevent the multiple failures which might occur if the hidden failure remained undetected.

For example, we cannot *prevent* the failure of a brake light bulb. So if there is no warning circuit to show that a bulb has failed, the only way to reduce the possibility that a burnt-out bulb will fail to warn other drivers of our intentions is to check if it is still working. But *how often* should we do so?

The Frequency of Failure-finding Tasks

This section of this chapter describes how to determine the frequency of failure-finding tasks.

Failure-finding frequency and availability

If we cannot prevent a hidden function from failing, it is still possible to influence its availability by carrying out failure-finding tasks. Figure 6.2 illustrates the relationship between the frequency of failure-finding and the availability of a hidden function. It takes the example of the brake lights a step further, as follows:

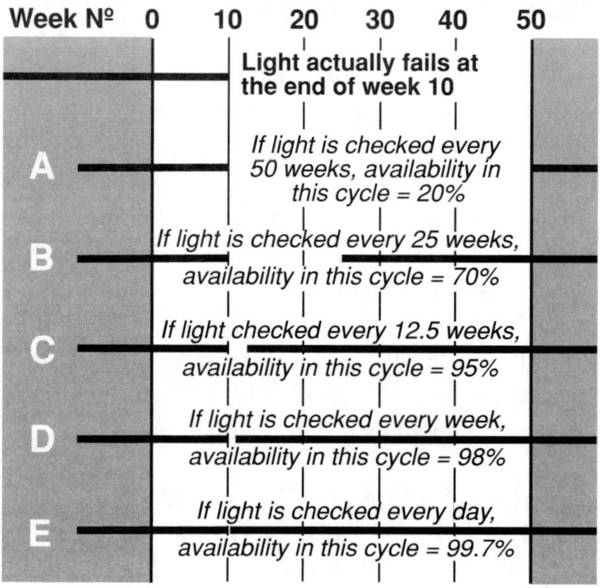

Figure 6.2:
Frequency of
failure-finding
vs availability

Figure 6.2 is based on a fifty week operating cycle. The brake lights actually fail at the end of week 10. Lines A to E show what happens if they are checked at different frequencies. (It is assumed that the lights are repaired as soon as the failure is discovered in each case). For instance, in case B the lights are checked every 25 weeks, so they would be down for 15 weeks out of the fifty week cycle. This corresponds to a downtime of 30%, or an availability of 70%. In case D, they are checked every 12.5 weeks, which means that they are down for 2.5 weeks out of 50. This corresponds to an availability of 95%, and so on.

This example is based on the assumption that the lights fail at the end of week ten. In practice, they could have failed at any point in the fifty week cycle. Clearly, the point at which the failure actually occurs (if it occurs at all) would influence the actual availability. However, the purpose of the example is to illustrate the fact that *the more often a hidden function is checked, the higher will be its overall availability.*

Failure-finding frequency and reliability

The example shown in Figure 6.2 is based on the assumption that the brake lights fail only once in the fifty week cycle. In fact they could fail any number of times, and the number of times that they are found to be in a failed state might also influence our opinion about how often we ought to be checking them.

For example, if we had been checking our brake lights every day for ten years and had never found them to be failed, we might start forming the opinion that it might be in order to check them once every two days, or maybe even once a week. On the other hand, if we had been in the habit of checking them once a year and found them to be failed every time we checked them, we might start getting the feeling that we ought to be checking them more often.

This suggests that in general, the more often we find out that a hidden function is in a failed state, the lower will be our opinion of its "reliability" and the more often we will want to check it. In practice, reliability can be measured by the mean time between failures (whether the failure is random or age-related). The more reliable the component, the less often it will fail and so the greater will be its MTBF. Conversely, less reliable components will fail more often and so they will have shorter mean times between failures.

This indicates that there is a relationship between failure-finding task frequencies and the MTBF. But we have just seen that there is also a connection between the failure-finding task frequency and the availability of a hidden function. This means that we must take *both* factors into account when setting failure-finding frequencies.

Failure-finding frequency, availability and reliability

For random hidden failures, the relationship between mean time between
failures, the required availability and failure-finding task frequencies is
shown in Table 6.1.

Availability we require for the hidden function	99.5%	97.5%	95%	93%	91%	89%
Failure-finding frequency (as a % of the MTBF)	1%	5%	10%	15%	20%	25%

Table 6.1: Failure-finding frequencies, availability and reliability

Having established the relationship between these three factors, the next
step to consider is how we actually go about setting a failure-finding task
frequency. The following paragraphs review how this can be done on a
rigorous basis, and then how it can be done less formally.

A rigorous approach to setting failure-finding frequencies

When using Table 6.1 the first step is to decide what availability is needed
for the hidden function. If this is to be done on a rigorous basis, Part 4.1
of Chapter 4 explained that three steps must be followed:

1: first ask what probability the organisation is prepared to accept for the
   multiple failure which could occur if the hidden function was not working when called upon to do so

2: then determine the probability that the *protected* function will fail in
   the period under consideration

3: finally determine what availability the *hidden* function must achieve
   during the same period to reduce the probability of the multiple failure
   to the desired level

In addition to carrying out these three steps, we need to find out the mean
time between failures of the hidden function. Once this has been done, we
are in a position to look at Table 1 and select the task frequency which
corresponds to the level of availability established in step 3.

Chapter 4 gave an example of a duty and stand-by pump where:

• in step 1 above, the users decided that they wanted the probability of the multiple failure to be less than 1 in 1000

• in step 2 they established that the probability of the unanticipated failure of the
  duty pump could be reduced to 1 in 10 in any one year

- this meant that the downtime of the stand-by pump must not exceed 1%, so the availability of this pump has to be 99% or better (step 3).

Table 6.1 suggests that to achieve an availability of 99.5% for the stand-by pump, someone would need to carry out a failure-finding task (in other words, check that it is fully functional) at an interval of 1% of its mean time between failures. Records might show that the stand-by pump has a mean time between failures of 8 years (or about 400 weeks), so the failure-finding task frequency should be 1% of 400 weeks = 4 weeks.

If the consequences of the multiple failure could be catastrophic, then it is essential that this rigorous approach be used to establish the failure-finding frequency.

If accurate records about the probability of failure of the protected function and the mean time between failures of the hidden function are available, this can be done quite quickly and easily. If this information is not available – and very often it is not – then it is necessary to estimate what these variables are likely to be *in the context under consideration.* In rare cases, it might be possible to obtain data from one of the following:
- the manufacturers of the equipment
- commercial data banks
- other users of similar equipment.

More often, however, the estimates have to be based on the knowledge and experience of the people who know the most about the equipment, which in many cases turns out to be the operators and the maintenance craftsmen. (When making use of data from external sources, take special note of the operating context of the items for which the data was gathered compared to the context in which your equipment is operating.)

Once a failure-finding task frequency has been established and the tasks are being done on a regular basis, it becomes possible to verify the assumptions used to determine the frequency quite rapidly. However, this does require the keeping of absolutely meticulous records, not only about when each failure-finding task is done, but also about:

- whether or not the hidden function is found to be functional each time the task is done

- how often the protected function fails (this can often be inferred from the number of times the protected function makes use of the protective device – for instance, from the number of times a pressure relief valve actually has to relieve the pressure in the system).

On the basis of this information the actual mean time between failures can be calculated and, if necessary, the task frequency revised accordingly.

A less formal approach to setting failure-finding frequencies

Most modern industrial undertakings possess several thousand protected systems, the majority of which incorporate hidden functions. The multiple failures associated with many of these systems will be serious enough to justify using the rigorous approach to failure-finding described above. This is particularly true of multiple failures which could affect safety or the environment.

However, not every hidden function is important enough to warrant the time and effort needed to do this analysis. This applies mainly to multiple failures which do not affect safety or the environment, although it could also apply to some multiple failures which could affect safety but where the protected function is inherently very reliable and the threat to safety is marginal.

In these cases, it is usually sufficient to take a general view of the entire protected system in its operating context, and go straight to a decision on a desired level of availability for the hidden function. This decision is then used in conjunction with the MTBF of the hidden failure to set a task frequency, using Table 6.1.

(Some organisations even go so far as to use an availability of 95% for all hidden functions where the associated multiple failure cannot affect safety or the environment. However, general policies of this nature can be dangerous so they should only be used by people who have extensive experience with this type of analysis.)

Once again, if adequate records about hidden failures are not available – and they seldom will be – it will be necessary to guess at the MTBF's to begin with. But again these records should be compiled as quickly as possible to validate the initial estimates.

Failure-finding is a Default Action!

It is always preferable to prevent a failure from occurring rather than to check whether it has occurred, so scheduled failure-finding should only be specified if a more effective preventive task cannot be found.

We have also seen that scheduled failure-finding tasks only apply to hidden functions. This is because, by definition, the failure of an evident function inevitably becomes apparent to the operating crew, so there is no need to carry out regular checks to find out whether such a failure has occurred.

This means that:

> *Failure-finding tasks should only be considered if:*
> * *a functional failure will not become evident to the operating crew under normal circumstances*
> * *the failure is one for which a suitable preventive task cannot be found.*

The Technical Feasibility of Failure-finding

The fundamental reason for checking whether a hidden function is still working is to satisfy ourselves that it will provide the necessary protection if it is called upon to do so. As a result, the *entire* function should be checked. This applies especially to hidden functions which consist of a number of components, such as electrical circuits or instrument loops. In these cases, the complete circuit should be checked, from sensor to actuator. Wherever possible this should be done:

* by simulating the conditions the circuit should respond to, and checking if the *actuator* gives the right response

  For example, a pressure switch may be designed to shut down a machine if the lubricating oil pressure drops below a certain level. Wherever possible switches like this should be checked by dropping the oil pressure to the required level and checking whether the machine shuts down.

* without disconnecting and otherwise disturbing any of the components of the circuit. (This is especially important, because taking an item to bits to check if it is still working greatly increases the chances that something will go wrong either while it is in pieces or when it is being put back together. This of course is what failure pattern F is all about.)

If it is not possible to simulate the conditions *in situ*, then the conditions under which it is checked should be such that there can be no doubt that it will work when called upon to do so in real life. Secondly, if the item really cannot be checked without being disturbed in some way, then this disturbance should be kept to the absolute minimum.

In reality, there is a very small but still significant number of situations where it is impossible to carry out a scheduled failure-finding task of any sort. These are:

* when the function of the protective device cannot be checked without destroying it (as in the case of fusible devices and rupture discs)
* where it is impossible to gain access to the protective device in order to check it (this is almost always a result of thoughtless design)

- where any attempts to simulate the conditions to which the protective device should respond would simply be too dangerous.

There are also cases where failure-finding is possible, but the frequency is impractical. In these cases, the frequency might be too high or too low, as follows:

- to attain the desired level of availability of a hidden function, Table 1 sometimes gives very high failure-finding task frequencies. This has several implications:
  * sometimes the frequency is simply far too high to be practical. An example is a failure-finding task which calls for a major item of plant to be shut down every few days (or even every few hours)
  * the task could begin to increase the chance of causing the failure which it is supposed to detect (which might happen if a switch is tested too often)
  * the task could cause habituation (which might happen if a fire alarm is tested too often).

- Table 1 can also produce very low failure-finding task frequencies – sometimes as low as fifty years or more. Here the theory is clearly suggesting that we really need not worry about doing the task at all. In these cases the proposed "task" should be stated as follows: *"the risk/ reliability profile is such that failure-finding is felt to be unnecessary".*

This all means that for a failure-finding task to be technically feasible, it should be possible to do the task without increasing the risk of the multiple failure, and it should be practical to do it at the required frequency.

Failure-finding is technically feasible if:

- *it is possible to do the task without increasing the risk of a multiple failure*
- *it is practical to do the task at the required frequency*

When Failure-finding is Worth Doing

The objective of a failure-finding task is to secure adequate availability for a hidden function. We have seen that what is meant by "adequate" depends on the nature and the consequences of the multiple failure, the reliability of the protected function and the reliability of the protective device. In general, however, failure-finding is only worth doing if it secures the desired availability of the hidden function.

A failure-finding task is only worth doing if it secures
the desired availability of the hidden function

What if Failure-finding is Not Suitable?

In the situations where a failure-finding task is not technically feasible or worth doing, we have exhausted all the possibilities which might enable us to extract the required performance from the existing asset.

As we saw in Chapter 3, if an existing asset is incapable of delivering the performance we want it to deliver, we have two choices. We can either lower our expectations and live with its inadequacies, or we can change it in such a way that it *can* deliver the required performance. In the case of hidden failures, how we respond is once again governed by the consequences of the multiple failure, as follows:

• if a suitable failure-finding task cannot be found and the multiple failure could affect safety or the environment, redesign is compulsory

• if a suitable failure-finding task cannot be found and the multiple failure does not affect safety or the environment, then it is acceptable to take no action, but redesign may be desirable if the consequences of the multiple failure are particularly expensive.

This decision process is summarised in Figure 6.3 (note that this diagram is a fuller description of this aspect of the decision process than the two boxes at the foot of the left hand column in Figure 6.1):

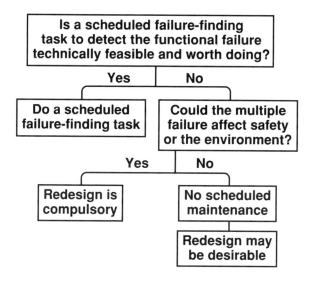

Figure 6.3:
Failure-finding:
the decision
process

6.2   No Scheduled Maintenance

We have seen that failure-finding is the initial default action if a suitable preventive task cannot be found for a *hidden failure*. However, if a suitable failure-finding task cannot be found, then redesign is the compulsory secondary default action if the multiple failure has safety or environmental consequences. We have also seen that if an evident failure has *safety* or *environmental consequences* and a suitable preventive task cannot be found, the item must also be redesigned.

However, if the failure is not hidden and it does not affect safety or the environment, or if it is hidden and the multiple failure does not affect safety or the environment, the initial default decision is to do *no scheduled maintenance*. In these cases, the items are left in service until a functional failure occurs (although it may be worth reconsidering the design under circumstances which are explained in the next part of this chapter). In other words, "no scheduled maintenance" is only valid if:

• a suitable scheduled task task cannot be found for a hidden function, and the associated multiple failure does not have safety or environmental consequences

• a cost-effective preventive task cannot be found for failures which have operational or non-operational consequences.

Note that if a suitable preventive task cannot be found for a failure under either of these circumstances, it simply means that we do not carry out *scheduled maintenance* on that component in its present form. It does not mean that we simply forget about it. As we see in the next section of this chapter, there may be circumstances under which it is worth redesigning the component to reduce overall costs.

6.3   Redesign

The question of equipment design has arisen again and again as we have traced the steps which must be followed to develop a successful maintenance programme. In this part of this chapter, we consider three general issues which affect the relationship between design and maintenance, and then consider the part played by redesign in the task selection process.

The term "redesign" is used in its broadest sense in this chapter. Firstly, it refers to any change to the specification of any item of equipment. Basically this means any action which should result in a change to a drawing or a parts list. It includes *changing the specification of a component, adding a new item, replacing an entire machine* with one of a different make or type, or *relocating a machine*. It also means any other change to a *process* or *procedure* which affects the operation of the plant.

Design and Maintenance

Three general issues which need to be placed in perspective before considering redesign as a specific default option are as follows:
• the relationship between inherent reliability and desired performance
• what do we consider first - design or maintenance?
• the management of modifications.

Inherent reliability vs desired performance

Among other things, Part 3.1 of Chapter 3 stressed that the inherent reliability of any item is established by its design and by how it is made, and that maintenance cannot yield reliability beyond that inherent in the design. This led to two important conclusions.

Firstly, if the inherent reliability or built-in capability of an item is greater than the desired performance, maintenance can help achieve the desired performance. Most equipment *is* adequately specified, designed and built, so it is usually possible to develop a satisfactory maintenance programme, as described in previous chapters.

On the other hand, if the desired performance exceeds the inherent reliability of an item, then no amount of *maintenance* can deliver the desired performance. In these cases "better" maintenance cannot solve the problem, so we need to look beyond maintenance for the solutions. Options include:
• modifying the equipment
• changing operating procedures
• lowering our expectations and deciding to live with the problem.
This reminds us that maintenance is not *always* the answer to chronic reliability problems. It also reminds us that we must establish as soon and as precisely as possible what *we want each piece of equipment to do* in its operating context before we can consider its maintenance requirements with confidence.

Which comes first - redesign or maintenance?

The above paragraphs indicate that reliability, design and maintenance are inextricably linked. This can lead to a temptation to start reviewing the design of existing equipment before considering its maintenance requirements. In fact, maintenance should be considered first for two reasons.

Firstly, most modifications take from six months to three years from conception to commissioning, depending on the cost and complexity of the new design. On the other hand, the maintenance person who is on duty *today* has to maintain the equipment as it exists *today*, not what should be there or what might be there some time in the future. So today's realities must be dealt with before tomorrow's design changes.

Secondly, most organisations are faced with many more apparently desirable design improvement opportunities than are physically or economically feasible. By focusing on failure consequences, RCM does much to help us to develop a rational set of priorities for these projects, especially because it separates those which are essential from those which are merely desirable. Clearly, such priorities can only be established after the review has been carried out.

The management of modifications

Modifications are expensive. They involve the cost of redesign, the cost of making components (or even whole new items) and the cost of installing the parts. Further indirect costs are incurred if the equipment has to be taken out of service while it is being modified. There is also the risk that a modification will fail to eliminate or even alleviate the problem it is meant to solve. In some cases, it may even create more problems.

As a result, the whole question of modifications should be approached with great caution. This means that all modifications should be:

- *properly justified* (this is covered in more detail later)
- *correctly designed* by suitably qualified engineers
- *properly implemented*. This means ensuring that the modification is carried out as intended in terms of time, cost and quality, and that all drawings, manuals and parts lists are updated correctly
- *properly managed*. This means ensuring that modifications do not interfere with essential routine maintenance activities in other parts of the plant, and that the maintenance requirements of every modified item of equipment are correctly assessed and implemented.

Redesign as the Default Action

Figure 6.1 shows that redesign appears at the bottom of all four columns of the decision diagram. In the case of failures which have safety or environmental consequences, it is the compulsory default action, and in the other three cases, it "may be desirable". In this part of this chapter, we consider each case in more detail, starting with the safety case.

Safety or environmental consequences

If a failure could affect safety or the environment and no preventive task or combination of tasks can be found which reduces the risk of the failure to an acceptable level, something must be changed, simply because we are dealing with a safety or environmental hazard which cannot be adequately prevented. In these cases, redesign is usually undertaken with one of two objectives:

- to reduce the probability of the failure mode occurring to a level which is acceptable. This is usually done by replacing the affected component with one which is stronger or more reliable.

- to change the item or the process in such a way that the failure no longer has safety or environmental consequences. This is most often done by installing one or more of the five types of protective devices which were categorised as follows in Chapter 3:
  * to alert operators to abnormal conditions
  * to shut down the equipment in the event of a failure
  * to eliminate or relieve abnormal conditions which follow a failure and which might otherwise cause more serious damage
  * to take over from a function which has failed
  * to prevent dangerous situations from arising.
  Remember that if such a device is added, its maintenance requirements must also be analysed. (Safety or environmental consequences can also be reduced by eliminating hazardous materials from a process, or even by abandoning a dangerous process altogether.)

As mentioned in Chapter 4, when dealing with safety or the environment, RCM does not raise the question of economics. If the level of risk associated with any failure is regarded as unacceptable, we are obliged either to prevent the failure, or to make the process safe. The alternative is to accept conditions which are unsafe or environmentally unsound. This is no longer acceptable in most industries.

Hidden failures

In the case of hidden failures, the risk of a multiple failure can be reduced by modifying the equipment in one of four ways:

- ***make the hidden function evident by adding another device:*** Certain hidden functions can be made evident by adding another device which draws the attention of the operator to the failure of the hidden function.

  For example, a battery used to power a smoke detector is a classical hidden function if no additional protection is provided. However, a warning light is fitted to most such detectors in such a way that the light goes out if the battery fails. In this way the additional protection makes the function of the battery evident.

  Special care is needed in this area, because extra functions installed for this purpose also tend to be hidden. If too many layers of protection are added, it becomes increasingly difficult – if not impossible – to define sensible failure-finding tasks. A much more effective approach is to substitute an evident function for the hidden function, as explained in the next paragraph.

- ***substitute an evident function for the hidden function***: In most cases this means substituting a genuinely fail-safe protective device for one which is not fail-safe. This is surprisingly difficult to do in practice, but if it is done, the need for a failure-finding task falls away at once.

  For example, one commonly used way to warn the driver of a vehicle that his brake lights have failed is to install a warning light which is switched on if the brake lights fail. (In many cases, this light is also switched on for a short while when the ignition is switched on. However, so are all the other lights on the dashboard. Under these circumstances one missing warning light is likely to be overlooked, so its function is effectively hidden.)

  The system might also be configured in such a way that its full function can only be tested by disabling a brake light and seeing if the warning light comes on. This is a clumsy and invasive task which is likely to cause more problems than it solves, so it is likely to be dismissed on the grounds of impracticality. The multiple failures associated with this system could have serious safety consequences, so it is necessary to reconsider the design.

  One way to eliminate this problem is to make the function of the brake lights *and* of the warning system evident. This can be done by substituting fibre-optic cables for the warning light. The cables can be mounted so that the driver looks through the cables at the brake lights every time he uses the brakes. (In fact, he sees a pinprick of light at the end of each cable.) In this situation, it is apparent to the driver if either a brake light or a cable fails. In other words, the function of this protective device is now evident, which means that failure-finding is no longer necessary.

- *substitute a more reliable (but still hidden) device for the existing hidden function:* Table 6.1 suggests that a more reliable hidden function (in other words, one which has a higher mean time between failures) will enable the organisation to achieve one of three objectives:
  - * to reduce the probability of the multiple failure without changing the failure-finding task frequency. This increases the level of protection
  - * to reduce the task frequency (in other words, increase the interval between tasks) without changing the probability of the multiple failure. This reduces ongoing resource requirements
  - * to reduce the probability of the multiple failure *and* reduce the task frequency, giving increased protection with less effort

- *duplicate the hidden function:* If it is not possible to find a single protective device which has a high enough MTBF to give the desired level of protection, it is still possible to achieve any of the above three objectives by duplicating (or even triplicating) the hidden function.

Let us return to the example of a duty pump with a stand-by. Earlier in this chapter it was explained that if the users want the probability of a multiple failure to be less than 1 in 1000, and the probability of the unanticipated failure of the duty pump is reduced to 1 in 10 in any one year, then the availability of the stand-by pump has to be 99% or better.

This led to the conclusion that a failure-finding task should be done on the stand-by pump every four weeks in order to achieve an availability of 99.5% (based on an MTBF for this pump of 400 weeks).

However, now let us assume that someone has decided that the probability of a multiple failure in this system should not exceed 1 in 100 000 (or 10^{-5}), rather than 1 in 1000. Assume also that it is not possible to improve the probability of failure of the duty pump beyond 1 in 10. This means that the downtime of the stand-by pump must now not exceed 10^{-4} (or 0.01%), which corresponds to an availability of 99.99%. Extrapolating the figures in Table 6.1 suggests that this can be achieved by doing a failure-finding task at 0.02% of the MTBF of the stand-by pump. 0.02% of 400 weeks is about 13 hours. Activating a stand-by pump at this frequency is plainly impractical, so more thought has to be given to the design of this system.

In fact, the required level of protection can be achieved by adding a second stand-by pump, and ensuring that the availability of each stand-by pump on its own exceeds 99% (corresponding to a downtime of 1%, or 10^{-2}). In this case the probability of the multiple failure would be:

$$10^{-1} \times 10^{-2} \times 10^{-2} = 10^{-5}$$

or 1 in 100 000. This can be achieved easily by doing a failure-finding task on each pump at the original frequency of once every four weeks. In other words, a much higher level of protection has been achieved without changing the task frequency. This is summarised in Figure 6.4 overleaf.

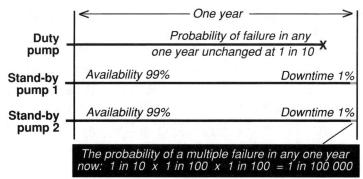

Figure 6.4:
The effect of duplicating a hidden function

Operational and non-operational consequences

If a technically feasible preventive task cannot be found which is worth doing for failures with operational or non-operational consequences, the immediate default decision is no scheduled maintenance. However, it may still be desirable to modify the equipment to reduce total costs. To achieve this, the plant could be modified to:

• reduce the number of times the failure occurs, or possibly eliminate it altogether, again by making the component stronger or more reliable

• reduce or eliminate the consequences of the failure (for example, by providing a stand-by capability)

• make a preventive task cost-effective (for instance, by making a component more accessible).

Note that in this case the failure consequences are purely economic so modifications must be cost-justified, whereas they were the compulsory default action if the failure had safety or environmental consequences.

There is no one way to determine whether a modification will be cost-effective. Each case is governed by a different set of variables, which include a before-and-after assessment of maintenance and operating costs, the remaining technologically useful life of the asset, the likelihood that the modification will work, the number of other projects competing for the capital resources of the company and so on.

A detailed cost-benefit study which takes all these factors into account can be very time-consuming, so it is helpful to know beforehand whether this effort is likely to be worthwhile. The decision diagram in Figure 6.4 can be used to do a quick preliminary assessment.

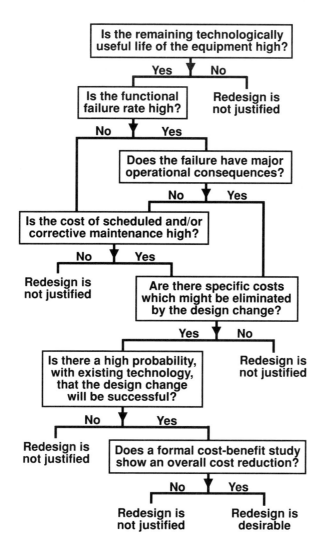

Figure 6.5:
Decision diagram
for a preliminary
assessment
of a proposed
modification

No matter how reliable, all equipment is eventually rendered obsolete by new developments. So the first issue to consider is whether the asset is going to be superseded by new technology in the near future. If it is, then it is clearly not worth modifying it. However, it is still going to be around for a while, the modification will have a chance to pay for itself. This is why the first question in Figure 6.5 asks:

Is the remaining technologically useful life of the equipment high?

Some organisations demand that modifications should pay for themselves within a specified period – say, two years. This effectively sets the operational horizon of the equipment at two years. This type of policy reduces the number of projects initiated on the basis of projected cost-benefits and ensures that only projects which will pay for themselves quickly are submitted for approval. So if the answer to the first question in Figure 6.5 is no, redesign is probably not justified.

Figure 6.6:
A stainless
steel hopper

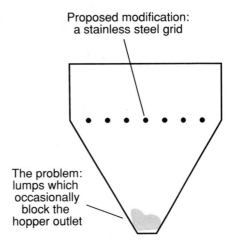

Proposed modification:
a stainless steel grid

The problem:
lumps which
occasionally
block the
hopper outlet

For example Figure 6.6 illustrates a simple stainless steel hopper which is periodically blocked by lumps. So far, the RCM process has revealed that this failure mode costs £200 in lost production every time it occurs, but that it cannot be prevented by maintenance. It has been suggested that one way to eliminate the failure mode might be to install a stainless steel grid above the hopper outlet at a cost of £3000.

If the hopper were due to be superseded within two years, it is highly unlikely that this modification would be worth doing, especially in view of the fact that several months would almost certainly elapse before it could be commissioned. On the other hand, if the hopper were to remain in service for several more years, the modification would be worth further consideration.

If the answer to the first question is yes, the next question to consider is whether the failure is happening often enough to be a real problem:

Is the functional failure rate high?

This question eliminates items which fail so seldom that the cost of redesign would probably be greater than the benefits to be derived from it (unless of course a preventive task is the reason for a low failure rate. This is why a "no" answer to this question does not immediately abort the modification – the maintenance task itself might be so expensive that the modification is still justified.)

For example if the blockage in the hopper occurred once every two or three years, no-one would pay much attention to it. If it occurred once a month, it would be worth investigating further.

If the failure rate is high, we start considering the economic implications of the failure:

Does the failure involve major operational consequences?

If the answer is yes, then the question of redesign should be taken further.

In the case of the hopper, the operational consequences would probably not be classified as "major", but are sufficiently costly to warrant further investigation.

A "no" to this question means that the failure only has a minor effect on operating costs, but we must still consider the maintenance costs associated with the failure by asking:

Is the cost of scheduled and/or corrective maintenance high?

Note that this question is approached from two directions. As we have seen, we may get a "no" answer to the failure rate question only because a very costly preventive task is preventing functional failures. A "no" answer to the question of operational consequences means that failures may not be affecting operating capability, but they may result in excessive repair costs. So a "yes" answer to either of these two questions brings us to the design change itself:

Are there specific costs which might be eliminated by the design change?

This question refers to the operational consequences and the direct costs of preventive and/or corrective maintenance. However, if these costs are not related to a specific design feature, it is unlikely that the problem will be solved by a design change. So a "no" answer to this question means that it may be necessary to live with the economic consequences of the failure. On the other hand, if the problem can be pinned down to a specific cost element, then the economic potential of redesign is high.

In the case of the hopper, it is hoped that the grid would prevent the lumps from reaching the hopper outlet, and so eliminate the cost of £200 per blockage.

But will the new design work? In other words:

Is there a high probability, with existing technology, that the modification will be successful?

Although a particular design change might be very desirable economically, there is a chance that it will not have the desired effect. A change directed at one failure mode may reveal other failure modes, requiring several attempts to solve the problem. So if a cold-blooded assessment of the proposed change indicates that the probability of success is low, the change is highly unlikely to be economically viable.

For instance, in the case of the hopper we would need to be sure that lumps would not simply accumulate on the grid and coagulate into a possibly much more costly problem in the long term.

Any proposed design change which makes it this far deserves a detailed cost-benefit study:

Does an economic trade-off study show an expected cost saving?

Such a study compares the expected reduction in costs over the remaining useful life of the equipment with the costs of carrying out the modification. To be on the safe side, the expected benefit should be regarded as the projected saving if the first attempt at improvement is successful, multiplied by the probability of success at the first try. Alternatively it might be considered that the design change will always be successful, but only some of the savings will be achieved.

If we are certain that the modification to the hopper will work, a discounted cash flow analysis on the figures provided for the hopper (at a discount rate of 10%) shows that the modification will pay for itself
* in five years if the blockage occurs four times per year,
* in seven years if it occurs three times per year and
* in more than ten years if it occurs twice per year.

This type of justification is not necessary, of course, if the reliability characteristics of an item are the subject of contractual warranties or if the changes are needed for reasons other than cost (such as safety).

6.4 Lubrication

Most lubrication tasks tend to be determined as part of the task selection process. This is because they are directed at specific failure modes with serious consequences (such as *gearbox seizes due to lack of oil*, or *hydraulic oil fails due to oxidation*). The nature and frequency of the appropriate preventive tasks can usually be determined readily using the RCM decision diagram. These tasks tend to focus on checking levels, checking oil quality and/or changing oil, and on the maintenance of central lubrication systems.

However, "total loss" lubrication points (such as grease nipples, small oil bottles and manually lubricated gears and lead screws) are seldom subjected to a full RCM review. These items tend to be lubricated whether or not they need it because the cost of doing so is tiny compared to the cost of inadequate lubrication – in other words, the cost of doing this type of task is too low to justify studies to determine the most economic task interval. This is why total loss lubrication points are seldom analysed in depth when developing a maintenance programme.

However, this does not mean that these points should be ignored altogether. Every item of equipment should always be studied carefully at the end of an RCM review programme with a view to picking up any lubrication points which may have been overlooked, and the requirements of these points should be incorporated in the appropriate schedules.

(In fact, total loss lubrication really constitutes the scheduled discard of a single component – the old lubrication film. This task is applicable because the film deteriorates with age and shows wear-out characteristics. Usually the condition of the lubricant film cannot be determined, so it is replaced at conservatively short intervals.)

6.5   Zonal Inspections and Walk-around Checks

Zonal inspections and walk-around checks also fall outside the formal RCM decision process.

Walk-around checks

Walk-around checks serve two purposes. The first is to spot accidental damage. These checks may include a few specific on-condition tasks for the sake of convenience, but damage in general can occur at any time and is not related to any definable level of failure resistance.

As a result, there is no basis for defining an explicit potential failure condition or a predictable P-F interval. Similarly, the checks are not based on the failure characteristics of any particular item, but are intended to spot unforeseen exceptions in failure behaviour.

Walk-around checks are also meant to spot problems due to ignorance or negligence, such as hazardous materials or foreign objects left lying around, spillage, and other items of a housekeeping nature. They also give management an opportunity to ensure that general standards of maintenance are satisfactory, and can be used to check whether maintenance routines are being done correctly. Again, there are rarely any explicit potential failure conditions and no predictable P-F interval.

Some organisations distinguish between the two types of checks on the pretext that one is mainly technical and the other predominantly managerial, so they are sometimes done by different people. In fact it does not matter who does them, as long as both are done frequently and thoroughly enough to ensure a reasonable degree of protection from the consequences of the failures concerned.

Zonal inspections

Zonal inspections are also not directed at any particular failure mode but they focus more clearly on specific zones or areas of the plant. They also tend to be more intensive. They include checks of assemblies and connecting lines for security, obvious signs of damage or leaks, and wear and tear which is not covered by formal preventive tasks.

The need for and frequency of inspections in each zone are very much influenced by the extent to which functions are generally hidden or evident, by the consequences of failure, by the stresses to which equipment and structures are subjected, and by the skill and motivation of the workforce. However, it should always be understood that zonal inspections complement, and are not a substitute for, formal preventive maintenance activities.

7 The RCM Decision Diagram

7.1 Integrating Consequences and Tasks

Chapters 4 to 6 have provided a detailed explanation of the criteria used to answer the last three of the seven questions which make up the RCM process. These questions are:

- *in what way does each failure matter?*
- *what can be done to prevent each failure?*
- *what should be done if a suitable preventive task cannot be found?*

This chapter summarises the most important of these criteria. It also describes the RCM Decision Diagram, which integrates all the decision processes into a single strategic framework. This framework is shown in Figure 7.1, and is applied to each of the failure modes listed on the RCM Information Worksheet.

Finally, this chapter describes the RCM Decision Worksheet, which is the second of the two key working documents used in the application of RCM (the information worksheet being the first).

7.2 The RCM Decision Process

The RCM Decision Worksheet is illustrated in Figure 7.2. The rest of this chapter demonstrates how it is used to record the answers to the questions in the Decision Diagram, and in the light of these answers, to record:

- what routine maintenance (if any) is to be done, how often it is to be done and by whom
- which failures are serious enough to warrant redesign
- cases where a deliberate decision has been made to let failures happen.

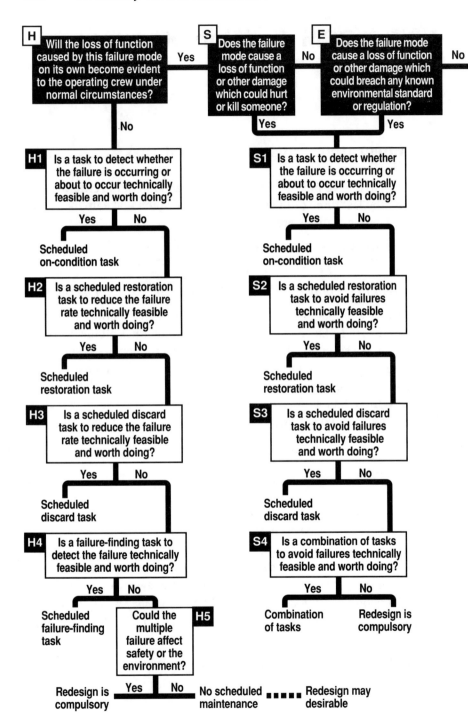

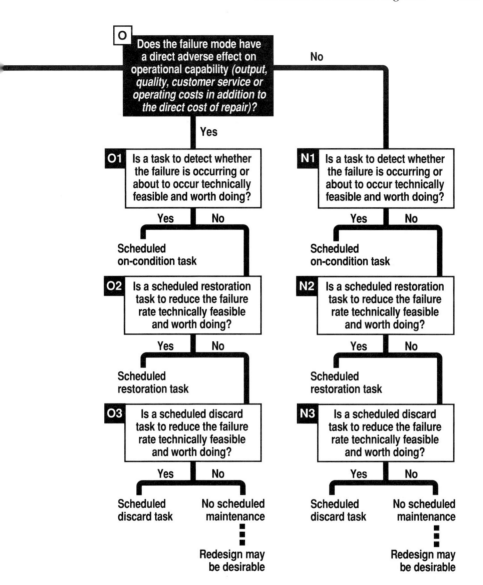

Figure 7.1:
THE RCM // DECISION DIAGRAM
© 1991 Aladon Ltd

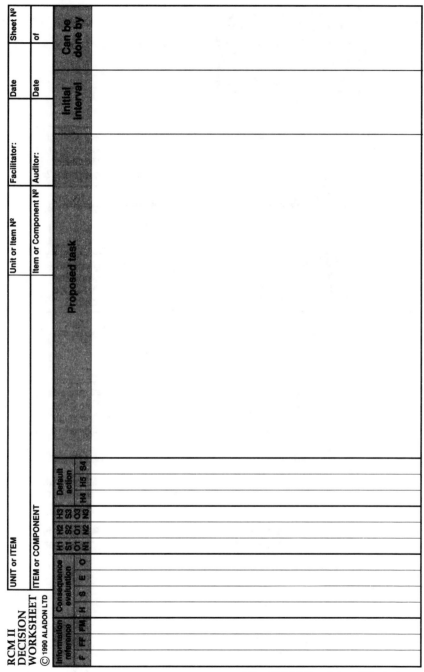

Figure 7.2: *The RCM Decision Worksheet*

The decision worksheet is divided into sixteen columns. The columns headed F, FF and FM identify the failure mode under consideration. They are used to cross-refer the information and decision worksheets, as shown in figure 7.3 below:

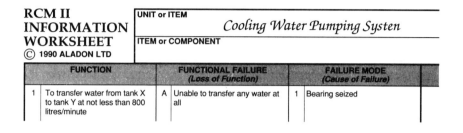

Figure 7.3:
Cross-referring
the information
and decision
worksheets

The headings on the next ten columns refer to the questions on the RCM Decision Diagram in Figure 7.1, as follows:

- the columns headed H, S, E, O and N are used to record the answers to the questions concerning the consequences of each failure mode
- the next three columns (headed H1, H2, H3 etc) record whether a preventive task has been selected, and if so, what type of task
- if it becomes necessary to answer any of the default questions, the columns headed H4 and H5, or S4 are used to record the answers.

The last three columns record the task which has been selected (if any), the frequency with which it is to be done and who has been selected to do it. The "proposed task" column is also used to record the cases where redesign is required or it has been decided that the failure mode does not need scheduled maintenance.

In the following paragraphs, each of these four sections of the decision worksheet is reviewed in the context of the associated questions on the Decision Diagram.

Failure Consequences

The precise meanings of questions H, S, E and O in Figure 7.1 are discussed at length in Chapter 4. These questions are asked for each failure mode, and the answers recorded on the decision worksheet on the basis shown in Figure 7.4 below.

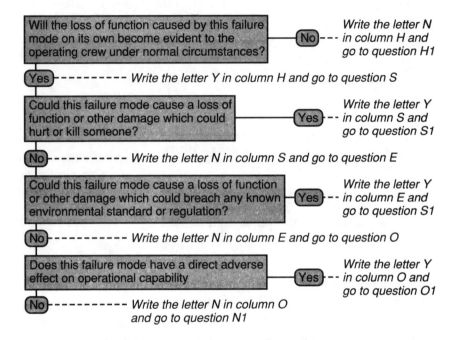

Figure 7.4: Using the decision worksheet to record failure consequences

Figure 7.5 shows how the answers to these questions are recorded on the decision worksheet. Note that:

- each failure mode is dealt with in terms of one category of consequences only. So if it is classified as having environmental consequences, we do not also evaluate its operational consequences (at least when performing the first analysis of any asset). This means that if for instance a "Y" is recorded in column E, nothing is recorded in column O.

- once the consequences of the failure mode have been categorised, the next step is to seek a suitable preventive task. Figure 7.5 also summarises the criteria used to decide whether such tasks are *worth doing*.

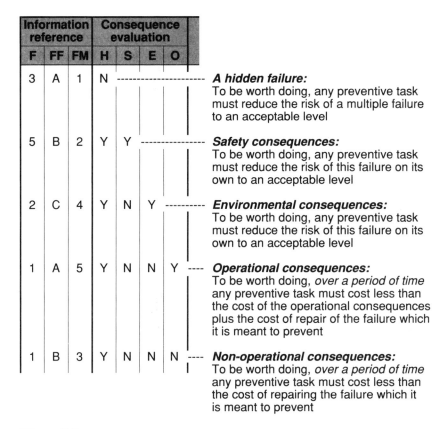

Information reference			Consequence evaluation			
F	FF	FM	H	S	E	O
3	A	1	N			
5	B	2	Y	Y		
2	C	4	Y	N	Y	
1	A	5	Y	N	N	Y
1	B	3	Y	N	N	N

A hidden failure:
To be worth doing, any preventive task must reduce the risk of a multiple failure to an acceptable level

Safety consequences:
To be worth doing, any preventive task must reduce the risk of this failure on its own to an acceptable level

Environmental consequences:
To be worth doing, any preventive task must reduce the risk of this failure on its own to an acceptable level

Operational consequences:
To be worth doing, *over a period of time* any preventive task must cost less than the cost of the operational consequences plus the cost of repair of the failure which it is meant to prevent

Non-operational consequences:
To be worth doing, *over a period of time* any preventive task must cost less than the cost of repairing the failure which it is meant to prevent

Figure 7.5:
Failure consequences - a summary

Preventive Tasks

The eighth to tenth columns on the decision worksheet are used to record whether a preventive task has been selected, as follows:

- the column headed H1/S1/O1/N1 is used to record whether a suitable on-condition task could be found to anticipate the failure mode in time to avoid the consequences

- the column headed H2/S2/O2/N2 is used to record whether a suitable scheduled restoration task could be found to prevent the failures

- the column headed H3/S3/O3/N3 is used to record whether a suitable scheduled discard task could be found to prevent the failures.

In each case, a task is only suitable if it is worth doing *and* technically feasible. Chapter 5 explained in detail how to establish whether a task is technically feasible, and these criteria are summarised in Figure 7.6.

In essence, for a task to be technically feasible and worth doing it must be possible to provide a positive answer to *all* of the questions shown in Figure 7.6 which apply to that category of tasks, *and* the task must fulfil the "worth doing" criteria in Figure 7.5. If the answer to any of these questions is "no" or unknown, then that task as a whole is rejected. If all of the questions can be answered positively, then a Y is recorded in the appropriate column.

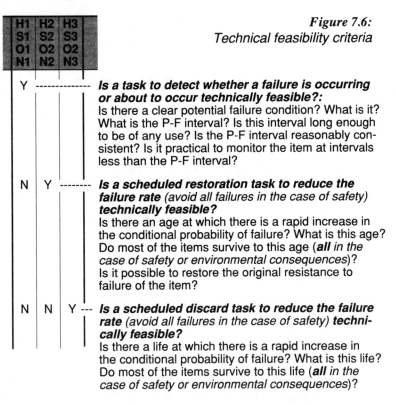

Figure 7.6:
Technical feasibility criteria

Is a task to detect whether a failure is occurring or about to occur technically feasible?:
Is there a clear potential failure condition? What is it? What is the P-F interval? Is this interval long enough to be of any use? Is the P-F interval reasonably consistent? Is it practical to monitor the item at intervals less than the P-F interval?

Is a scheduled restoration task to reduce the failure rate (avoid all failures in the case of safety) **technically feasible?**
Is there an age at which there is a rapid increase in the conditional probability of failure? What is this age? Do most of the items survive to this age (**all** in the case of safety or environmental consequences)? Is it possible to restore the original resistance to failure of the item?

Is a scheduled discard task to reduce the failure rate (avoid all failures in the case of safety) **technically feasible?**
Is there a life at which there is a rapid increase in the conditional probability of failure? What is this life? Do most of the items survive to this life (**all** in the case of safety or environmental consequences)?

If a task is selected, a description of the task and the frequency with which it must be done are recorded as explained later in this chapter, and the analysts move on to the next failure mode. However, as mentioned in Chapter 5, bear in mind that if it seems that a lower order task may be more cost-effective than a higher order task, then the lower order task should also be considered and the more effective of the two chosen.

The Default Questions

The columns headed H4, H5 and S4 on the decision worksheet are used to record the answers to the three default questions. The basis on which these questions are answered is summarised in Figure 7.7. (Note that the default questions are only asked if the answers to the previous three questions are all "no".)

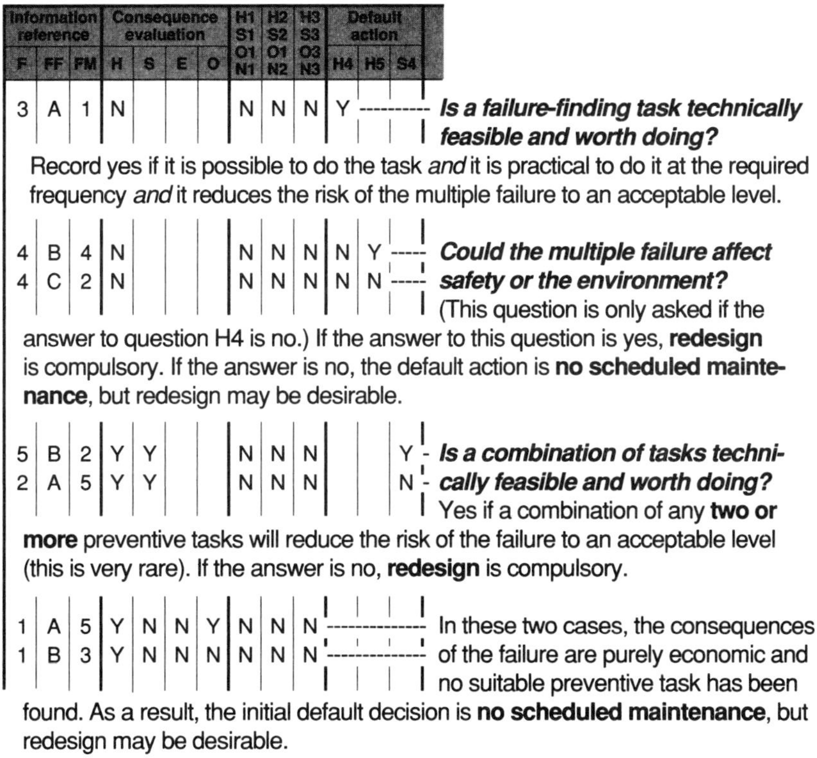

Information reference			Consequence evaluation				H1 S1 O1 N1	H2 S2 O1 N2	H3 S3 O3 N3	Default action		
F	FF	FM	H	S	E	O				H4	H5	S4

| 3 | A | 1 | N | | | | N | N | N | Y | | | *Is a failure-finding task technically feasible and worth doing?* |

Record yes if it is possible to do the task *and* it is practical to do it at the required frequency *and* it reduces the risk of the multiple failure to an acceptable level.

| 4 | B | 4 | N | | | | N | N | N | N | Y | | *Could the multiple failure affect* |
| 4 | C | 2 | N | | | | N | N | N | N | N | | *safety or the environment?* |

(This question is only asked if the answer to question H4 is no.) If the answer to this question is yes, **redesign** is compulsory. If the answer is no, the default action is **no scheduled mainte-nance**, but redesign may be desirable.

| 5 | B | 2 | Y | Y | | | N | N | N | | | Y | *Is a combination of tasks techni-* |
| 2 | A | 5 | Y | Y | | | N | N | N | | | N | *cally feasible and worth doing?* |

Yes if a combination of any **two or more** preventive tasks will reduce the risk of the failure to an acceptable level (this is very rare). If the answer is no, **redesign** is compulsory.

| 1 | A | 5 | Y | N | N | Y | N | N | N | | | | In these two cases, the consequences |
| 1 | B | 3 | Y | N | N | N | N | N | N | | | | of the failure are purely economic and |

no suitable preventive task has been found. As a result, the initial default decision is **no scheduled maintenance**, but redesign may be desirable.

Figure 7.7: The default questions

Proposed Task

The selected tasks are recorded on the decision worksheet in the column headed "Proposed Task". The task description should be written in a way which is easy to read and easy to understand. After all, if the person doing the task cannot understand exactly what is expected, all the work which has gone into identifying it is wasted.

This may seem obvious, yet it is surprising how often vague instructions like "check bearings" appear in practice. In Chapter 5 we saw how bearings can suffer from a variety of potential failure conditions, including noise, vibration, heat, measurable wear, loose mountings, and so on. This means that if an instruction is too vague, there is a good chance that the person receiving it will not do the task which was intended. Not only is this a waste of time, but it could be dangerous.

This problem is avoided if the task is specified as clearly as possible. Ideally, the task should be specified as precisely on the decision worksheet as it will be on the final document (usually a maintenance schedule or an operating procedure.)

Further examples of the right and the wrong way to specify tasks are shown in Figure 7.8.

Wrong	**Right**
Check coupling	Check feedscrew coupling for loose bolts *or* Check feedscrew coupling for missing bolts *or* Check pump coupling rubber for deterioration *or* Check agitator coupling flange for cracks...etc
Calibrate gauge	Fit 0 - 20 bar test gauge to test point and check if reading on pressure gauge PI1204 is within 1 bar of the reading on the test gauge when the test gauge is reading 18 bar *or* Remove pressure gauge PI1204 to workshop and calibrate following procedure in manual 27A

Figure 7.8: Task descriptions

Initial Interval

The frequency with each task should be done is recorded on the decision worksheet in the column headed "Initial Interval". Chapter 5 explained that the frequency for each task is based on the characteristics of the failure and of the task itself, as summarised below:

• on-condition task frequencies are governed by the *P-F intervals*. For different tasks, these can range from fractions of a second to years, so the associated task frequencies also range from continuous observation to several years.

• scheduled restoration and scheduled discard task frequencies depend on the *useful life* of the item under consideration. The frequencies of these tasks are usually measured in months or years.

• the frequencies of failure-finding tasks are governed by the *consequences of the multiple failure*, which dictate the availability needed, and the *mean time between occurrences of the hidden failure*. These frequencies range from weeks to years.

This highly rigorous approach to the selection of tasks and frequencies helps to avoid unnecessary duplication.

For example when preventive maintenance programmes are drawn up in a traditional manner, it often happens that one person is asked to listen to a bearing at one frequency while someone else is asked to carry out vibration analysis on the same bearing at some other frequency.

Such duplication is needlessly expensive and does nothing for the credibility of planned maintenance. (The only exceptions are the rare cases where the consequences of the failure are serious enough to make it worth applying on-condition tasks to components which are also subject to scheduled discard. However, even here both tasks must satisfy the criteria for technical feasibility.)

   Two further points which arise at this stage are whether the frequency of any task should be influenced by the frequency of any other tasks, and whether such frequencies should be based on elapsed time or running time. These issues are discussed in the following paragraphs.

The interaction between task frequencies

When completing the decision worksheet, the *frequency* of each task must be recorded entirely on its own merits – in other words, without reference to any other maintenance tasks. This is because the reason for doing a task at a particular frequency can change over time – indeed the reason for doing the task at all could disappear. So if the frequency of task X is based on the frequency of task Y and task Y is later eliminated, the frequency of task X becomes meaningless.

   As explained in the next chapter, if we are confronted with a number of tasks which need to be done at a wide range of different frequencies, the time to consider consolidating them into a smaller number of work packages is when compiling maintenance schedules. However, the initial task frequencies should always remain on the decision worksheet to remind us how the schedule frequencies were derived.

Elapsed time vs running time

When maintenance programmes are being developed, considerable time is often spent debating whether task intervals should be based on elapsed time or running time. In practice, the issue needs to be considered from two different perspectives – the *technical* viewpoint and the *administrative* viewpoint. From the *technical* viewpoint, the issue is quite simple:

• elapsed time is suited to cases where deterioration is a function of elapsed time, or where it is a function of operating time and the item is operated consistently.

• running time (or any of its variants such as units of output or distance travelled) should be used where deterioration is a function of operating time and the equipment works intermittently.

Some tasks can be a function of elapsed time *and* operating time.

For example, lubricating oil degenerates due to oxidation when equipment is idle, while many of its additives deteriorate with usage. This leads to an instruction (say) to "change oil every 12 months or 20 000 km, whichever comes first".

This task is actually addressing two different failure modes, but they are combined because if the task is done at the one frequency, it is not necessary to do it at the other.

From the *administrative* viewpoint, planning on the basis of elapsed time is essentially static, so it is usually possible to plan a balanced routine maintenance workload throughout the year. Once the planning system has been set up, operating it becomes a matter of producing the schedules and associated lists at pre-set intervals. The planning system is refined steadily over a period of time and only suffers major dislocations if the operating context changes (from five to seven day working, for example).

On the other hand, planning based on running time is more dynamic. The operating time (or output) of each item must be recorded at regular intervals, and the planning system updated accordingly. This causes the following problems:

• some sort of instrument usually has to be installed to monitor the operating time. This instrument itself needs maintenance of some sort

• someone has to transcribe the information, which is used by someone else to update the planning system (unless this process is automated).

These two factors make running time systems expensive to use. They are also error-prone, because they depend on human and/or mechanical or electronic recorders, which can fail themselves. The final disadvantage of planning on this basis is that routine workloads fluctuate, so it is diffi-cult to predict these workloads even a short way into the future without sophisticated forecasting tools.

These comments all suggest that it is wise to select elapsed time as a basis for planning routine maintenance activities where possible. Run-ning time or output should only be used if it is already routinely recorded, as in the case of vehicles, or if output relates directly to the operation of the equipment.

Can Be Done By

The last column on the decision worksheet is used to list who should do each task. Note that the RCM process considers this issue one failure mode at a time. In other words, it does not approach the subject with any preconceived ideas about who should (or should not) do maintenance work. It simply asks who has the competence and confidence to do *this task* correctly.

The answer could be anyone at all. While the majority of tasks tend to be allocated to craftsmen and operators (depending on the frequency of the task and the level of skill required), it could be agreed that some of the tasks will be done by insurance inspectors, the quality function, specialist technicians, structural inspectors, vendors or laboratory technicians.

As with most of the other decisions in the RCM process, this decision is made best by the people who know the equipment best. This issue is discussed at greater length in Chapter 10.

7.3 Completing the Decision Worksheet

To illustrate how the decision worksheet is completed, we consider three failure modes which have been discussed at length in previous chapters. These are:
• the bearing which seizes on a pump with no stand-by, as discussed on page 95
• the bearing which seizes on an identical pump which does have a stand-by, as discussed on pages 102 and 103
• the failure of the stand-by pump set as a whole, as discussed on pages 77 and 138/139.

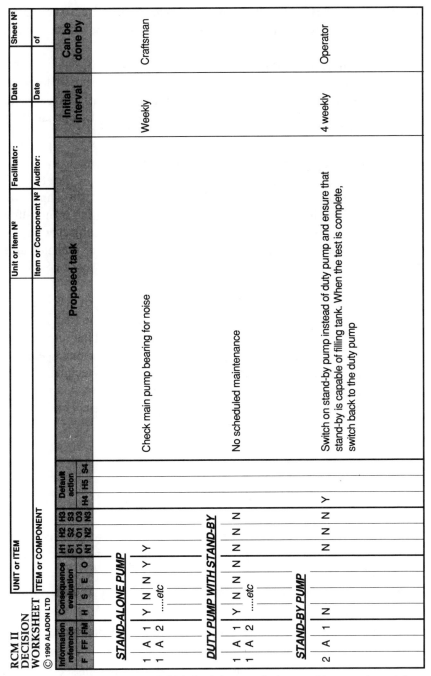

Figure 7.9: *An RCM decision worksheet with sample entries*

The associated decisions are recorded on the decision worksheet in Figure 7.9. Please note three important points about these examples:

- the first two pumps could suffer from many more failure modes than the failure under consideration. Each of these other failures would also be listed and analysed on its own merits.
- a number of other preventive tasks could have been chosen to anticipate the failure of the bearing – the decisions in the example are for the purpose of illustration only.
- the stand-by pump is treated as a "black box". In practice, if such a pump were known to suffer from one or more dominant failure modes, these failures would be analysed individually.

In essence, the RCM worksheets not only show *what* course of action has been selected to deal with each failure mode, but they also show *why* it was selected. This information is invaluable if the need to do any maintenance task is challenged at any time.

The ability to trace each task right back to the functions and desired performance of the asset also make it a simple matter to keep the maintenance programme up to date. This is because users can readily identify and reassess tasks which are affected by a change in the operating context of the asset (such as a change in shift arrangements or a change in safety regulations), and avoid wasting time on tasks which are not likely to be affected by the change.

8 Planning, Organising and Controlling the Proposed Tasks

We have seen how the formal application of the RCM process ends with completed decision worksheets. Among other things, these specify a large number of *maintenance tasks* which need to be done at regular intervals, and a smaller number of one-off tasks where the *process or the design of the asset needs to be changed.*

Once they have been approved by senior managers, these tasks need to be put into effect. Design or process changes are usually dealt with by forwarding the suggestions to appropriate specialists. The role of these specialists is to ensure that the suggested changes are properly justified and designed before they are implemented, as mentioned in Chapter 6.

This chapter focuses on the implementation of the routine tasks. Three key issues are considered, as follows:

• grouping the tasks into suitable work packages
• implementing planning and control systems which ensure that the tasks end up in the hands of the right people at the right time and which ensure that the tasks are done correctly
• ensuring that any faults found are dealt with speedily.

In most organisations, maintenance planning and control systems will already be in place to deal with many if not most of these issues, so this chapter only highlights the main points.

8.1 Packaging the Tasks

The previous chapter explained that each routine task should be defined as clearly as possible on the decision worksheet. Not only does this save the duplication of effort which occurs if detailed procedures have to be written up later by someone else, but it also reduces the possibility of transcription errors. However, if time does not permit the procedures to be specified during the RCM analysis, then they must be specified later.

Once the maintenance procedures have been fully specified, they need to be packaged in a form which can be presented to the people who will be doing the tasks. This can be done in two ways:

• some of the simpler, high-frequency maintenance procedures can be incorporated into the operating procedures of the equipment

• the balance of the maintenance routines are packaged into maintenance schedules.

Standard Operating Procedures

If a set of standard operating procedures already exists for the equipment, it is a simple matter to incorporate the relevant maintenance routine at the appropriate frequencies.

For example, the RCM process might reveal a maintenance task which needs to be done once per shift on a machine which is always started up at the beginning of each shift. The operating procedures for this machine could direct the operator to do this task as a matter of course just before or just after starting up the machine.

If a set of operating procedures do not exist already, then they must either be written, or the affected maintenance tasks must be incorporated into maintenance schedules and treated as described below.

Maintenance Schedules

A maintenance schedule is a document listing a number of maintenance tasks to be done by a person with a specified level of skill on a specified asset at a specified frequency. Figure 8.1 shows the relationship between these schedules and the RCM decision worksheets:

Proposed task	Initial interval	Can be done by
Check main coupling visually for loose or missing bolts	**Monthly**	**Fitter**
No scheduled maintenance	N/A	N/A
Check oil level on agitator gearbox and top up with Wonderoil 900 if necessary	**Monthly**	**Fitter**
Check main bearing for noise	Daily	Operator
etc...		

MAINTENANCE SCHEDULE	
FREQUENCY	TO BE DONE BY
Monthly	*Fitter*
1: *Check main coupling visually for loose or missing bolts*	
2: *Check oil level on agitator gearbox and top up with Wonderoil 900 if necessary*	

Figure 8.1: *Transferring tasks from decision worksheets to schedules*

Compiling schedules from RCM decision worksheets is a fairly straight-forward process. However, a few additional factors need to be taken into account as explained in the following paragraphs.

Basic information

In addition to a clear description of the tasks which have been determined using RCM, every schedule should carry the following information:

- *a description of the equipment* for which it is written together with an equipment number where relevant
- *who should do the schedule* (operator, electrician, fitter, technician, etc)
- *the frequency* with which the schedule is to be done
- *the estimated time* to do the schedule. This is important for planning downtime (if it is needed), for day-to-day workshop planning and for assessing routine workloads
- *whether the equipment should be stopped* and/or isolated while the schedule is done, together with any other safety precautions which must be taken
- *special tools and prescribed spares.* Listing these items can save much unproductive walking to and fro after the job has started.

Contradictions

When a low frequency schedule incorporates a higher frequency schedule, should the latter be incorporated as a global instruction, or should it be rewritten in full? In other words, should (say) an annual schedule include an instruction like "do the three monthly schedule", or should all the tasks from the three monthly schedule be written out in the annual schedule?

In fact it is wise to rewrite the schedules in order to avoid the problem of contradictions.

For instance, consider what could happen in a situation where a three monthly schedule includes the instruction "check gearbox oil and top up if necessary", and the annual schedule for the same machine starts with the instruction "do the three monthly schedule", and later says "drain, flush and refill gearbox".

Too many anomalies and contradictions of this nature rapidly erode the credibility of the system in the eyes of the people doing the work, so it is worth taking a little extra time to ensure that they don't occur.

"If necessary"

Instructions like "Check component A for condition B and replace if necessary" appear on many schedules. These should be avoided because the "check" part of the task might only take a few seconds, while the "replace" part could take several hours. This can play havoc with the duration of planned downtime. Instructions of this sort should in fact be written as "check component A for condition B and report defects to foreman". Only use "if necessary" for quick servicing routines, such as "check oil filter and replace if necessary".

Consolidating frequencies

In Chapter 7 it was mentioned that if we are confronted with a wide range of different task frequencies on a decision worksheet, they should be consolidated into a smaller number of work packages when compiling the schedules which are based on the worksheets. Figure 8.2 gives a somewhat extreme example of the variety of task frequencies which could appear on a decision worksheet, and how they might be consolidated into a smaller number of schedule frequencies.

Frequencies of tasks on decision worksheets	Frequencies of maintenance schedules
Daily	Daily
Weekly	Weekly
2-weekly	
Monthly	Monthly
6-weekly	
2-monthly	
3-monthly	3-monthly
4-monthly	
6-monthly	6-monthly
9-monthly	9-monthly
12-monthly	12-monthly

Figure 8.2:
Consolidating task frequencies

The most expensive tasks, in terms of the direct cost of doing them and the amount of downtime needed to do them, tend to dictate basic schedule frequencies. However, planning is simplified if the schedule frequencies are multiples of one another, as shown in the example.

Note also that if a task frequency is changed in this fashion, it should *always* be incorporated into a schedule of a *higher* frequency. Task frequencies should never be arbitrarily reduced (in other words, the intervals between tasks should not be arbitrarily increased), because doing so could move an on-condition task frequency outside the P-F interval for that failure, or it could move a scheduled discard task past the end of the "life" of the component.

Adding tasks

When compiling schedules on the basis described above, there is often a great temptation to start adding tasks to the completed schedule. This is most often done on the basis that "when we do A and B, we might as well do X, Y and Z". This should be avoided for the following reasons:

• extra tasks increase the routine workload. If too many tasks are added, the workload is increased to the point where there is either insufficient labour to do all the tasks, or the equipment cannot be released for the amount of time required to do them, or both

• the people doing the schedules soon realise that X, Y and Z are not strictly necessary, and *they judge the schedule as a whole accordingly*. As a result, they start looking for reasons why they cannot do the schedule as a whole. When they find them, tasks A and B are also not done and the whole maintenance programme begins to fall apart.

This problem is common in shutdowns. Many shutdown tasks are done, not because they are really needed, but because the plant is stopped and it is possible to "get at" the equipment. This adds greatly to the cost and sometimes to the duration of the shutdown. Unnecessary work also leads to an increase in infant mortality when the plant starts up again.

(This does not mean that people who do routine tasks should concentrate only on the specified tasks and ignore any other potential and functional failures which they may encounter. Of course they should keep their eyes and ears open. The point is that the schedule itself should only specify what really needs to be done at that frequency.)

8.2 Maintenance Planning and Control Systems

High- and Low-frequency Maintenance Schedules

Once the tasks have been grouped into sensible work packages, the next step is to set up planning and control systems which ensure that they are done by the right person at the right time. A key factor which influences the design of such systems is the frequency of the schedules.

In particular, high- and low-frequency schedules are handled differently because both the work content and the planning horizons differ.

High-frequency schedules are defined as *daily* or *weekly* schedules. Most high-frequency tasks are simple on-condition, failure-finding and servicing tasks. They usually have a low work content, and hence can be done quickly. Most of them can also be done while the plant is running, so they can be done at more or less any time. These two factors mean that the associated planning systems can be kept very simple.

However, high-frequency schedules also exist in large numbers, so if careful thought is not applied to their administration the associated paperwork can easily get out of hand. For example, daily schedules which have to be done for 350 days of the year on 1000 items of plant could generate 350 000 pieces of paper annually if each schedule is issued separately every time it is to be done. An avalanche of paper of this magnitude is clearly nonsense, and the problems it creates are a common reason why high-frequency schedules are often administered badly or not at all.

But high-frequency tasks are the backbone of successful routine maintenance, so some way must be found to ensure that they are done without creating an excessive administrative burden.

Low-frequency schedules are those which are done at intervals of *a month or longer*. Their longer planning horizon makes them less amenable to simple planning systems of the type which can be used for high-frequency schedules. They usually have a higher work content so more time is needed to do them, and the plant usually has to be stopped while they are done. As a result, they need more complex planning and control systems.

The next sections of this chapter suggest some of the options which can be used to manage both types of schedules, under the following headings:
- schedules done by operators
- "schedules" done by the quality function
- high-frequency schedules done by maintenance people
- low-frequency schedules done by maintenance people.

Schedules done by Operators

From the maintenance viewpoint, the most valuable attribute of operators is that they are near the equipment for much of the time. As discussed on page 126, this puts them in an ideal position to do many on-condition and failure-finding tasks. These tend to be very high-frequency tasks – most will be daily or even once or twice per shift – so special care must be taken to keep the associated administrative systems as simple as possible.

MAINTENANCE CHECKLIST	PLANT SECTION		TO BE DONE BY	WEEK ENDING DATE
	Boiler House		Mechanical	

ITEM Nº	DESCRIPTION	SCHEDULE	M	T	W	T	F	S	S	REMARKS
29-01-02	Grate assembly	M-441								
29-01-04	ID Fan	M-603								
29-01-07	Feed pump A	M-211								
29-01-08	Feed pump B	M-217								
29-01-11	Control system	M-376								
29-02-02	Grate assembly	M-441								
29-02-04	ID Fan	M-603								
29-02-07	Feed pump A	M-211								
29-02-08	Feed pump B	M-217								
29-02-11	Control system	M-376								
29-03-02	Grate assembly	M-441								
29-03-04	ID Fan	M-603								
29-03-07	Feed pump A	M-211								
29-03-08	Feed pump B	M-217								
29-03-11	Control system	M-376								
29-04-00	Water treatment plant	M-155								

ALLOCATED TO	TIME SPENT		COMPLETED BY	FOREMAN

Figure 8.3: A checklist for high-frequency maintenance schedules

Simple reminder systems which can be used for operator tasks instead of formal checksheets include:

- incorporating the maintenance checks into standard operating procedures, as discussed earlier
- mounting the schedule permanently onto a wall or on a control cabinet where the operators can see it easily
- training the operators in such a way that the inspections become second nature (a high-risk approach).

Formal written checklists should only be used for operator checks when the failure consequences are likely to be particularly severe, and there is reason to doubt whether the tasks will be done without a formal reminder. The checklists can be the same as those described later for high-frequency tasks done by maintenance people.

Schedules and Quality Checks

We have seen how performance standards of equipment are being defined increasingly often in terms of product quality standards. This means that more and more potential and functional failures are being revealed by quality checks. These checks are often being done already (for example, using SPC as discussed on page 123). Key points to note are as follows:

- quality checks must be recognised as a valid and valuable source of maintenance information (it is surprising how many maintenance people *still* regard product quality as being someone else's problem)
- steps must be taken to ensure that quality-related potential failures are attended to as soon as they are noticed. This issue is discussed in more detail later.

High-frequency Schedules done by Maintenance

Despite all the earlier comments about the merits of using operators to do high-frequency maintenance work, many of these tasks still need to be done by maintenance people. These usually need to be more formally planned than operators' checks, because maintenance people cover more machines spread over a wider area than operators, and they usually do a wider variety of tasks.

One approach is to divide the plant into sections, and prepare a checklist of the type shown in Figure 8.3 for each section.

Note the following points about this type of checklist:

- the checklist only lists the *schedules* to be done, not individual tasks. The schedules are issued separately, often in book form, and bound in plastic covers for protection. In this way, only one checklist is issued per section per week, rather than dozens of schedules every day.

- roughly the same amount of work should be planned for each day, and it should not exceed between half an hour and an hour per day.

- the checklist shown can be used to plan at intervals between daily and weekly. Jobs can be planned for alternate days and twice per week, so the checklist encompasses a wider range of the shorter P-F intervals.

- the checklist can start and finish on any five or seven day cycle - it is not essential to stick to the Monday/Sunday cycle shown in the example.

- the checklists embody the schedule plans and they are issued automatically every week, so there is no need for any sort of planning board.

- the checklists are not used for any tasks which are to be done at intervals of longer than a week.

- each checklist involves one or two sheets of paper per week per plant section. This amounts to no more than fifty photocopies per week for a plant containing 1000 items subject to these checks. As a result, it is usually unnecessary to use a computer for these checklists.

Some high-frequency performance monitoring tasks call for written records of meter readings. Reading a meter is a task, while the checklist described above is designed for complete schedules, so this cause problems. For instance some people start issuing separate documents for these records alongside the checklists. This should be avoided, as the volumes of paper simply start climbing again. Possible alternatives are as follows:

- ask operators to collect the readings on a separate document

- develop a special sheet of paper for *all* the meter readings in each section, and attach this one sheet to the checklist for that section each week

- use one person to carry out all the meter readings in the entire plant

- ask the people reading the meters to record only those readings which are outside acceptable limits in the remarks column of the checklist (to make this possible, these limits need to be specified on the schedule or on the meter itself, as shown on page 124)

- automate the recording process.

Issuing high-frequency schedules

The checklists are issued to the relevant supervisor the week before they are to be done, and the supervisor issue them to the craftsmen. Preferably, they should be the first activity which each craftsman does each day. Note the following additional features of a well-run checklist system:

- if the craftsman cannot complete the planned tasks on any day, the tasks are done the following day. If the craftsman is continually unable to complete the prescribed checks, something is fundamentally wrong and the situation should be investigated.

- the craftsman notes any potential or functional failures in the remarks column of the checklist – not on the schedules themselves.

- the craftsman reports to the supervisor at the end of each daily round. The supervisor decides what corrective action should be taken and when. This will vary from arranging for the plant to stop at once to arranging for the fault to be corrected at the next shutdown. This decision is based on the possible consequences of the failure and the nett P-F interval. (Note however that these issues should have been considered as part of the RCM process when the routine task was originally specified.)

- as in the case of operators, it is important that the supervisor takes action, or else explains why action is unnecessary or being deferred, or the craftsmen will also lose interest in the system.

- at the end of each cycle, the completed checklists are returned to the maintenance planning office. As a rule it is not necessary to record the completion of high-frequency schedules which have revealed no problems in a history recording system, but there may be some merit in recording any problems which are found, as discussed in Chapter 9.

Controlling high-frequency schedules

A problem associated with most checklist systems is the "tearoom tick syndrome". This means that people indicate that the checklist has been done when in fact it has not. To avoid this problem, the supervisor should conduct random over-inspections. These entail doing the schedules on the checklist in the company of the craftsman who normally does it. If the checklist is not being done correctly, unreported failures soon become apparent, and the supervisor takes appropriate action.

Low-frequency Schedules done by Maintenance

We have seen that high-frequency schedules can be planned, organised and controlled using one carefully structured checklist. In contrast, the long planning horizon associated with low-frequency schedules means that the steps needed to plan, organise and control them are carried out separately. What is more, the procedures used to *plan* schedules based on elapsed time differ markedly from those used for schedules based on running time, but similar procedures can be used to *organise* and *control* the two types of schedule. As a result, we consider the planning process separately in the following paragraphs, but consider the subsequent steps together.

Elapsed time planning

The basic principles of elapsed time planning are well known, and are used for a wide range of purposes in addition to maintenance planning. For low-frequency schedules, elapsed time planning is usually based on a planning board similar to that shown in Figure 8.4 (or its computerised equivalent).

ITEM Nº	DESCRIPTION	1	2	3	4	5	6	7	8	9	10	11	12	----	47	48	49	50	51	52

Figure 8.4: A typical low-frequency planning board

Most of these systems use an overall planning horizon of one year, divided into 52 weeks. When setting up these systems, bear in mind all the issues which affect operational consequences of failure. This is because low-frequency schedules nearly always involve equipment stoppages, and these can have operational consequences in exactly the same way as the stoppages which they are supposed to prevent, unless special care is taken. (These consequences are discussed at length in Chapter 4.) Points to watch for include the following:

- peaks and troughs in the production cycle. The most time consuming schedules should be planned for periods of lowest activity, in order to minimise their effect on operations
- two machines which require the same special resource at the same time (such as a crane)

- cases where it is only possible to do a schedule if other machines are stopped at the same time. This applies especially to services like boilers and compressors.

On the other hand, wherever such constraints permit, try to spread the routine maintenance workload as evenly as possible over the year in order to stabilise labour requirements.

A final point about elapsed-time-based low-frequency schedule planning is that it looks deceptively simple to use computers for this purpose. However, bear in mind that all the issues discussed above introduce a very wide range of completely unrelated constraints into the calendar time planning process.

For this reason, approach with caution calendar-time-based systems which plan schedules on the basis of predetermined parameters, or which automatically re-plan schedules that have not been done. Such systems move schedules from week to week, usually regardless of policy constraints. This can become chaotic, especially if schedules which should only be done in the low season are gradually moved into the middle of the high season and so on.

Running time planning

Running time planning involves the following steps:

- the number of cycles each machine has completed in each period are recorded (they can be measured in terms of time, distance travelled, units of output, etc)
- this record is fed into the planning system
- the cumulative total of hours run is updated to reflect the time run since the last schedule was done.

Manual running time systems can range from sophisticated boards costing hundreds – even thousands – of pounds to counters which move along pieces of string. If possible, these systems should count *down* to zero, so that planners can see at a glance how much time is left before schedules are due. This also provides visual early warning of peaks that could overload the workshop.

Running time planning systems lend themselves readily to the use of computers because they entail processing and storing large quantities of data. Also the dynamism of running time systems means that they have fewer policy constraints than elapsed time systems.

However, as discussed on page 168, if the collection of the run time data is not automated it can be expensive and prone to errors, so if computers are to be used for running time planning, data capture should also be automated if possible. The system should also be designed to provide a continuously updated forecast of the scheduled workload on each workshop as far as possible into the future. This gives managers time to smooth any peaks and troughs which appear in the forecast.

Organising low-frequency schedules

Most planning systems start organising low-frequency schedules the week before the schedules are due (except for shutdown schedules). The organising process contains the following elements:

- a list is prepared which shows the schedules due the following week. They are usually separated by craft and plant section

- meetings are held with the operations department to agree on which day and at what time the schedules will be done (especially those which require equipment downtime)

- the schedules themselves are issued to the relevant supervisors, who plan who will do them and arrange any other resources which may be needed as they would for any other incoming maintenance job.

Computers are widely used for this aspect of schedule management. They can be used in one of three ways:

- to produce a list of schedules due, while the schedules and associated job cards are produced manually

- to produce a list of schedules due *plus* the job cards, in which case the schedules themselves can either be copied manually or kept in each plant section in the same book as high-frequency schedules

- to produce the list of schedules due plus the job cards plus the schedules themselves. In this case, the schedules are stored on the computer. Such schedules should be easily accessible so that they can be changed without difficulty.

The second option is usually the most popular, possibly because it offers most of the data sorting advantages of the computer and the lowest total set-up cost. If the schedules are stored in books in each section of the plant, this option also generates the lowest quantity of paper and requires the least manual clerical effort.

Controlling low-frequency schedules

Low-frequency schedules are subject to the same performance controls as any other type of maintenance work. This applies to the time taken to do the schedules, standards of workmanship, and so on.

Two additional factors need to be considered. Firstly, the planning system should indicate when any schedule is overdue. As mentioned earlier, such schedules should not be reprogrammed automatically, but should be managed on an exception basis.

Finally, maintenance schedules should be reviewed continuously in the light of changing circumstances (especially circumstances which affect the consequences of failure) and new information. In this context, bear in mind that the more everyone associated with the equipment is involved in determining its maintenance requirements to begin with, the more they are likely to offer thoughtful and constructive feedback about these requirements in future.

8.3 Reporting Defects

In addition to ensuring that the tasks are done, we also need to ensure that any potential failures which are found are rectified before they become functional failures, and that hidden functional failures are rectified before the multiple failure has a chance to occur. This means that anyone who might discover a potential or functional failure must have unrestricted access to a simple, reliable and direct procedure for reporting it immediately to whoever is going to repair it.

This communication takes place instantaneously if the person who operates the machine is also the person who maintains it. The speed and accuracy of the response to defects which can be achieved under these circumstances are a major reason why people who operate machines should also be trained to maintain them (or vice versa). A second benefit of this approach is that formal defect reporting systems are only needed for failures which the operator/maintainer is unable to deal with on his own.

If this organisation structure is not possible or not practical, the next best way to ensure that defects are attended to quickly is to allocate maintenance people permanently to a specific asset or group of assets. Not only do such people get to know the machines better, which improves their diagnostic skills, but the speed of response also tends to be quicker than it would be if they work in a central workshop. It is also still possible to keep the defect reporting systems simple and informal.

If it is not possible to organise close maintenance support of either sort, then it becomes necessary to implement more formal defect reporting systems. In general, the further away the maintenance function is from the assets it is to maintain – in other words, the more heavily centralised it is – the more formal the defect reporting process becomes. This is also true of defects which can only be dealt with during major shutdowns.

Basically, formal defect reporting systems enable anyone to inform the maintenance department in writing (electronically or manually) about the existence of a potential or functional failure. The chief criteria of such systems should always be simplicity, accessibility and speed.

Manual defect reporting systems are usually based on simple job cards of the type shown in Figure 8.5. (These job cards can also be used by the maintenance department to plan and record work, but this aspect of their use is beyond the scope of this book.) If a computerised defect reporting system is used, the screen is formatted in much the same way as the card.

JOB CARD	DEPARTMENT		DATE		
PLANT Nº	**PLANT DESCRIPTION**			Potential failure	
JOB REQUEST	TO (FOREMAN)	JOB REQUESTED BY		Functional failure	
				Maintenance schedule	
Please attend to the following _____				Modification	
				Capital	
				Approved by	
				SHUTDOWN JOB	
				Yes No	
JOB INSTRUCTION	ALLOCATED TO	DATE		ESTIMATED TIME	
				FOREMAN	

Figure 8.5: A typical job request

The final point about systems of this sort is that people must be properly motivated to use them. This means that defects which are reported must be acted upon, or the user must be told why if no action is taken. Nothing will kill such a system more quickly than if defects are reported and nothing apparently happens.

9 The Nature of Failure and Technical History

Chapter 1 explained that maintenance means doing whatever is necessary to ensure that any physical asset continues to fulfil its intended functions to the desired level of performance. Subsequent chapters have explained how RCM contributes to this objective by enabling users to select the most appropriate blend of tools for detecting, anticipating, preventing or correcting failures. In discussing this process, extensive use has been made of terms such as "life", "mean time between failures", "random failure", "potential failure" and "conditional probability of failure".

This chapter explores the meaning of these terms in more detail. In so doing, it looks more deeply at the processes by which failures occur, and relates these to the six failure patterns first introduced in Chapter 1. It also takes a brief look at the role of historical data in maintenance decision making, and considers what sort of data (if any) need to be recorded on a formal basis.

Inherent reliability, desired performance and failure

Previous chapters have stressed repeatedly that if the desired performance of any asset exceeds its built-in capability, it is in a failed state right from the outset and no amount of maintenance will deliver the desired performance. This problem can only be solved by redesigning the asset to increase its built-in capability, or by lowering performance expectations to a level at which the asset can cope.

However, we have also seen that if what we want the asset to do is within the envelope of what it can do, then maintenance can deliver the desired performance. The rest of this chapter deals with assets which *are* capable of delivering the desired performance at the outset, and which only fail as a result of phenomena which occur after they have been put into service.

9.1 The Failure Process

Any physical asset which is required to fulfil a function which brings it into contact with the real world will be subjected to a variety of stresses. These stresses cause the asset to deteriorate by lowering its *resistance to stress*. Eventually this resistance drops to the point at which the asset can no longer deliver the desired performance – in other words, it fails. This is illustrated in Figure 9.1.

Chapters 5 and 8 explained that exposure to stress is measured in a variety of ways, including output, calendar time, distance travelled, or running time. These units are all related to time, so it is common to refer to total exposure to stress as the *age* of the item. This connection between stress and time suggests that there should be a direct relationship between the rate of deterioration and the age of the item. If this is so, then it follows that the point at which the item fails also depends on the age of the item, as shown in Figure 9.2.

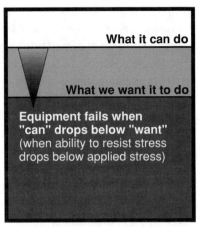

Figure 9.1:
Can, want and failure

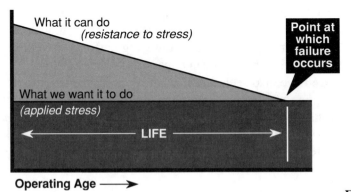

Figure 9.2:
Absolute predictability

However, Figure 9.2 is based on two key assumptions:

• deterioration is directly proportional to the applied stress, and

• the stress is applied consistently.

If this were true of all assets, we would be able to predict the life of most equipment with great precision. The classical view of preventive maintenance suggests that this can be done – all that is needed is enough information about failures.

In reality, however, the situation is much less clear cut. Let us start looking at the real world by considering a situation where there is a clear relationship between age and failure, and then move on to a more general view of reality.

Age-related Failures

Even parts which seem to be identical vary slightly in their initial resistance to failure. The rate at which this resistance declines with age also varies. Furthermore, no two parts are subject to exactly the same stresses throughout their lives. Even when these variations are quite small, they can have a disproportionate effect on the age at which the part fails. This is illustrated in Figure 9.3, which shows two components which are put into service with similar resistance to failure.

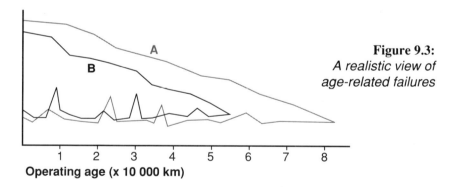

Figure 9.3:
A realistic view of age-related failures

Operating age (x 10 000 km)

Part B is exposed to a generally higher level of stress throughout its life than part A, so it deteriorates more quickly. Deterioration also accelerates in response to the two stress peaks at 18 000 km and 30 000 km. On the other hand, for some reason part A seems to deteriorate at a steady pace despite two stress peaks at 23 000 km and 37 000 km. So one component fails at 53 000 km and the other at 85 000 km.

This shows that the failure age of identical parts working under apparently identical conditions varies widely. Although the failures of a large number of these parts would tend to congregate around some average age, some last much longer than others. In the example shown, some last almost twice as long.

So even when resistance to failure does decline with age, the point at which failure occurs is often much less predictable than common sense would suggest. The quantitative implications of this situation are explored in greater depth in Part 2 of this chapter. However, from the maintenance management viewpoint, a more important issue is that surprisingly few items actually do show a relationship between age and failure. Why this should be so is discussed in the following paragraphs.

Random Failures

Simple items

Contrary to the assumptions listed above:

• deterioration is not always proportional to the applied stress, and

• stress is not always applied consistently.

For example, graph A in Figure 9.4 shows a situation where resistance remains constant, and failure is caused by a sudden increase in the applied stress *(a rock smashes a window pane)*. In an ideal world, "preventing" this type of failure should be a matter of preventing whatever causes the increase in stress levels, rather than a matter of doing anything to the asset.

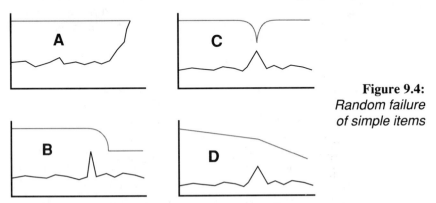

Figure 9.4:
*Random failure
of simple items*

For example, many such increases in stress are caused by errors on the part of operators (starting up a machine too quickly, accidentally putting it into reverse while it is going forward, feeding material into a process too quickly, etc). In such cases, the best method of prevention is of course to train the operator not to do whatever it is that causes the failure.

Other stress increases can be caused by external factors such as lightning, the "thousand-year flood", earthquakes, and so on. In these cases, failure could theoretically be avoided by designing the asset to withstand the very worst case. If this is too costly, the alternatives are either to live with the failure, or to try to anticipate the increase in stress as discussed later.

In case B, the stress peak permanently reduces the resistance to failure, but does not actually cause the item to fail *(an earthquake cracks a structure but does not cause it to fall down)*. The reduced failure resistance makes the part vulnerable to the next peak, which may or may not occur before the part is replaced for some other reason. In C, the stress peak only temporarily reduces failure resistance *(as in the case of thermoplastic materials which soften when temperature rises and harden again when it drops)*.

Finally, D shows a case where a stress peak accelerates the decline of failure resistance, and eventually greatly shortens the life of the component. When this occurs, the cause and effect relationship can be very difficult to establish, because the failure could take place months or even years after the stress peak.

This often happens when a part is damaged during installation (which might happen if a ball-bearing is misaligned), if it is damaged prior to installation (the bearing is dropped on the floor in the parts store) or if it is mistreated in service (dirt gets into the bearing while it is in service). In these cases, failure prevention is ideally a matter of ensuring that maintenance and installation work is done correctly and that parts are looked after properly in storage.

In all four of these examples, when the items enter service it is not possible to predict when any of the failures will occur. For this reason, they are described as "random".

Complex items

The failure processes described in Figure 9.4 apply to fairly simple mechanisms. In the case of complex items, the situation becomes even less predictable. Items are made more complex to improve their performance (by incorporating new or additional technology or by automation) or to make them safer (using protective devices).

For example, Nowlan and Heap[1978] cite developments in the field of civil aviation. In the 1930's, an air trip was a slow, somewhat risky affair, undertaken in reasonably favourable weather conditions in an aircraft with a range of a few hundred miles and space for about twenty passengers. The aircraft had one or two reciprocating engines, fixed landing gear, fixed pitch propellers and no wing flaps.

Today an air trip is much faster and very much safer. It is undertaken in almost any weather conditions in an aircraft with a range of thousands of miles and space for hundreds of passengers. The aircraft has several jet engines, anti-icing equipment, retractable landing gear, moveable high-lift devices, pressure and temperature control systems for the cabin, extensive navigation and communications equipment, complex instrumentation and complex ancillary support systems.

In other words, better performance and greater safety are achieved at the cost of greater complexity. This is true in most branches of industry.

Greater complexity means balancing the lightness and compactness needed for high performance, with the size and mass needed for durability. This combination of complexity and compromise:

- increases the number of components which can fail, and also increases the number of interfaces or connections between components. This in turn increases the number and variety of failures which can occur.

  For example, a great many mechanical failures involve welds or bolts, while a significant proportion of electrical and electronic failures involve the connections between components. The more such connections there are, the more such failures there will be.

- reduces the margin between the initial capability of each component and the desired performance (in other words, the "can" is closer to the "want"), which reduces scope for deterioration before failure occurs.

These two developments in turn suggest that complex items are even more likely to suffer from random failures than simple items. The quantitative aspects of random failure are discussed in more detail in Part 2 of this chapter.

However, the main conclusion from the maintenance management viewpoint is that the idea of a wear-out age simply does not apply to random failures, so the idea of routine replacement or overhaul prior to such an age cannot apply.

Potential Failures

Even though most failures are not related to the age of the item, most of them give some warning of the fact that they are either occurring or are about to occur. As explained in Part 6 of Chapter 5, this warning is known as a potential failure. The final stages of deterioration are described by the P-F curve, and the interval between potential and functional failure is called the P-F interval. In this part of this chapter, we consider these concepts in more detail, starting with a look at what happens in the final stages of deterioration just before failure.

The final stages of deterioration

Figure 5.6 on Page 117 suggests that the deterioration process usually accelerates in the final stages. To see why this should be so, let us consider in more detail what happens when a ball bearing fails due to "normal wear and tear".

Figure 9.5 overleaf illustrates a typical vertically-loaded ball bearing which is rotating clockwise. The most heavily and frequently loaded part of the bearing will be the bottom of the outer race. As the bearing rotates, the inner surface of the outer race moves up and down as each ball passes over it. These cyclic movements are tiny, but they are sufficient to cause sub-surface fatigue cracks which develop as shown in Figure 9.5.

Figure 9.5 also explains how these cracks eventually give rise to detectable symptoms of deterioration. These are of course potential failures, and the associated P-F intervals are shown in Figure 5.12 on page 127. This example raises several further points about potential failures, as follows:

- failure only becomes detectable when the fatigue cracks migrate to the surface and the surface starts breaking up. The point at which this happens in the life of any one bearing depends on the speed of rotation of the bearing, the magnitude of the load, the extent to which the outer race itself rotates, whether the bearing surface is damaged prior to or during installation, how hot the bearing gets in service, the alignment of the shaft relative to the housing, the materials used to manufacture the bearing, how well it was made, etc. Effectively, this combination of variables makes it impossible to predict how many operating cycles must elapse before the cracks will reach the surface, and hence when the bearing will start exhibiting the symptoms mentioned in Figure 9.5.

- in the example, the deterioration process accelerates. This suggests that if a quantitative technique such as vibration analysis is used to detect potential failures, we cannot predict when failure will occur by drawing a straight line based on just two observations.

  This in turn leads to the notion that after an initial deviation is observed, additional vibration readings should be taken at progressively shorter intervals until some further point is reached at which action should be taken. In practice, this can only be done if the P-F interval is long enough to allow time for the additional readings. It also does not escape the fact that the initial readings need to be taken at a frequency which is known to be less than the P-F interval.

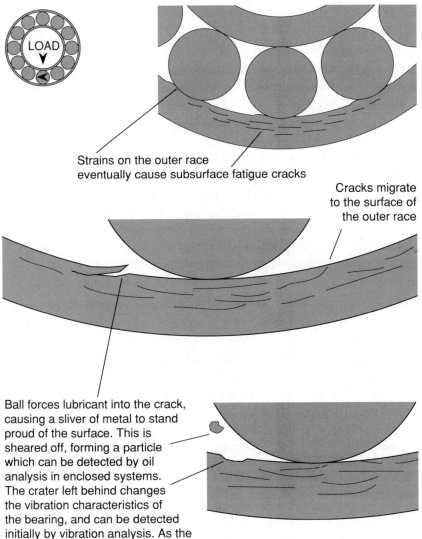

Strains on the outer race
eventually cause subsurface fatigue cracks

Cracks migrate
to the surface of
the outer race

Ball forces lubricant into the crack,
causing a sliver of metal to stand
proud of the surface. This is
sheared off, forming a particle
which can be detected by oil
analysis in enclosed systems.
The crater left behind changes
the vibration characteristics of
the bearing, and can be detected
initially by vibration analysis. As the
balls pass over the crater, they make it bigger. Soon the balls themselves get
damaged because they are no longer rolling on a smooth surface. At some point,
the bearing becomes audibly noisy, and then starts getting hotter. Deterioration
continues at an accelerating pace until the balls eventually disintegrate and the
bearing seizes.

Figure 9.5:
How a rolling element bearing fails due to "normal wear and tear"

(In fact, if the shape of the P-F curve is fairly well known and the P-F interval is reasonably consistent, it should not be necessary to take additional readings after the first sign of deviation is discovered. This suggests that the process of deterioration should only be tracked by taking additional readings if the P-F curve is poorly understood or if the P-F interval is highly inconsistent.)

• different failure modes can often exhibit similar symptoms.

For example, the symptoms described in Figure 9.5 are based on failure due to normal wear and tear. Very similar symptoms would be exhibited in the final stages of the failure of a bearing where the failure process has been initiated by dirt, lack of lubrication or brinelling.

In practice, the precise root cause of many failures can only be identified using sophisticated instruments. For instance, it might be possible to determine the root cause of the failure of a bearing by using a ferrograph to separate particles from the lubricating oil and examining the particles under an electron microscope.

However, if two different failures have the same symptoms and if the P-F interval is broadly similar for each set of symptoms – which it would be in the case of the bearing examples – the distinction between root causes is irrelevant from the failure *detection* viewpoint. (The distinction does of course become relevant if we are seeking to *eliminate* the root cause of the failure.)

Deterioration accelerates in the final stages of most failures. For instance, apart from bearings, deterioration is likely to accelerate when bolts start to loosen, when filter elements get blinded, when V-belts slacken and start slipping, when electrical contactors overheat, when seals start to fail, when rotating components become unbalanced and so on. But it does not accelerate in *every* case.

Linear P-F curves

If an item deteriorates in a more or less linear fashion over its entire life, it stands to reason that the final stages of deterioration will also be more or less linear. A close look at Figures 9.2 and 9.3 suggests that this is likely to be true of age-related failures.

For example, consider again the example of tyre wear discussed on page 130. The surface of the tyre is likely to wear in a more or less linear fashion until the tread depth reaches the legal minimum. If this minimum is (say) 2 mm, it is possible to specify a depth of tread greater than 2 mm which provides adequate warning that functional failure is imminent. This is of course the potential failure level.

If the potential failure is set at (say) 3 mm, then the P-F interval is the distance the tyre could be expected to travel while its tread depth wears down from 3 mm to 2 mm, as illustrated in Figure 9.6.

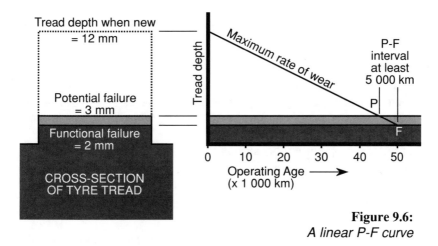

Figure 9.6:
A linear P-F curve

Figure 9.6 also suggests that if the tyre enters service with a tread depth of (say) 12 mm, it should be possible to predict the P-F interval based on the total distance usually covered before the tyre has to be retreaded. For instance, if the tyres usually last *at least* 50 000 km before they have to be retreaded, it is reasonable to conclude that the tread wears at a maximum rate of 1 mm for every 5 000 km travelled. This amounts to a P-F interval of 5 000 km. The associated on-condition task would call for the driver to:

"Check tread depth every 2 500 km and report tyres whose tread depth is less than 3 mm."

Not only will this task ensure that wear is detected before it exceeds the legal limit, but it also allows plenty of time – 2 500 km in this case – for the vehicle operators to plan to remove the tyre before it reaches the limit.

In general, linear deterioration between "P" and "F" is only likely to be encountered where the failure is caused by abrasion, erosion, corrosion or oxidation. This is not surprising, since these failure mechanisms are intrinsically age-related. (Figure 9.5 suggests that fatigue is a somewhat more complex case. This failure process is discussed in more detail later.)

Note that the P-F interval and the associated task frequency can only be deduced in this fashion if deterioration is linear. As we have seen, the P-F interval cannot be determined in this way if deterioration accelerates between "P" and "F".

A further point about linear failures concerns the point at which one should start to look for potential failures.

For example, Figure 9.6 suggests that it would be a waste of time to measure the overall depth of the tyre tread at ten or twenty thousand km, because we know that it only approaches the potential failure point at 50 000 km. So perhaps we should only start measuring the tread depth of each tyre after it has passed the point where we know tread depth will be approaching 3 mm – in other words, when the tyre has been in service for more than (say) 40 000 km.

However, if we want to ensure that this checking regime is adopted in practice, consider how the checks for a 4-wheeled truck would have to be planned if the actual history of a set of tyres is as follows:

Item	Distance travelled by truck and by each tyre			
Truck	140 000	142 500	145 000	147 500
Left front tyre	47 500	50 000	52 500	1 000*
Right front tyre	22 000	24 500	27 000	29 500
Left rear tyre	12 500	2 000†	4 500	7 000
Right rear tyre	38 000	40 500	43 000	45 500

* *Tread depth of L/F tyre dropped below 3 mm and tyre replaced at depot*
† *6 inch nail caused tyre to blow out at 13 000 km - replaced with new spare*

If we are seriously going to try to ensure that the driver only checks each tyre after it passes 40 000 km in service, we would have to devise a system which told him to:
• start checking the L/F tyre only when the truck reached 132 500 km
• check the L/F and R/R tyres when the truck reached 142 500 km
• and again at 145 000 km
• but check the R/R tyre only at 147 500 km.

Clearly this is nonsense, because the cost of administering such a planning system would be far greater than the cost of simply asking the driver to check the tread depth of every tyre on the vehicle every 2 500 km. In other words, in this example the cost of fine-tuning the planning system would be far greater than the cost of doing the tasks. So we would simply ask the driver to check the tread depth of every tyre at 2 500 km intervals, rather than direct his attention to specific tyres.

However, if the process of deterioration is linear and the task itself is very expensive, then it might be worth ensuring that we only start checking for potential failures when it is really necessary.

For instance, if an on-condition task entails shutting down and opening up a large turbine to check the turbine discs for cracks, and *we are certain that deterioration only becomes detectable after the turbine has been in service for a certain length of time (in other words, the failure is age-related)*, then we should only start taking the turbine out of service to check for the cracks after it has passed the age at which there is a reasonable likelihood that detectable cracks will start to emerge. Thereafter, the frequency of checking is based on the rate at which a detectable crack is likely to deteriorate into a failure.

In cases like these, the cost of doing the task would be much greater than the cost of the associated planning systems, so it is worth ensuring that we only start doing the tasks when it is really necessary. However, if it is felt that this fine-tuning is worthwhile, bear in mind that the planning process has to employ two completely different time-frames, as follows:

• the first time-frame is used to decide *when we should start* doing the on-condition tasks. This is the *operating age* at which potential failures are likely to start becoming detectable.

• the second time-frame governs *how often* we should do the tasks after this age has been reached. This time-frame is of course the *P-F interval*.

For example, it might be felt that the turbine disc is unlikely to develop any detectable cracks until it has been in service for at least 50 000 hours, but that it takes a minimum of ten thousand hours for a detectable crack to deteriorate into disc failure. This suggests that we don't need to start checking for cracks until the item has been in service for 50 000 hours, *but thereafter it must be checked at intervals of less than ten thousand hours.*

Planning with this degree of sophistication requires a very detailed understanding of the failure mode under consideration, together with highly sophisticated planning systems. In practice, few failure modes are this well understood. When they are, even fewer organisations possess planning systems which can switch from one time frame to another as described above, so this issue needs to be approached with care.

(This two stage approach to routine maintenance should also not be confused with the situations where a combination of preventive tasks is used, such as when an on-condition task is used in conjunction with scheduled discard as mentioned on page 133. In these cases, the on-condition task is usually done throughout the life of the component.)

In closing this discussion, it must be stressed that all the curves – P-F and age-related – which have been drawn in this part of this chapter have been drawn for *one failure mode at a time.*

For instance, in the example concerning tyres, the failure process was "normal" wear. Different failure modes (such as flat spots worn on the tyres due to emergency braking or damage to the carcass caused by hitting kerbs) would lead to different conclusions because both the technical characteristics and the consequences of these failure modes are different.

It is one matter to speculate on the nature of P-F curves in general, but it is quite another to determine the magnitude of the P-F interval in practice. This issue is considered in the next section of this chapter.

Determining the P-F Interval

It is usually a fairly simple matter to determine the P-F interval for age-related failure modes whose final stages of deterioration are linear. It is done by applying logic similar to that used in the tyre example on page 196. However, in the case of random failures where deterioration accelerates, the interval can be surprisingly difficult to establish.

The main problem with random failures is that we don't know when the next one is going to occur, so we don't know when the next failure mode is going to start on its way down the P-F curve. So if we don't even know where the P-F curve is going to start, how can we go about finding out how long it is?

The following paragraphs review five possibilities, only the fourth and fifth of which have any merit.

Continuous observation

In theory, the P-F interval could be determined by observing the item continuously until a potential failure occurs, noting when that happens, and then continuing to observe the item until it fails completely.

(Note that we cannot chart a full P-F curve by observing the item intermittently, because when we eventually discovered that it was failing we still wouldn't know precisely when the failure process started. What is more, if the P-F interval is shorter than the intermittent observation period we might miss the P-F curve altogether, in which case we would have to start all over again with a new item.)

Clearly this approach is impractical, firstly because continuous observation is very expensive – especially if we were to try to establish every P-F interval in this way. Secondly, waiting until the functional failure occurs means that the item actually has to fail. This might end up with us saying to the boss after (say) the compressor blew up: "Oh, we knew it was failing, but we just wanted to see how long it would take before it finally went so that we could determine the P-F interval!"

Start with a short interval and gradually extend it

The impracticality of the above approach leads some people to suggest that P-F intervals can be established by starting the checks at some quite short but arbitrary interval, and then gradually increasing it until "we find out what the interval should be". Unfortunately, this is again the point at which the functional failure occurs, so we would still end up blowing up the compressor. There is also no guarantee that the initial arbitrary inter-val, no matter how short, will be shorter than the P-F interval to begin with (unless serious consideration is given to the failure process itself).

In fact, choosing between these first two methods is like choosing whether to play Russian Roulette with one expensive bullet or with two cheaper ones.

Arbitrary intervals

The difficulties associated with these two approaches lead some people to suggest – quite seriously – that we should forget about P-F intervals and do the task at any interval which looks reasonably short. This arbi-trary approach causes the following problems:

- there is again no guarantee that the "reasonably short" arbitrary interval is shorter than the P-F interval. (Goodbye again to the compressor ... or the motor-generator set ... or the boiler ... .)

- on the other hand, the true P-F interval may be much longer – in some cases, several orders of magnitude longer – than the arbitrary interval. So people who adopt this approach could be committing substantially more effort to routine maintenance than they need to.

  For instance, if a daily task really only needs to be done once a month, that task is costing *thirty times* as much as it should.

This is in fact the least satisfactory and potentially the most dangerous way to set on-condition task frequencies.

Research

The best way to establish a precise P-F interval is to simulate the failure in such a way that there are no serious consequences when it eventually does occur. For example this is done when aircraft components are tested to failure in special rigs on the ground rather than in the air. Not only does this provide data about the life of the components, as discussed in Part 2 of this chapter, but it also enables the observers to study at leisure how failures develop and how quickly this happens.

However, laboratory testing is expensive and it takes time to yield results, even when it is accelerated. So it is only worth doing in cases where a fairly large number of components are at risk – such as an aircraft fleet – and the failures have very serious consequences.

A rational approach

The above paragraphs indicate that in the vast majority of cases, it is either impossible, impractical or too expensive to try to determine P-F intervals on an empirical basis. On the other hand, it is equally unwise simply to take a shot in the dark.

Despite these problems, P-F intervals can still be estimated with surprising accuracy on the basis of judgement and experience. *The first trick is to ask the right question.* Specifically, it is essential that anyone who is trying to determine a P-F interval understands that we are asking *how quickly the item fails.* In other words, we are asking how much time elapses from the moment the potential failure becomes detectable until the moment it reaches the functionally failed state. We are *not* asking how often it fails or how long it lasts.

The second trick is to ask the right people – people who have an intimate knowledge of the asset, the ways in which it fails and the symptoms of each failure. For most equipment, this usually means the people who operate it, the craftsmen who maintain it and their first-line supervisors. If the detection process requires specialised instruments such as condition monitoring equipment, then appropriate specialists should also take part in the analysis.

In practice, the author has found that an effective way to crystallise thinking about P-F intervals is to provide a number of mental "coat-hooks" on which people can hang their thoughts. For instance, one could ask: "do you think that the P-F interval is likely to be of the order of days, weeks or months?" If the answer is (say) weeks, the next step is to ask: " One, two, four or eight weeks?"

If everyone in the group achieves consensus, then the P-F interval has been established and the analysts go on to consider to consider other task selection criteria such as the consistency of the P-F interval and whether the nett P-F interval is long enough to avoid the failure consequences.

If the group cannot achieve consensus, then it is not possible to provide a positive answer to the question "what is the P-F interval?". When this happens, the associated on-condition task must be abandoned as a way of detecting the failure mode under consideration, and the failure must be dealt with in some other way.

The third trick is to concentrate on one failure mode at a time. In other words, if the failure mode is wear, then the analysts should concentrate on the characteristics of wear, and should not discuss (say) corrosion or fatigue (unless the symptoms of the other failure modes are almost identical and the rate of deterioration is also very similar).

Finally, it must be clearly understood by everyone taking part in such an analysis that the objective is to arrive at an on-condition task interval which is less than the P-F interval, but not so much less that resources will be squandered on the checking process.

The effectiveness of such a group is redoubled if management expresses an appreciation of the fact that it is made up of human beings, and that humans are not infallible. However, the analysts must also be aware that if the failure has safety consequences, the price of getting it badly wrong could (literally) be fatal for themselves or their colleagues, so they need to take special care in this area.

The Consistency of the P-F Interval

All the P-F curves which have appeared in illustrations so far in this book indicate that the P-F interval is constant. In fact, this is not the case – some can actually vary over a quite considerable range of values, as shown in Figure 9.7.

For example, when discussing the P-F interval associated with a change in noise levels, someone might say: "This thing rattles away for anything from two weeks to three months before it collapses." In another case, tests might show that anything from six months to five years elapses from the moment a crack becomes detectable at a particular point in a structure until the moment the structure fails.

Clearly, in these cases a task interval should be selected which is substantially less than the shortest of the likely P-F intervals. In this way, we can always be reasonably certain of detecting the potential failure before it becomes a functional failure. If this minimum interval is long enough not to require an unsustainable commitment of resources over the life of the asset, then the on-condition task is technically feasible, and the next step is to assess whether or not it is worth doing, as explained in Chapter 4.

On the other hand, if the P-F interval is wildly inconsistent – as some of them can be – then it is not possible to establish a meaningful task interval, and the task in question should again be abandoned in favour of some other way of dealing with the failure.

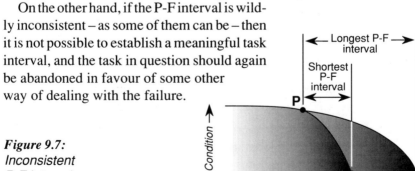

Figure 9.7:
Inconsistent
P-F intervals

9.2 The Six Failure Patterns

The last section of this chapter considers what role (if any) technical history records play in helping to draw conclusions about failure data. However, before considering this issue we need to define a number of key terms, and consider how these data can be correlated and presented in a way which permits meaningful conclusions to be drawn.

Specifically, we will examine the six principal failure patterns first introduced in Figure 1.5 on page 12 and shown again in Figure 9.8 below. We start with a detailed look at failure patterns B and E, because they represent the most widely held views of age-related and random failure. Next we review patterns C and F and end with a look at patterns D and A.

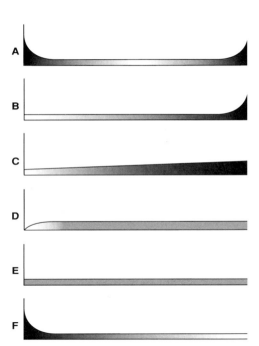

Figure 9.8:
Six patterns of failure

Failure Pattern B

So far in this book, it has been mentioned on numerous occasions that failure pattern B depicts age-related failures. Figure 9.3 showed that although these failures are the result of a more-or-less linear process of deterioration, there will still be considerable differences in the behaviour of any two components which are subject to the same nominal stresses. Figure 9.9 shows how this behaviour translates into failure pattern B.

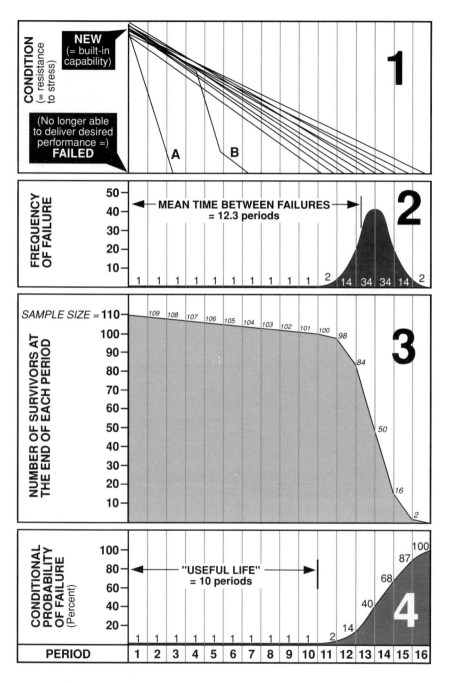

Figure 9.9: Failure pattern B

An example of a component which might behave as shown in Figure 9.3 is the impeller of a pump which is used to pump a moderately abrasive liquid. Part 1 of Figure 9.9 shows the wear-out characteristics of a dozen such impellers. Ten of them deteriorate at roughly the same rate, and last between 11 and 16 periods before failing. However, two of the impellers fail much sooner than expected, "A" perhaps because it was not properly case hardened and "B" because the proper- ties of the liquid changed for a while, causing it to wear more quickly than usual. *Note that this failure distribution only applies to impellers which fail due to wear. It does not apply to impellers which fail for other reasons.*

In Part 2 of Figure 9.9, the distribution of failure frequencies is plotted against operating age for a large sample of components. It shows that apart from a few "premature" failures, the majority of the components are likely to conform to a normal distribution about one point.

For example, assume that we have accumulated actual failure data for a sample of 110 impellers, all of which have failed due to wear. Ten of these impellers failed prematurely, one in each of the first ten periods. The other 100 impellers all failed between periods 11 and 16, and the frequency of these failures conforms to a normal distribution. (For a normal distribution, the failure frequencies in the last six periods would be roughly as shown if they are rounded to the nearest whole number.) On the basis of these figures, the mean time between failures of the impellers due to wear is 12.3 periods.

Part 3 of Figure 9.9 shows the survival distribution of the impellers based on this frequency distribution.

For example, 98 impellers lasted for more than 11 periods, and 16 impellers lasted for more than 14 periods.

Part 4 of Figure 9.9 is failure pattern B. It shows the probability that any impeller which has survived to the beginning of a period will fail during that period. This is known as the *conditional probability of failure*.

Allowing for a small degree of rounding error, this shows for instance that there is a 14% chance that an impeller which has survived to the beginning of period 12 will fail in that period. Similarly, 14 out of the sixteen impellers which make it to the beginning of period 15 will fail in that period – a conditional probability of failure of 87%.

The frequency curve in Part 2 and the probability curve in Part 4 are depic- ting the same phenomenon, but they differ markedly in the way they show it. In fact, the conditional probability of failure curve provides a better illustration of what is really happening than the frequency curve, because the latter could deceive us into thinking that things are getting better after the peak of the frequency curve.

These curves illustrate a number of additional points, as follows:

- the frequency and conditional probability curves show that the word "life" can actually have two quite distinct meanings. The first is the mean time between failures (which is the same as the *average life* if the whole sample has run to failure). The second is the point at which there is a rapid increase in the conditional probability of failure. For want of any other term, this has been named the *useful life*.

- if we were to plan to overhaul or replace components at the mean time between failures, half would fail before they reached it. In other words, we would only be preventing half of the failures, which is likely to have unacceptable operating consequences. Clearly, if we wish to prevent the majority of the failures, we would need to intervene at the end of the "useful life". Figure 9.9 shows that the useful life is shorter than the mean time between failures – if the bell curve is wide, it can be very much shorter.

    As a result, it can only be concluded that *the mean time between failures is of little or no use in establishing the frequency of scheduled restoration and scheduled discard tasks* for items which conform to failure pattern B. The key variable is the point at which there is a rapid increase in the probability of failure.

- if we do replace the component at the end of its useful life as defined above, the average service life of each component would be shorter than if we let it run to failure. As discussed on page 112, this would increase the cost of maintenance (provided that there is no secondary damage associated with the failures).

    For instance, if we were to replace all the surviving impellers in Figure 9.9 at the end of period 10, the average service life of the impellers would be about 9.5 periods, instead of 12.3 periods if they were allowed to run to failure.

- The fact that there are two "lives" associated with pattern B-type failures means that we must take care to specify which one we mean whenever we use the term "life".

    For example, we might phone the manufacturer of a certain component to ask what its "life" is. We may have in mind the useful life, but if we don't spell out exactly what we mean, he might in all good faith give us the mean time between failures. If this is then used to establish a replacement frequency, all kinds of problems arise, often resulting in wholly unnecessary unpleasantness.

These issues apart, perhaps the biggest problem associated with pattern B is that very few failure modes actually behave in this fashion. As mentioned in Chapter 1, it is much more common to find failure modes which show little or no long-term relationship between age and failure.

Failure Pattern E

Figure 5.13 on page 128 illustrated three components which failed on a random basis. A number of reasons why failures can occur on this basis were discussed in Part 1 of this chapter. This part of this chapter explores some of the quantitative aspects of random failure in more detail, and goes on to review some of the implications of failure pattern E. To begin with, Figure 9.10 overleaf shows the relationship between the frequency and conditional probability of random failures.

Part 1 of Figure 9.10 shows a number of components – in this case, ball bearings – whose failure seems to bear no relationship to their operating age. As in Figure 5.13, each failure is preceded by a (somewhat elongated) P-F curve.

Random failure means that the probability that an item will fail in any one period is the same as it is in any other. In other words, the conditional probability of failure is constant, as shown in Part 2 of Figure 9.10.

For example, if we accept the empirical evidence that rolling element bearings usually conform to a random failure pattern – a phenomenon first observed by Davis[1952] – the conditional probability of failure is constant as shown in Figure 9.10, Part 2. Specifically, this shows that there is 10% probability that a bearing which has made it to the beginning of any period will fail during that period.

Part 3 of Figure 9.10 shows how a conditional probability of failure which is constant translates into a survival distribution which is exponential.

For example, if we started with a sample of 100 bearings and the probability of failure in the first period is 10%, then 10 bearings would fail in period 1 and 90 bearings would survive for more than one period. Similarly, if there is a 10% probability that the bearings which survive beyond the end of period 1 will fail in period 2, then 9 bearings would fail in period 2, and 81 bearings would make it to the beginning of period 3. Part 3 of Figure 9.10 shows how many bearings would survive to the beginning of each subsequent period for the first sixteen periods.

Theoretically, this process of decay would continue until infinity. In practice, however, we usually stop at unity – in other words, when the survival curve drops below one.

In the example shown in Figure 9.10, a rate of decay of 10% per period means that unity is reached after about 43 periods. This suggests that one lone bearing might last for 43 periods, but the vast majority will have failed long before then.

Finally, Part 4 of Figure 9.10 shows the frequency curve derived from the survival curve in Part 3. This curve is also exponential. (The shape of this frequency curve often causes it to be confused with failure pattern F, which is a conditional probability curve based on a different frequency distribution.)

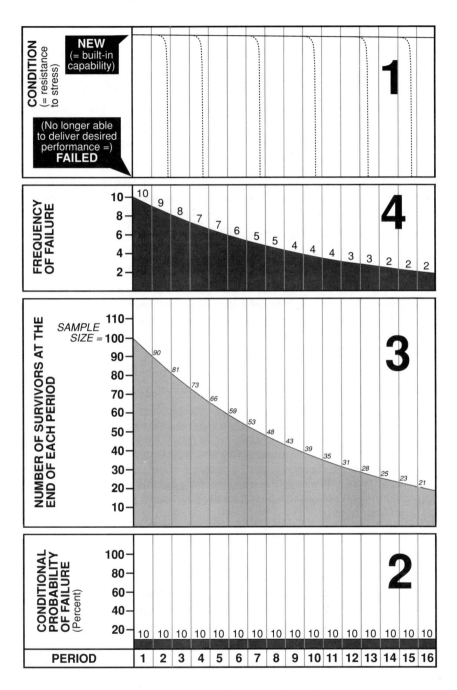

Figure 9.10: *Failure pattern E*

The fact that frequency and survival curves both carry on declining indefinitely means that the conditional probability curve also remains flat indefinitely. In other words, at no stage does Pattern E show a significant increase in the conditional probability of failure, so at no stage can an age be found at which we should contemplate scheduled rework or scheduled discard. Further points about Pattern E are as follows:

- *MTBF and random failures:* despite the fact that it is impossible to predict how long any one item which conforms to failure pattern E will last (hence the use of the term "random" failure), it is still possible to compute a mean time between failures for such items. It is given by the point at which 63% of the items have failed.

  For example, Part 3 of Figure 9.10 indicates that 63% of the items have failed about half way through period 10. In other words, the MTBF of the bearings in this example is 9.5 periods.

  The fact that these items have a mean time between failures but do not have a "useful life" as defined earlier means that we must be doubly careful when talking about the "life" of an item.

- *comparing reliability:* the MTBF provides a basis for comparing the reliability of two different components which both conform to failure pattern E, even though the failure is "random" in both cases. This is because the item with the higher MTBF will have a lower probability of failure in any given period.

  For example, assume that Brand X bearings conform to the failure distribution shown in Figure 9.10. If the conditional probability of failure of Brand Y is only 5% in each period, they would only be half as likely to fail and so would be considered much more reliable.

In the case of items which conform to failure pattern B, a more reliable component has a longer "useful life" than one which is less reliable. So in simple language it could be said of the pattern B components that one type *lasts longer* than the other, while in the case of the Pattern E components, one type *fails more often* than the other.

(In practice, the reliability of bearings is measured by the "B10" life. This is the life below which a bearing supplier guarantees that no more than 10% of his bearings will fail under given conditions of load and speed. This corresponds to one period on Part 2 of Figure 9.10. It also suggests that if a bearing conforms to a truly exponential survival distribution, then the MTBF of bearings due to "normal wear and tear" should be about 9.5 times the B10 life.

So if bearing Brand Y is twice as reliable as Brand X, the B10 life – which is also known as the L10 life or the N10 life – of Brand Y will be twice as long as that of Brand X. This is useful when making procurement decisions about bearings, but it still does not tell us how long any one bearing will last in service.)

- *P-F curves and random failures:* Figure 5.13 on page 128 and Part 1 of Figure 9.10 both show random failures preceded by P-F curves. This is not meant to suggest that *all* failures which happen on a random basis are preceded by such a curve. In fact a great many failure modes which conform to pattern E are not preceded by any sort of warning, or if they are, the warning period is often much too short to be of any use. This is especially true of most of the failures which affect light current electrical and electronic items.

  This does not detract in any way from the validity of the analysis. It simply means that no form of preventive maintenance – on-condition, scheduled restoration or scheduled discard – is technically feasible for these components, and they have to be managed on an appropriate default basis as discussed in Chapter 6.

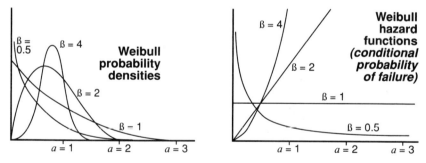

Figure 9.11: *Weibull distributions*

A Note on Weibull Distributions

At this stage, it is worth commenting on the Weibull distribution. This distribution is widely used because it has a great variety of shapes which enable it to fit many kinds of data, especially data relating to product life. The Weibull frequency distribution (or more correctly, *probability density function*) is:

$$f(t) = (\beta/a^\beta)t^{\beta-1}\exp[-(t/a)^\beta]$$

ß is called the *shape parameter* because it defines the shape of the distribution. *a* is the *scale parameter*. It defines the spread of the distribution and corresponds to the 63rd percentile $[100 (1 - e^{-1})]$ of the cumulative distribution. The Weibull probability density function and corresponding conditional probability curves are shown in Figure 9.11. (This shows that the conditional probability of failure is also known as the "hazard rate".)

When ß = 1, the Weibull distribution is the exponential distribution. When ß is between 3 and 4, it closely approximates the normal distribution. Later in this chapter we see how it describes other failure patterns.

Failure Pattern C

Failure pattern C shows a steadily increasing probability of failure, but no one point at which we can say "that's where it wears out". This part of this chapter looks at a possible reason why pattern C occurs, and then shows how it is derived.

The possible cause of pattern C which we consider is fatigue. Classical engineering theory suggests that fatigue failure is caused by cyclic stress, and that the relationship between cyclic stress and failure is governed by the *S-N curve*, as shown in Figure 9.12.

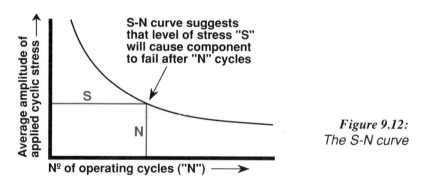

Figure 9.12:
The S-N curve

Figure 9.12 suggests that if the S-N curve is known, then we should be able to predict the life of the component with great accuracy for a given amplitude of cyclic stress. However, this is not so in practice because the average amplitude of the cyclic stress is not constant, and the ability of the component to withstand the stress – in other words, the location of the S-N curve – will not be exactly the same for every component.

Part 1 of Figure 9.13 overleaf suggests that the average amplitude of the applied stress might conform to a normal distribution about some

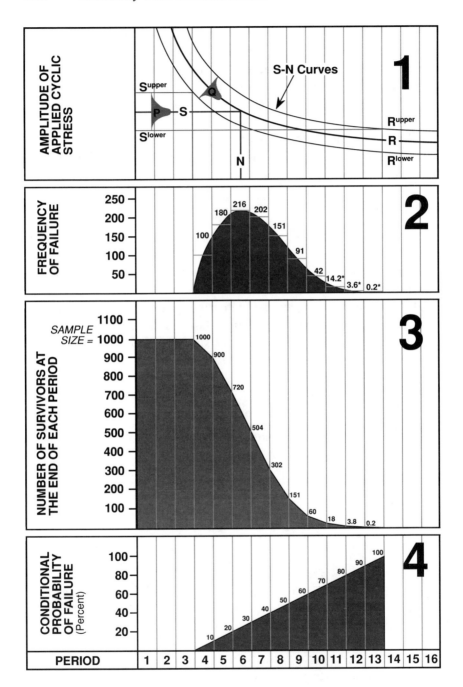

Figure 9.13: Failure pattern C (shifted)

mean, which is designated by "S" in Figure 9.13. This distribution is shown by curve P. Similarly, the distribution of the S-N curves might be designated by normal curve Q. The combination of these two curves will be such that the ages at which failure occurs will conform to a distribution skewed to the left. How much it is skewed depends on the shape of the S-N curve itself. For the sake of argument, Part 2 of Figure 9.13 suggests that it will conform to a Weibull distribution with shape parameter ß = 2. (Strictly speaking, this should be called a "shifted" Weibull distribution because it does not start at time zero.)

On the basis of this distribution, Part 2 of Figure 9.13 goes on to suggest how many failures might occur in each period if we were to test a sample of 1000 components to failure. (The fact that the numbers marked with an asterisk are not integers explains why this curve should be called a probability density rather than a frequency distribution.)

Part 3 of Figure 9.13 translates Part 2 into a survival curve, while Part 4 shows the conditional probability of failure based on the preceding two curves. Both of the latter curves are derived in the same way as the corresponding curves in Figure 9.9.

Further points about failure pattern C include the following:

• the shifted Weibull distribution means that the conditional probability curve starts at a point to the right of time t = 0. Figure 9.13 shows that this is the point where there is "a rapid increase in the conditional probability of failure", which is of course the useful life as defined earlier. In Figure 9.13 this is three periods. However, earlier depictions of pattern C show a conditional probability of failure starting above zero. This might occur in practice if a failure mode led to a *truncated* Weibull distribution (one which hypothetically starts to the left of time t = 0) with a shape parameter of ß = 2, as shown in Figure 9.14.

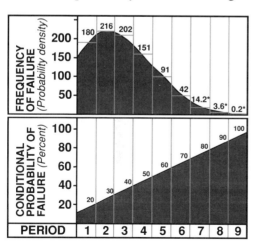

Figure 9.14:
Truncated Weibull
distribution and failure
pattern C

- the slope of pattern C appears to be quite steep in these examples. However, bear in mind that the actual slope is governed by the Weibull scale parameter a, which can be measured in anything ranging from weeks to decades (or even centuries), so the slope of pattern C can vary from quite steep to almost flat.

- pattern C is not only associated with fatigue. For instance, it has been found to fit the failure of the insulation in the windings of certain types of generators.

- conversely, not all fatigue-related failures necessarily conform to failure pattern C.

  For instance, if curve P in Figure 9.13 were skewed towards the S^{lower} limit and curve Q were skewed towards the R^{upper} limit, the failure frequency curve would be biased further towards the right. This would give a Weibull shape parameter greater than 2, which tends towards a normal distribution and so gives a conditional probability of failure curve which resembles pattern B.

  On the other hand, if the S^{lower} limit is below the point at which R^{lower} becomes asymptotic, then the frequency distribution will develop a long "tail" on the right. This corresponds to a Weibull distribution where ß is between 1 and 2, which in turn generates failure pattern D.

  Finally, the discussion on page 193 mentioned that a large number of factors influence the rate at which fatigue failures develop in ball bearings. This would make the spread of any distribution very wide, which would in turn lead to an almost flat conditional probability curve. Add to this the variety of additional bearing failure modes listed on page 195 which have the same symptoms as fatigue, and the overall probability density effectively becomes fully exponential, which leads to failure pattern E as we have seen.

  So fatigue could manifest itself as failure pattern B, C, D or even E.

Failure Pattern D

As mentioned above, failure pattern D is the conditional probability curve associated with a Weibull distribution whose shape parameter ß is greater than 1 and less than 2.

Failure Pattern F

Pattern F is perhaps the most interesting, for two reasons:
- it is the only pattern where the probability of failure actually *declines* with age (apart from A, which is a special case)
- it is the most common of the six patterns, as mentioned on page 13.

For these reasons, it is worth exploring in more detail the factors which give rise to this pattern.

The shape of failure pattern F indicates that the highest probability of failure occurs when the equipment is new or just after it has been overhauled. This phenomenon is known as "infant mortality", and it has a wide variety of causes. These are summarised in Figure 9.15 and discussed in the subsequent paragraphs.

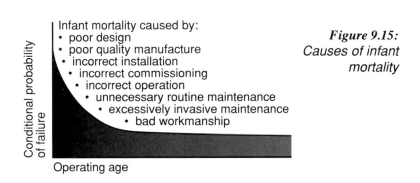

Figure 9.15:
Causes of infant
mortality

Design

Infant mortality problems attributable to design occur when part of an item is simply incapable of delivering the desired performance, and hence tends to fail soon after being put into service. These problems can only really be solved by redesign, as discussed in Chapter 6. They can be forestalled to some extent by

• using proven technology. *The author recently encountered one company which professed to be "in a headlong rush to be second" in adopting new technology, because it has found that being first usually means a huge investment in "de-bugging" new equipment - an involuntary investment made in the form of equipment downtime. On the other hand being second can be competitively disadvantageous in the long term.*

• using the simplest possible equipment to fulfil the required function *on the premise that bits which aren't there can't fail.*

Manufacture and installation

Infant mortality attributable to equipment manufacture occurs either because the manufacturer's quality standards are too loose, or because the parts concerned have been badly installed. These problems can only be solved by rebuilding the affected assemblies or replacing the affected parts. Two ways to forestall these problems are:

- to implement suitable SQA (Supplier Quality Assurance) and PQA (Project Quality Assurance) schemes. Such schemes usually work best when they are run by someone other than the prime contractor.
- to request extended warranties, perhaps with the full-time on-site support of the vendor's technicians until the equipment has been working as intended for a specified period.

Commissioning

Commissioning problems occur either when equipment is set up incorrectly, or when it is started up incorrectly. These problems are minimised if care is taken to ensure that everyone involved in commissioning knows exactly how the plant is supposed to work, and is given enough time to ensure that it does so.

Routine maintenance

A great deal of infant mortality is caused by routine maintenance tasks which are either unnecessary, or unnecessarily invasive. The latter are tasks which disrupt or disturb the equipment, and so needlessly upset basically stable systems. The way to avoid these problems is to stop doing unnecessary tasks, and in cases where scheduled maintenance is necessary, to select tasks which disturb the equipment as little as possible

Maintenance workmanship

Clearly, if something is badly put together it will fall apart quickly. This problem can only be avoided by ensuring that anyone who is called upon to do a preventive or corrective maintenance task is trained and motivated to do it correctly the first time.

Infant mortality and RCM

The above discussion suggests that infant mortality problems are usually solved by once-off actions rather than by scheduled maintenance (with the exception of a few cases where it may be feasible to use on-condition tasks to anticipate failures). However, despite the minimal role played by *routine* maintenance, using RCM to analyse a new asset before putting it into service still leads to substantial reductions in infant mortality for the following reasons:

- a detailed study of the functions of the asset usually reveals a surprising number of design flaws which, if not corrected, would make it impossible for the asset to function at all

- craftsmen and operators learn exactly how the asset is supposed to function, and so are less inclined to make mistakes which cause failures

- many weaknesses which would otherwise lead to premature failures are identified and dealt with *before* the asset enters service

- routine maintenance is reduced to the essential minimum, which means fewer de-stabilising interventions, but this essential minimum ensures that the early life of the asset is not plagued by failures which could have been anticipated or prevented.

Failure Pattern A

It is now generally accepted that failure pattern A – the bathtub curve – is really a combination of two or more different failure patterns, one of which embodies infant mortality and the other of which shows increasing probability of failure with age. Some commentators even suggest that the central (flat) portion of the bathtub constitutes a third period of (random) failure between the other two, as shown in Figure 9.16.

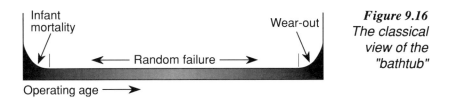

Figure 9.16
The classical view of the "bathtub"

This means that failure pattern A actually depicts the conditional probability of two or more different failure modes. From the failure management viewpoint, each of these must be identified and dealt with in the light of its own consequences and its own technical characteristics.

Similar conclusions can be drawn about failure pattern B as it is shown in Figure 9.9. This is because the failures which occur between periods 11 and 16 are caused by "normal" wear, while those occurring between periods 1 and 10 are caused by other "random" factors which still cause the impeller to wear out, but cause it to do so faster than normal.

This starts to raise a number of questions about the meaning of these patterns, which are considered at length in the next part of this chapter.

9.3 Technical History Data

The Role of Actuarial Analysis in Establishing Maintenance Policies

A surprising number of people believe that effective maintenance policies can only be formulated on the basis of extensive *historical* information *about failure*. Thousands of manual and computerised technical
history recording systems have been installed around the world on the
basis of this belief. It has also led to great emphasis being placed on the
failure patterns described in Part 2 of this chapter. (The fact that the
bathtub curve still appears in nearly every significant text on maintenance
management is testimony to the almost mystical faith which we place in
the relationship between age and failure.)

Yet from the maintenance viewpoint, these patterns are fraught with
practical difficulties, conundrums and contradictions. Some of these are
summarised below under the following headings:
• complexity
• sample size and evolution
• reporting failure
• the ultimate contradiction.

Complexity

Chapter 2 noted that most industrial undertakings consist of hundreds, if
not thousands of different assets. These are made up of dozens of different
components, which between them exhibit every extreme and intermediate aspect of reliability behaviour. This combination of complexity and
diversity means that it is simply not possible to develop a complete analy-
tical description of the reliability characteristics of an entire undertaking
– or even any major asset within the undertaking.

Even at the level of individual functional failures, a comprehensive
analysis is not easy. This is because many functional failures are caused
not by two or three but by two or three *dozen* failure modes. As a result,
while it may be fairly easy to chart the incidence of the functional failures,
it is a major statistical undertaking to isolate and describe the failure
pattern which applies to each of the failure modes which falls within the
envelope of each functional failure. What is more, many failure modes
have virtually identical physical symptoms, which makes them easy to
confuse with each other. This in turn makes sensible actuarial analysis
almost impossible.

Sample size and evolution

Large industrial processes usually possess only one or two assets of any one type. They also tend to be brought into operation in series rather than simultaneously. This means that sample sizes tend to be too small for statistical procedures to carry much conviction. For new assets which embody high levels of leading-edge technology, they are always too small.

These assets are also usually in a continuous state of evolution and modification, partly in response to new operational requirements and partly in an attempt to eliminate failures which either have serious consequences or which cost too much to prevent. This means that the amount of time which any asset spends in any one configuration is relatively short.

So actuarial procedures are not much use in these situations because the database is both very small and constantly changing. (As discussed later, the main exception is undertakings which use large numbers of identical components in a more-or-less identical manner.)

Reporting failure

The problem of analysing failure data is further complicated by differences in reporting policy from one organisation to another. One area of confusion is the distinction between potential and functional failures.

For instance, in the tyre example discussed on pages 196 and 197, one organisation might classify and record the tyres as "failed" when they are removed for retreading after the tread depth drops below 3 mm. However, as long as the tread depth is not allowed to drop below 2 mm, this "failure" is actually a potential failure as defined in Chapter 5. So other organisations might choose to classify such removals as "precautionary", because the tyres have not actually failed in service, or even as "scheduled", because the tyres are "scheduled" for replacement at the earliest opportunity after the potential failure has been discovered. In both of the latter cases, it is likely that the removals will not even be reported as failures.

On the other hand, if for some reason the tread depth does drop below 2 mm, then there is no doubt that the tyre has failed.

Similar differences might be caused by different performance expectations. Chapter 3 defined a functional failure as the inability of an item to meet a desired standard of performance, and these standards can of course differ for the same asset if the operating context is different.

For instance, page 53 gives the example of a pump which has failed if it is unable to deliver 800 litres per minute in one context and 900 litres per minute in another.

This shows that what is a failure in one organisation – or even one part of an organisation – might not be a failure in another. This can result in two quite different sets of failure data for two apparently identical items.

Further differences in the presentation and interpretation of failure data can be caused by the different perspectives of the manufacturers and users of an asset. The manufacturer usually considers it his responsibility to provide an asset capable of delivering a warranted level of performance (if there is one) under specific conditions of stress. In other words, he warrants a certain basic design capability, and often makes this conditional upon the performance of certain specified maintenance routines.

On the other hand, we have seen that many failures occur because users operate the equipment beyond its design capabilities (in other words, the "want" exceeds the "can", as discussed on page 45.) While users are naturally inclined to incorporate data about these failures in their own history records, manufacturers are naturally reluctant to accept responsibility for them. This leads many manufacturers to "censor" failures caused by operator error from failure data. As Nowlan and Heap[1978] put it, the result is that users talk about what they actually saw, while the manufacturer talks about what they should have seen.

The ultimate contradiction

An issue which bedevils the whole question of technical history is the fact that if we are collecting data about failures, it must be because we are not preventing them. The implications of this are summed up most succinctly by Resnikoff[1978] in the following statement:

*"The acquisition of the information thought to be most needed by maintenance policy designers – information about critical failures – is in principle unacceptable and is evidence of the failure of the maintenance programme. This is because critical failures entail potential (in some cases, certain) loss of life, **but there is no rate of loss of life which is acceptable to (any) organisation as the price of failure information to be used for designing a maintenance policy**. Thus the maintenance policy designer is faced with the problem of creating a maintenance system for which the expected loss of life will be less than one over the planned operational lifetime of the asset. This means that, both in practice and in principle, the policy must be designed without using experiential data which will arise from the failures which the policy is meant to avoid."*

Despite the best efforts of the maintenance policy designer, if a critical failure should happen to occur, Nowlan and Heap[1978] go on to make the following comments about the role of actuarial analysis:

"The development of an age-reliability relationship, as expressed by a curve representing the conditional probability of failure, requires a considerable amount of data. When the failure is one which has serious consequences, this body of data will not exist, since preventive measures must of necessity be taken after the first failure. Thus actuarial analysis cannot be used to establish the age limits of greatest concern – those necessary to protect operating safety."

In this context, note also the comments made on page 114 about safe-life limits and test data. These data are usually so scanty that the safe-life limit (if there is one) is established by dividing the test results by some conservatively large arbitrary factor rather than by the tools of actuarial analysis.

The same limitation applies to failures which have really serious operational consequences. The first time such a failure occurs, immediate decisions are usually made about preventive or corrective action without waiting for the data needed to carry out an actuarial analysis.

All of which brings us to the ultimate contradiction concerning the prevention of failures with serious consequences and historical information about such failures: *that successful preventive maintenance entails preventing the collection of the historical data which we think we need in order to decide what preventive maintenance we ought to be doing.*

This contradiction applies in reverse at the other end of the scale of consequences. Failures with minor consequences tend to be allowed to occur precisely because they don't matter very much. As a result, large quantities of historical data will be available concerning these failures, which means that there will be ample material for accurate actuarial analyses. These may even reveal some age limits. However, because the failures don't matter much, it is highly unlikely that the resulting scheduled restoration or scheduled discard tasks will be cost-effective. So while the actuarial analysis of this information may be precise, it is also likely to be a waste of time.

The chief use of actuarial analysis in maintenance is to study reliability problems on the middle ground, where there is an uncertain relationship between age and failures which have significant economic consequences but no safety consequences. These failures fall into two categories:

• those associated with large numbers of identical items whose functions are to all intents and purposes identical, and whose failure might only have a minor impact when taken singly but whose cumulative effect can be an important cost consideration.

Examples of items which fall into this category are street lights, vehicle components (especially from large fleets) and many of the components used by the armed forces and in the electricity, water and gas *distribution* industries. Items of this type are used in sufficient numbers for precise actuarial analyses to be carried out, and detailed cost-benefit studies are justified (in many cases, if only to minimise the amount of travelling involved in maintaining the items).

• the second category of failures which merit actuarial investigation are those which are less common but are still thought to be age-related, and where both the cost of any preventive task and the cost of the failure are very high. As mentioned on page 110, this applies especially to gradually increasing failure probabilities typified by failure pattern C.

The way forward

The above paragraphs indicate that except for a limited number of fairly specialised situations, the actuarial analysis of the relationship between operating age and failure is of very little use from the maintenance management viewpoint. Perhaps the most serious shortcoming of historical information is that it is rooted in the past, whereas the concepts of anticipation and prevention are necessarily focused on the future.

So a fresh approach to this issue is needed – one which switches the focus from the past to the future. In fact, RCM is just such an approach. Firstly, it deals with the specific problems identified above as follows:

• *defining failure:* by starting with the definition of the functions and the associated performance standards of each asset, RCM enables us to define with great precision what we mean by "failed". By distinguishing clearly between built-in capability and desired performance, and between potential (anticipated) failures and functional (unanticipated) failures, it eliminates further confusion.

• *complexity:* RCM breaks each asset down into its functions and each function into functional failures, and only then identifies the failure modes which cause each functional failure. This provides an orderly framework within which to consider each failure mode. This in turn makes them much easier to manage than if we were to start out at the failure mode level (which is the starting point of most classical FMEA's and FMECA's).

• *evolution:* by providing a comprehensive record of all the performance standards, functional failures and failure modes associated with each asset, RCM makes it possible to work out very quickly how any change to the design or to the operating context is likely to affect the asset, and to revise maintenance policies and procedures only in those areas where changes need to be made

- *the ultimate contradiction:* RCM deals with the ultimate contradiction in several ways. Firstly, by obliging us to complete the Information Worksheet described in Chapter 3, it focuses our attention on *what could happen.* Compare this with the actuarial emphasis on *what has happened.* Secondly, by asking how, and how much, each failure matters as described in Chapter 4, it ensures that we focus our energies on the failures which have serious consequences and that we do not waste time on those which don't. Finally, by adopting the structured approach to the selection of preventive tasks and default actions described in Chapters 5 and 6, RCM ensures that we do whatever is necessary to prevent serious failures from happening, and as far as humanly possible, avoid having to analyse them at all.

Secondly, the RCM process focuses attention on the information needed to support specific decisions. It does not ask us to collect a whole lot of data in the hope that they will eventually tell us something. This point is discussed in more detail in the next section of this chapter.

Specific Uses of Data in Formulating Maintenance Policies

In spite of all the above comments, the successful application of RCM needs a great deal of information. As explained at length in Chapters 3 to 6, much of this information is descriptive or qualitative, particularly on the RCM Information Worksheet. However, in view of the emphasis which has been placed on quantitative issues in this chapter, Table 9.1 summarises the principal types of quantitative data which are used to support different stages of the maintenance decision process. It does so under the following headings:

- *datum:* the piece of information of interest.

- *application:* a very brief summary of the use to which each datum is put. Note that some are used in conjunction with others to reach a final decision, and that many are only used when qualitative data are not strong enough to make an intuitive decision possible.

- *comments:* where each datum is most likely to be found. Note that in some cases, they are established by the user of the asset.

- *pages:* refers to the pages in this book where the use of each datum is discussed at greater length.

DATUM	APPLICATION	COMMENTS	PAGES
Desired standards of performance	These standards define the objectives of maintenance for each asset. They cover output, product quality/customer service, energy efficiency, safety and environmental integrity	Set by the users of the assets (and by regulators for environmental and some safety standards)	43 - 47 50 - 53
ASSESSING OPERATIONAL AND NON-OPERATIONAL FAILURE CONSEQUENCES			
Downtime	Assessing whether each failure will affect production/operations, and if so how much	Not the same thing as MTTR ("mean time to repair")	64 - 65 95 - 96
Cost of lost production	Used together with downtime to evaluate total cost of each failure which affects operations	Only needed when the cost-benefit of scheduled maintenance is not intuitively obvious	95 - 96
Cost of repair	Used together with MTBF to evaluate cost effectiveness of scheduled maintenance	Only needed when the cost-benefit of scheduled maintenance is not intuitively obvious (Operational and non-operational consequences only)	102 - 103
Mean time between failures	Used with downtime, cost of lost production (if any) & repair cost to compare cost of scheduled maintenance with the cost of a failure over a period of time	Only needed when the cost-benefit of scheduled maintenance is not intuitively obvious (Operational and non-operational consequences only)	95 - 96
ASSESSING SAFETY AND ENVIRONMENTAL FAILURE CONSEQUENCES			
Acceptable risk of a single failure	Used to assess whether scheduled maintenance is worth doing for failures which could have a direct adverse effect on safety or the environment	Almost always assessed by the users of the assets/likely victims on an intuitive basis	88 - 92
ESTABLISHING ON-CONDITION TASK FREQUENCIES			
Potential failure	Point at which imminent failure becomes detectable	Based on the nature of the P-F curve and the monitoring technique: usually quantified for performance monitoring, condition monitoring and SPC	116 - 118 192 - 198
P-F interval	Used to establish the frequency of on-condition tasks	"How quickly it fails": very seldom formally recorded	118 - 121 199 - 202

Table 9.1: Summary of key maintenance decision-support data

DATUM	APPLICATION	COMMENTS	PAGES
SCHEDULED RESTORATION AND SCHEDULED DISCARD TASK FREQUENCIES			
Age at which there is a rapid increase in the conditional probability of failure	Used to establish the frequency of most scheduled restoration and scheduled discard tasks	"Useful life": Based on formal records if these are available: more often based on consensus of people who have the most knowledge of the asset	203 - 206
Actuarial analysis of relationship between age and failure	Optimising restoration/discard intervals for large numbers of identical parts whose failure is known to be age-related, or for expensive pattern C-type failures	Worth doing for no more than 1 - 2% of failure modes in most industries: needs extensive and reliable historical data: used for failure modes which have operational and non-operational consequences only	221 - 222
HIDDEN FAILURE CONSEQUENCES AND FAILURE-FINDING TASK FREQUENCIES			
Acceptable probability of a multiple failure	Used to establish maintenance policies for protected systems	Set by the users of the asset: only used when a rigorous analysis is to be done	75 - 78
Mean time between failures of a protected function	Used together with "acceptable probability of a multiple failure" to determine the desired availability of a protective device	Based on past and anticipated future performance of the protected function: Only used to support a rigorous analysis – not needed for the intuitive approach *(see below)*	75 - 78
Desired availability of a protective device	Used together with the MTBF of the protective device to establish failure-finding task frequency	Derived from the two above variables if the task frequency is to be derived on a rigorous basis: otherwise set directly by the users of the asset on the basis of an intuitive assessment of the risks of the multiple failure	75 - 78 136 - 140
Mean time between failures of a protective device	Used with desired availability to establish a failure-finding task frequency	Based on records of *failures found* if these are available: if not, any suitable data source should be used to begin with (including educated guesses) but a suitable database should be started immediately	136 - 140

A number of final points concerning quantitative data are reviewed under the following headings:
• management information
• a note on the MTBF
• technical history.

Management information

Table 9.1 only describes data which are used directly to formulate policies designed to deal with specific failure modes. It does not include data which are used to track the overall performance of the maintenance function and which are usually classified as "management information". Typical examples of such information are plant availability statistics, safety statistics and information about expenditure on maintenance against budgets.

Monitoring the overall performance of the maintenance function is of course an essential aspect of maintenance management, but the compilation and presentation of the associated information is a major topic in its own right, and is beyond the scope of this book.

A note on the MTBF

In recent times, the concept of the "mean time between failures" seems to have acquired a stature which is quite disproportionate to its real value in maintenance decision-making. For instance, it has nothing to do with the *frequency* of on-condition tasks, and virtually nothing to do with the *frequency* of scheduled restoration and scheduled discard tasks.

However, it does have certain very specific uses. Table 9.1 mentions three of these:

• to establish the *frequency* of failure-finding tasks.

• to help decide whether scheduled maintenance is *worth doing* in the case of failure modes which have operational or non-operational consequences only. (In other words, it helps us to decide *whether* such tasks need to be done, but not *how often* they need to be done.)

• to help establish the *desired availability* of a protective device.

In the first case, the MTBF is always needed to make the appropriate decision, but in the second two it is only used if the nature and consequences of the failures are such that a rigorous analysis must be carried out.

The MTBF also has a number of uses outside the field of maintenance policy formulation, as follows:

- *in the field of design:* to carry out a detailed cost-justification of a proposed modification, as mentioned briefly on page 154
- *in the field of procurement:* to evaluate the reliability of two different components which are candidates for the same application, as mentioned on page 209
- *in the field of management information:* one way to assess the overall effectiveness of a maintenance programme is to track the mean time between unanticipated failures of any asset.

However, as mentioned earlier, a detailed exploration of the last three issues is beyond the scope of this book.

Technical history

Together with the above comments about the MTBF, Table 9.1 can be used to help decide what sorts of data really need to be recorded in a technical history recording system.

Perhaps the most important information which needs to be recorded on a formal basis is **what is found** *each time a failure-finding task is done.* Specifically, we need to record whether the item was found to be fully functional or whether it was in a failed state. Such records enable us to check the validity of the task frequency against the desired availability of the protective device, and if necessary to revise the frequency. *This information should be recorded for **all** hidden functions – in other words, for all protective devices which are not fail-safe.*

In addition to hidden failures, Table 9.1 identifies two further areas where historical failure data can be used to make (or to validate) decisions about maintenance policies, as follows:

- *the occurrence of failure modes which have significant operational consequences.* This information can be used to compute the mean time between the failures in order to assess the cost effectiveness of scheduled maintenance. However, as mentioned in Table 9.1, this only needs to be done if the cost-benefit of preventive action is not intuitively obvious. If it is, such action – be it scheduled maintenance or redesign – would be taken and so there should be no more failures to record (except perhaps as potential failures if the preventive action is an on-condition task).

Table 9.1 mentions that in rare cases, it may also be worth capturing these data in order to carry out full actuarial analyses with a view to optimising scheduled restoration and scheduled discard frequencies.

- *the mean time between failures of a protected function.* This is again only needed if assumptions about the desired availability of a protective device are to be validated on a rigorous basis, which may be the case if the associated multiple failure has particularly serious consequences. This can be done by logging the number of times the protective device is called upon to function by the failure of the protected function.

  For instance, a record can be made every time the over-pressurisation of a boiler causes a relief valve to start passing.

If any of these data are to be captured, the failure reporting systems should be designed to identify the datum which is required – usually the *failure mode* – as precisely as possible. This can be done by asking the person who does the task (or who discovers the failure in the case of failure-finding) either to:

- complete a suitably designed form which is then used to enter the data into a manual or computerised history recording system, or
- enter the data directly if an on-line computer system is used to store it.

In most organisations, the records themselves can be stored in:

- a simple proprietary PC-based database, or
- a specialised computerised or manual maintenance history recording system.

The design of such systems is also beyond the scope of this book. However, Table 9.1 suggests that if technical history recording systems are used to capture specific data for specific reasons, rather than to record everything in the hope that it will eventually tell us something, they become useful and powerful contributors to the practice of maintenance management rather than the expensive white elephants which so many of them tend to be.

10 Implementing RCM

10.1 Who Knows?

The seven basic questions which make up the RCM process have been considered at length in Chapters 3 to 7. Chapter 9 looked more deeply at the information which is needed to answer some of the questions, and concluded that historical records are of limited value for this purpose. Yet the questions must still be answered, so the required information still has to be obtained from somewhere.

More often than not, "somewhere" actually turns out to be "someone" – someone who has intimate knowledge and experience of the asset under consideration. There are also occasions when the information-gathering process reveals widely differing viewpoints which have to be reconciled before decisions can be made.

Later sections of this chapter describe how small groups can be used to gather the information, reconcile differing views and make the decisions. However, before considering these groups, this part of this chapter reviews the information needed to answer each question, and considers who is most likely to possess it. It does so with reference to earlier sections of the book where the questions have been discussed in detail.

- *What are the functions and associated performance standards of the asset in its present operating context?*

RCM is based on the premise that every asset is acquired to fulfil a specific function or functions, and that maintenance means doing whatever is necessary to ensure that it continues to perform to the desired standard. The people who usually have the clearest view of the desired performance on a day-to-day basis are *operations and production managers*, so they have a central role to play in the entire process. (In areas such as hygiene or the environment, the advice of appropriate *specialists* may also be needed.)

The performance standards associated with each function specify the objectives of maintenance for the asset. However, we have also seen that the built-in capability of the asset – what it *can* do – is the most that maintenance can actually deliver. *Maintenance and design people, often at supervisory levels,* tend to be the custodians of this information, so they too are an essential part of this process.

If this information is shared at a single forum, maintenance people begin to appreciate much more clearly what production is trying to achieve, while production people gain a clearer understanding of what maintenance can – and cannot – deliver.

• *In what ways does it fail to fulfil its functions?*
The example on pages 50 and 51 showed why it is essential that the performance standards used to judge functional failures should be set by *maintenance and operations people* working together.

• *What causes each functional failure?*
Part 3 of Chapter 3 explained how maintenance is really managed at the failure mode level. It went on to stress the importance of identifying the real root causes of each functional failure. The example on page 57 showed how these root causes are often most clearly understood by the shop-floor and first-line supervisory people who work most closely with each machine (especially the *craftsmen and technicians* who have to diagnose and repair each failure).

In the case of new equipment, a valuable source of information about what can fail is a *field technician who is employed by the vendor* and who has worked on the same or similar equipment.

• *What happens when each failure occurs?*
Part 4 of Chapter 4 lists a wide variety of information which needs to be recorded as failure effects. These include:

- the evidence that the failure has occurred, which is most often obtained from the *operators* of the equipment
- the amount of time the machine is usually out of action each time the failure occurs, again obtained from *operators or first-line supervisors*
- the hazards associated with each failure, which may need *specialist advice* (especially concerning such issues as the toxicity and flammability of chemicals, or the hazards associated with mechanical items such as pressure vessels, lifting equipment and large rotating components)
- what must be done to repair the failure, which is usually obtained from the *craftsmen or technicians* who carry out the repairs.

- **In what way does each failure matter?**
Failure consequences are discussed at length in Chapter 4 and summarised in the four questions at the head of Figure 7.1 on pages 158/159. The
assessment of failure consequences can only be done in close consultation
with production/operations people, for the following reasons:

- *hidden failures:* The analysis of hidden functions requires at least four
  items of information, especially if a rigorous approach is used to determine failure-finding task frequencies (see pages 138 -139). These are
  as follows:

  * *evidence of failure:* the first question on the RCM Decision Diagram
    asks if the loss of function caused by this failure mode on its own *will
    become evident* to the operating crew under normal circumstances.
    Clearly, this question can only be answered with assurance by con-
    sulting *the operating crew* concerned.

  * *normal circumstances:* as explained on page 85, different people can
    attach quite different meanings to the term "normal" in the same situ-
    ation, so it is wise to ask this question in the presence of the *operators
    and their supervisors.*

  * *acceptable probability of a multiple failure:* as explained on pages 75
    - 78, this must be determined on either a quantitative or a qualitative
    basis. The discussion about who should evaluate risk on pages 91 and
    92 suggests that this should be done by a group consisting of the *likely
    victims of the multiple failure, the people who would bear the respon-
    sibility if it were to occur, and if necessary, an expert on the specific
    characteristics of the multiple failure.*

  * *the mean time between failures of a protected function:* this is needed
    if the desired availability of a protected device is to be determined on
    a rigorous basis. If this information has not been recorded in the past,
    it can sometimes be obtained by asking the *operators* of the equipment
    how often the protective device is called upon to operate by the failure
    of the protected function.

- *safety and environmental consequences:* if the effects of a failure mode
  are explained reasonably thoroughly, it should be quite easy to assess
  whether it is likely to affect safety or the environment. The main difficulty in this area lies in deciding what level of risk is acceptable, a
  process which also involves the *group described on pages 91 and 92.*

- *operational consequences:* a failure has operational consequences if it affects output, product quality or customer service, or if it leads to an increase in costs other than the direct costs of repair. Clearly, the people who are in the best position to assess these consequences are *operations managers and supervisors*, perhaps with some assistance from *cost accountants*.

- *non-operational consequences:* the people who are usually in the best position to assess direct repair costs are *first- and second-line maintenance supervisors*

• **What can be done to prevent each failure?**
The information needed to assess the technical feasibility of different types of preventive tasks was discussed in Chapters 5 and 9, and the key questions are summarised on page 164. If clear actuarial or research-based data are not available to provide the answers, then the questions must again be answered on the basis of judgement and experience, as follows:

- *on-condition tasks:* page 126 stressed how important it is to consider as many different potential failures as possible when seeking on-condition tasks. The monitoring possibilities range from sophisticated condition monitoring techniques through product quality and primary effects monitoring to the human senses, so we should consult *operators, craftsmen, supervisors* and, if necessary, *specialists in the different techniques.*

    A similar group would need to consider the duration and consistency of the associated P-F intervals, as explained on pages 201 and 202.

    The amount of time needed to avoid the consequences of the failure (in other words, the nett P-F interval) is established jointly by *maintenance and operations supervisors*

- *scheduled restoration and scheduled discard:* in the absence of suitable historical data, the people who are usually most likely to know whether any failure mode is age-related, and if so whether and when there is a point at which there is a rapid increase in the conditional probability of failure, are again the *operators, craftsmen and supervisors* who are closest to the asset.

    Whether it is possible to restore the original resistance to failure of the asset is usually decided by *maintenance supervisors* or in doubtful cases, by *technical specialists.*

• *What if a suitable preventive task cannot be found?*
The two default actions which need active consideration are failure-finding tasks and redesign:

- *failure-finding:* If the frequency of a failure-finding task is to be established without performing a rigorous analysis of the protected system (see page 140), the desired availability of the protective device should be determined by a *group of the sort described on pages 91 and 92.*

  In the absence of formal records, the MTBF of the protective device can be derived initially either by asking the manufacturer of the device for this information, or by asking anyone who might have done any functional checks in the past what they found when they did the checks. As mentioned on page 139, this is usually an *operator or craftsman.*

  Maintenance craftsmen and supervisors are usually the people who are best qualified to assess whether it is possible to do a failure-finding task in accordance with the criteria set out on pages 141 and 142.

- *redesign:* the question of redesign is discussed at length in Part 3 of Chapter 6. Note that the formal RCM process is only meant to identify situations where redesign is either compulsory or desirable. An RCM review group should not attempt to develop new designs during RCM meetings for two reasons:

  * the design process requires skills which are usually not present at an RCM forum.

  * done properly, developing even one new design takes a great deal of time. If this time is spent during RCM review meetings, it slows down and can even paralyse the rest of the programme. (This is not to suggest that designers should not consult the users and maintainers of the assets – just that it should not be done as part of the RCM review process.)

The above paragraphs demonstrate that it is impossible for one person, or even for a group of people from one department, to develop a viable maintenance programme on their own. The diversity of the information which is needed and the diversity of the people from whom it must be sought mean that it can only be done on the basis of extensive consultation and cooperation, especially between production/operations and maintenance people. The most efficient way to organise this is to arrange for the key people to apply the process in small groups.

10.2   RCM Review Groups

In the light of the issues raised in Part 1 of this chapter, we now consider who should participate in a typical RCM review group, what each group actually does, and what the participants get out of this process.

Who should participate

The people mentioned most frequently in Part 1 of this chapter were first-line supervisors, operators and craftsmen. This suggests that a typical RCM review group should include the people shown in Figure 10.1.

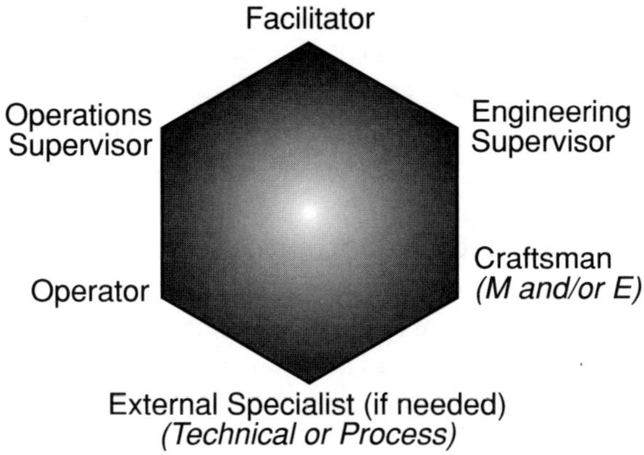

Facilitator

Operations Supervisor

Engineering Supervisor

Figure 10.1
A typical RCM review group

Craftsman
(M and/or E)

Operator

External Specialist (if needed)
(Technical or Process)

In practice, the places on every group do not have to be filled by exactly the same people as shown in Figure 10.1. The objective is to assemble a group which can provide most if not all of the information described in Part 1 of this chapter. These are the people who have the most extensive knowledge and experience of the asset and of the process of which it forms part. To ensure that all the different viewpoints are taken into account, this group should include a cross-section of users and main-tainers, and a cross-section of the people who do the tasks and the people who manage them. In general, it should consist of not less than four and not more than seven people, the ideal being five or six.

The group should consist of the same individuals throughout the analysis of any one asset. If the faces present at each meeting change, too much time is lost going over ground which has already been covered for the benefit of the newcomers.

As suggested in Part 1 of this chapter, "specialists" can be specialists in any of the following:

- some aspect of the process. These usually tend to be dangerous or environmentally sensitive issues.
- a particular failure mechanism, such as fatigue or corrosion.
- a specific type of equipment, such as hydraulic systems.
- some aspect of maintenance technology, such as vibration analysis or thermography.

Unlike other group members, specialists only need to attend meetings at which their speciality is under discussion.

What each group does

The objective of each group is to use the RCM process to determine the maintenance requirements of a specific asset or a discrete part of a process. Under the guidance of a facilitator, the group analyses the context in which the asset is operating, and then completes the RCM Information Worksheet as explained in Chapter 3. (The actual writing is done by the facilitator, so the group members do not have to handle any paper if they don't wish to.) They then use the RCM Decision Diagram shown on pages 158 and 159 to decide how to deal with each of the failure modes listed on the Information Worksheet. Their decisions are recorded on RCM Decision Worksheets as explained in Chapter 7.

The watchword throughout this process is *consensus*. Each group member is encouraged to contribute whatever he or she can at each stage in the process, as shown in Figure 10.2. Nothing should be recorded until it has been accepted by the whole group. (As discussed in Part 3 of this chapter, the facilitator has a crucial role to play in this aspect of the process.)

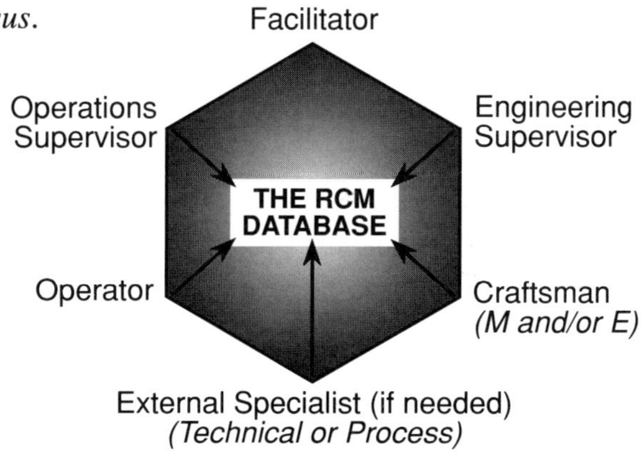

Facilitator

Operations Supervisor

Engineering Supervisor

THE RCM DATABASE

Operator

Craftsman (M and/or E)

External Specialist (if needed) (Technical or Process)

Figure 10.2
The flow of information
into the RCM database

This work is done at a series of meetings which last for about three hours each, and which are held at an average rate of one or two per week. If the group includes shift workers, the meetings need to be planned with special care.

The asset should be sub-divided and allocated to groups in such a way that any one group can complete the entire process in no more than six to ten meetings – certainly no more than twenty.

What participants get out of the process

The flow of information which takes place at these meetings is not only *into* the database. When any one member of the group makes a contribution, the others immediately learn three things:

- more about the asset, more about the process of which it forms part and more about what must be done to keep it working. As a result, instead of having five or six people who each know a bit – often a surprisingly little bit – about the asset under review, the organisation gains five or six experts on the subject.

- more about the objectives and goals of their colleagues. In particular, maintenance people learn more about what their production colleagues are trying to achieve, while operations people learn much more about how maintenance can – and cannot – help them to achieve it.

- more about the individual strengths and weaknesses of each team member. On balance, much more tends to be learned about strengths than weaknesses, which has a salutary effect on mutual respect as well as mutual understanding.

In short, participants in this process gain a much better understanding of
- what each group member (themselves included) should be doing,
- what the group is trying to achieve by doing it and
- how well each group member is equipped to make the attempt.
This changes the group from a collection of highly disparate individuals from two notoriously adversarial disciplines (operations and maintenance) into a team.

The fact that they have each played a part in defining the problems and identifying solutions also leads to a much greater sense of ownership on the part of the participants. For instance, operators start talking about "their" machines, while maintenance people are much more inclined to offer constructive criticism of "their" schedules.

This process has been described as "simultaneous learning", because the participants identify what they need to learn at the same time as they learn it. (This is much quicker than the traditional approach to training, which starts with a training needs analysis, proceeds through the development of a training programme and ends with the presentation of training courses – a process which can take months.)

One limitation of group learning in this fashion is that, unless specific steps are taken to disseminate the information further, the only people who benefit directly are the members of each group. Two ways to overcome this problem are as follows:

- to ensure that anyone in the organisation can gain access to the RCM database at any time
- to use the output of the RCM process to develop formal training courses.

The RCM meetings also provide a very efficient forum for key people to learn how to operate and maintain *new* equipment, especially if one of the vendor's field technicians attends meetings held during the final stages of commissioning. The RCM process provides a framework for such technicians to transfer everything they know about the asset to the other group members in an orderly and systematic fashion. The RCM worksheets enable the organisation to capture the information in writing for dissemination to anyone else who needs to know.

10.3 Facilitators and Auditors

In Part 2 of this chapter it was mentioned that the facilitator has a crucial role to play in the implementation of RCM. This part of this chapter considers this role in more detail, and also looks briefly at the auditing process.

Facilitators

The facilitators are the most important people in the RCM review process. Their role is to:

- ask a structured series of questions of a group of people who are thought to know a great deal about a specific asset or process
- ensure that the group achieves consensus about the answers
- record those answers on the RCM worksheets.

In fulfilling this role, the facilitator needs to do the following:

- *Decide on the level at which the analysis is to be carried out*, ensure that the operating context of the asset is fully defined and understood by the group, and ensure that no significant item or component is overlooked.

- *Ensure that the meetings are conducted professionally*. To do this, the facilitator must
  - ensure that everyone understands the overall purpose of the exercise
  - establish meeting norms (dealing with issues such as punctuality, the use of first names, smoking, etc)
  - set objectives for each meeting.

- *Ensure that the RCM process is applied correctly*. This entails ensuring that all the questions are asked correctly in the correct sequence, and that they have been correctly understood by all the group members. In particular, the facilitator needs to ensure that people do not answer questions which have not been asked (such as talking about the MTBF when asked for the P-F interval) and do not jump to conclusions.

  However, *the facilitators themselves should not attempt to answer any of the questions*. This is perhaps the most difficult aspect of facilitating. It means that while a facilitator should have a reasonable understanding of the process and of the technology incorporated in the asset under review, he or she should *not* be an expert on either subject. This whole approach is based on the notion that the other group members are the experts in these areas. (It may also explain why line maintenance managers and supervisors very seldom make good RCM facilitators.)

  The field in which the facilitator *should* of course be an expert is RCM. If possible, he or she should also be a full-time employee of the organisation which is using the asset, in order to secure the highest possible level of "ownership" of and long-term commitment to the conclusions drawn during the process. It has been the experience of the author that outsiders should only be used as facilitators when there is absolutely no alternative.

- *Secure genuine consensus*. Consensus means that every group member accepts the decisions of the group, even if on occasion he or she may disagree with them. In the rare cases where a group becomes deadlocked, the facilitator should resolve it by calling in an arbitrator – usually a technical expert – who is acceptable to both parties. On no account should the facilitator be seen to be "taking sides" by exercising a casting vote.

- *Ensure that the exercise proceeds at a steady pace.* As mentioned earlier, attempts to redesign the asset should not be made during RCM meetings. Facilitators must also be able to:
  - recognise when it is time to move on to the next point – not so quickly that the exercise becomes superficial but not lingering for so long that it becomes tedious
  - recognise when the group genuinely doesn't know the answer to a question and needs to seek a missing fact or facts between meetings (perhaps by consulting a specialist)
  - control digressions, allowing enough time for the group to take an occasional mental breather but not so much time that the whole process comes to a halt.

- *Motivate the group.* Occasionally a group which starts out enthusiastically loses it way, especially if a large number of meetings is needed to review a big asset. The best way to avoid this problem is to subdivide the asset in such a way that any one group is able to complete a review in six to ten meetings, as explained earlier. Other motivational or related issues which facilitators may have to deal with include:
  - people who don't believe that management will really accept their views (no matter what may have been said to the contrary)
  - people who use the RCM forum to air totally unrelated grievances
  - people with strong personalities who try to dominate the proceedings
  - people who are not comfortable taking part in meetings of this sort.

To be able to handle both the technical and the cultural issues listed above, facilitators need a strong technological background together with highly developed people skills (but they do not necessarily have to be engineers). Above all, however, they need very extensive training and practice in the application of the RCM philosophy.

Auditors

The process described above is a comprehensive exercise in empowerment, in that some remarkably sophisticated decisions are made and implemented by first-line supervisors and shop-floor people. However, this does not absolve higher levels of management of their responsibilities for the overall performance, safety and environmental integrity of each asset.

As a result, they need to satisfy themselves that they agree with the decisions made by the RCM groups, usually by checking the contents of the RCM Information and Decision Worksheets. This is known as "auditing", and the auditors should check the following:

- the definition of the functions and desired standards of performance, and the assessment of failure consequences
- that the group has overlooked no important failure modes.

If the auditors disagree with any findings or conclusions, they should discuss the matter with the group, usually through the facilitator. In so doing, the auditors should be prepared to accept that they themselves may be wrong. (In most cases, no more than 5% of the decisions are queried.)

As mentioned in Chapter 1, the senior managers do not necessarily have to do the audits themselves, but may delegate them to anyone in whose judgement they have sufficient confidence. However, if this is done, it should always be understood that the auditors are acting on behalf of senior management, and hence that the latter still bear the ultimate responsibility for the decisions. (Whoever carries out the audits should also be thoroughly trained in RCM.)

It is important that the audits are carried out immediately after each review has been completed, for three reasons:

- group members are easily able to recall the basis upon which they made their decisions
- group members are understandably keen to see the results of their efforts put into practice. (If this happens too slowly, they start to lose interest in the process, and more seriously, they begin to question whether management were serious about involving them in the first place.)
- the sooner the decisions are implemented, the sooner the organisation will derive the full benefits of the exercise.

When overall agreement is reached about each analysis, the decisions are fed into appropriate implementation systems as described in Chapter 8.

Logistics

Three further issues which need to be dealt with either by the facilitator or (preferably) an RCM project co-ordinator are as follows:

- *Meeting venues:* the meetings should be held in a venue which is reasonably secluded and big enough to accommodate all the participants comfortably

- *Administrative support:* all the participants and their superiors need to be notified formally about the date, times and locations of meetings, and appropriate action needs to be taken if any participants fail to arrive
- *Data entry:* if the information on the RCM worksheets is to be stored in a computerised database, and if the facilitator is unable to input the information, arrangements must be made for someone else to do so.

10.4 Implementation Strategies

In very broad terms, RCM can be implemented in one of two ways:

- the first focuses primarily on assets and processes, with less emphasis on people *(the short-term approach)*
- the second seeks to take advantage of the opportunities which RCM offers on the human front as well as on the technological front *(the long-term approach).*

The first approach is most often used by organisations that wish to achieve results in the shortest possible time. This is done by assembling a few groups of specialists – sometimes as few as one group – and asking them to concentrate only on the assets which offer the biggest returns.

- The main disadvantage of this approach is that *it does nothing to secure the long-term involvement and commitment* of all the people in the organisation to the results, so the results are much *less likely to endure.*
- The main advantages are that it is *quick*, because only one or two groups have to make their way up the RCM learning curve, and it is *easy to manage*, because only a small number of people are involved.

The second approach enables RCM to be used to improve the knowledge and motivation of individuals and to improve teamwork between the users and the maintainers of the assets, in addition to improving the performance of the assets themselves. It entails the use of a large number of groups - in a large plant, this can amount to dozens of groups and may even involve most of the workforce. Since the people who could benefit from this approach often substantially outnumber the assets, it is usually necessary to analyse most if not all of the assets to give everyone an opportunity to take part in the process.

- The main disadvantages of this approach are that it is *slower*, because more people have to become familiar with the RCM methodology, and it is *more difficult to manage*, because many more people are involved.

- The main advantage is that it secures much more *broadly-based owner-ship of maintenance problems and their solutions*. This not only improves individual motivation and teamwork, but it also ensures that the results of the exercise are *far more likely to endure*. (Best practice becomes "part of the way we do things around here".)

Parts 5 and 6 of this chapter consider these two approaches in more detail.

10.5 The Short-term Approach

As mentioned above, the main reason for adopting a short-term approach is to achieve the quickest possible return on the investment of time and money needed to carry out an RCM project. This approach can be applied in two different ways:

- the "task force" approach to acute problems
- the selective approach.

The key elements of these two approaches are discussed below.

The Task Force Approach

The quickest and biggest returns are usually achieved when RCM is applied to assets or processes suffering from intractable problems which have serious consequences. Such problems can often be solved surprisingly quickly by training a small group (the "task force") to carry out a comprehensive RCM analysis of the affected system. Such groups should consist of members drawn from the same disciplines as the groups described in Part 2 of this chapter. They often work full-time on the review project until it is complete, and the group is then disbanded.

(If the need arises, task forces are often used in parallel with the long-term approach described in Part 5 of this chapter.)

The Selective Approach

If the organisation is not suffering from any acute problems which lend themselves to the task force approach, the next best way to secure a quick return is to apply RCM to the assets which are most likely to benefit from this process. This can be done in three stages:

- identify "non-significant" assets. These are assets which are not likely to benefit much from the RCM process.
- rank the assets which are significant in descending order of importance.
- decide whether to use a "template" approach for very similar assets .

Significant assets

If a quick return is the main objective, the last thing anyone wants to do is waste time analysing assets which are unlikely to benefit from the RCM process in the short-term. One way to avoid doing this is to decide to analyse only those assets which are "significant", and not to analyse those which are not. An asset is judged to be significant if it could suffer from any failure mode which on its own:

- could threaten safety or breach any known environmental standard
- would have significant economic consequences.

Items are also judged to be significant if they contain hidden functions whose failures would expose the organisation to a multiple failure with significant safety, environmental or operational consequences.

Conversely, for any item to be classified as non-significant, we must be sure that:

- none of its failure modes will affect safety or the environment
- none of its failure modes will have significant operational consequences
- it does not contain a hidden function whose failure exposes the organisation to the risk of a significant multiple failure.

The process of identifying significant items is quick, approximate and conservative. In other words, if it is not certain that any asset is not significant in the sense defined above, then it should be subjected to a full RCM review. The assessment of significance is usually done at the "item" level as defined in Chapter 2 (although this is not necessarily the level at which the RCM review is conducted).

In the civil aviation industry, a surprisingly high percentage of items can be classified as non-significant in the sense described above. However, for twenty years this industry has been designing aircraft specifically to avoid or minimise the consequences of failure, so there is a very high (but still not infallible) level of redundancy and protection built into their assets.

Assets in other industries, however, tend to enjoy a much lower level of redundancy, so a rather higher proportion of items end up being classified as significant, especially if due consideration is given to failures which could affect safety or the environment. This means that most organisations will still be confronted with a large number of items which should be analysed. So the next question becomes: "Where should we start?"

Ranking significant items in order of importance

In addition to acute problems which lend themselves to the task force approach, many organisations also have assets or processes which are more susceptible than others to chronic problems which are less easy to identify. These problems usually manifest themselves as equipment downtime, poor product quality, poor customer service or excessive maintenance costs. Other areas might be confronted with unacceptable safety or environmental hazards which need to be tackled on systematic basis.

Given hundreds if not thousands of items to choose from in a large undertaking, it makes sense to start applying a problem-solving – or more accurately, a problem-preventing – technique with the power of RCM in areas where the worst of these problems are encountered. Once these have been dealt with, a decision is taken as to whether RCM will be used to analyse assets with less serious problems, and so on. (If the worst problems are not immediately obvious and if suitable hard performance and/ or cost data are available, Pareto analyses can be used to identify suitable starting points.)

However, when selecting the most important of the significant items, bear in mind that the RCM process is applied to every item in its operating context. This context is a function of the process or system of which the item forms part, so the starting point of an RCM analysis should always be an item or a group of items taken in the context of a specific process or system (such as a packing line, a rolling mill, a crane or even a single protected system).

The selection of important items should never be based on generic items or components (all pumps, all bearings, all relief valves), because these would necessarily have to be taken out of context.

Templating

The final way to get quick results from RCM is to use the analysis of one asset as a "template" for another. For reasons which were stressed repeatedly throughout Chapters 3 and 4, this approach can only be applied to assets or processes which are very similar, if not identical, and which are operating in virtually the same context.

When this approach is adopted, an RCM group carries out a comprehensive, zero-based analysis of the first item or process in a series of very similar items or processes, and then uses this analysis as the basis for a review of the other items in the series. To do this, the group ask themselves if the functions and performance standards of each subsequent item differ in any way from those listed on the worksheets for the zero-based item. The differences (if any) are recorded on the worksheets for second item, and the analysts move on to compare the functional failures in the same way, and so on until they have completed the entire analysis.

If the items are technically virtually identical and the operating context is very similar, this approach can save considerable amounts of time and effort because in most cases, a substantial proportion of the analysis remains unchanged for the subsequent items.

However, while it is technically appealing, templating can also have quite serious drawbacks from the motivational viewpoint. This is because the operators and maintainers of the subsequent assets are being asked to accept decisions made by others, which naturally reduces their sense of ownership. In extreme cases, the latter people may even reject the initial analysis out of hand because "it was not invented here". This phenomenon has led one or two major undertakings not to use templating at all, but to start all analyses from a zero-base. (Interestingly, this can lead to some quite different maintenance programmes as different groups select different methods of dealing with the same failure. One way in which this can occur quite legitimately was explained in Figure 5.12 on page 127.)

10.6 The Long-term Approach

Part 4 of this chapter mentioned that the long-term approach to RCM needs a much greater commitment of resources and management time than the short-term approach. It also requires the whole-hearted co-operation of large number of people. As a result, it is wise to adopt this approach in stages.

Since managers have to commit the resources to RCM, it makes sense to start by giving them the opportunity to learn what RCM is all about, to assess for themselves what resources are required to apply it and to judge for themselves what potential benefits it offers in their areas of responsibility. The best way to do this is usually to arrange for them to attend an introductory training course.

If the response is favourable, the next step is to run one or two pilot projects. These enable the organisation to gain first-hand experience of the dynamics of the whole RCM process, what it achieves, and what resource commitments are needed to achieve it.

When the pilot project(s) are complete, the participants are in a position to evaluate the results for themselves and to decide whether, where, and how quickly RCM should be applied to the remaining assets in the organisation. The two alternatives which are most often used are:

• to analyse all the assets on the site in one short, intensive project. Projects of this nature usually last from six months to a year on most sites. Up to twenty or even more groups can be active at once, working under the direction of three or four full-time facilitators. As soon as a group completes the analysis of their asset or process, a new group is activated. In this way, the entire project is finished quickly and the organisation enjoys the benefits equally quickly. In fact, it is an excellent way to achieve lasting step changes in maintenance performance for companies which need to do so in a hurry and which are prepared to make the investment.

   However, this approach is highly resource intensive, so it needs a great deal of careful planning and management attention. It should not really be considered if a number of other initiatives are to be undertaken in parallel with RCM.

• a second possibility is still to review all the equipment on the site, but to do so in stages. Perhaps four or five groups are activated at a time, working under the direction of one or two part-time facilitators. On this basis, it could take five to ten years to analyse all the equipment on a large site (three to four on a smaller one). The organisation still derives all the benefits of RCM, but it takes much longer to do so. This approach is less disruptive in the short term, but if expectations are not very carefully managed, it could be seen to be "dragging on forever", and hence could become demotivating. On the other hand, it means that RCM can be applied in parallel with other initiatives and vice versa.

Chapter 11 explains that an RCM implementation project can yield substantial returns, but that the nature of these returns varies widely from one organisation to another. As a result, the best time for any one organisation to decide which approach to adopt is after a pilot project has been completed and it is able to judge for itself what returns RCM offers in relation to what inputs.

10.7 RCM in Perpetuity

The application of RCM leads to a much more precise understanding of the functions of the assets which have been reviewed, and a much more scientific view of what must be done to cause them to continue to fulfil their intended functions. However, the analysis will not be perfect – and never will be perfect – for two reasons:

• as explained at length in Part 3 of Chapter 9, the evolution of a maintenance policy is inherently imprecise. Numerous decisions have to be made on the basis of incomplete or non-existent hard data, especially about the relationships between age and failure. Other decisions have to be made about the likelihood and the consequences of failure modes which haven't happened yet, and which may never happen. In an environment like this, it is almost inevitable that some failure modes and failure effects will be overlooked completely, while some failure consequences and task frequencies will be assessed incorrectly.

• the assets and the processes of which they form part will be changing continuously. This means that even parts of the analysis which are wholly valid today may become invalid tomorrow.

The people involved in the process will also change. This is partly because the perspectives and priorities of those who take part in the original analysis inevitably change with time, and partly because people simply forget things. In other cases, people leave and their places are taken by others who need to learn why things are as they are.

All these factors mean that the both the validity of the RCM database and people's attitudes towards it will inevitably deteriorate if no attempt is made to prevent this from happening.

One way to do this is to use the RCM process to analyse all significant unanticipated failure modes which occur after the initial analysis has been completed. This is usually done by convening an ad-hoc group which uses RCM to determine the most effective way of dealing with the failure. The results of their deliberations should be woven into the RCM database for the affected asset. The ad-hoc group itself should include as many as possible of the people who carried out the original analysis.

A second – and much surer – way to ensure that RCM databases remain current *in perpetuity* is to ask the original groups to review the database for "their" asset on a formal basis once every nine to twelve months. Such a review meeting need not last for more than one afternoon. Specific questions which should be considered include the following:

- has the *operating context* of the equipment changed enough to change any of the decisions made during the initial analysis? (Examples include a change from single shift operation to double-shifting, or vice-versa.)
- have any *performance expectations* changed enough to necessitate revisions to the performance standards recorded on the RCM worksheets?
- since the previous meeting, have any *failure modes* occurred which should be recorded on the Information Worksheets, or has anyone thought of any more failures which could occur and which should be analysed?
- should anything be added to or changed in the descriptions of *failure effects?* (This applies especially to the evidence of failure and estimates of downtime.)
- has anything happened to cause anyone to believe that *failure* consequences should be assessed differently? (Possibilities here include changes to environmental regulations.)
- is there any reason to believe that any of the *tasks* selected initially is not in fact technically feasible or worth doing?
- has any evidence emerged which suggests that the *frequency* of any task should be changed?
- has anyone become aware of a *preventive technique* which could be superior to one of those selected previously? (In most cases, "superior" means "more cost effective", but it could also mean technically superior.)
- is there any reason to suggest that a task or tasks should be *done by* someone other than the person selected originally?
- has the asset been *modified* in a way which adds or subtracts any functions or failure modes, or which changes the technical feasibility of any tasks? (Special attention should be paid to control systems and protective systems.)

If such reviews are carried out on a regular basis, they only take a small fraction of the time and effort which is needed to set up the database to begin with, but they ensure that the organisation continues to enjoy the benefits of the original exercise in perpetuity. These benefits are discussed in more detail in Chapter 11.

10.8 Building Skills in RCM

RCM provides a common framework which enables people from diverse backgrounds to achieve consensus about a wide range of highly technical issues. However, this process itself embodies many concepts which are new to most people. They need to learn what these are and how they fit together before they can use the process successfully. (Some people who have been steeped in traditional approaches to maintenance also need to unlearn a great deal.)

   The best way to ensure that large numbers of people acquire the relevant skills quickly is to provide suitable training. The most appropriate mix of courses for people at different levels is as follows:

- *craftsmen and operators:* a two-day course in the basic principles of RCM. Such a course should incorporate a variety of case studies and practical exercises which enable delegates to gain an appreciation of how the theory works in practice.

- *engineers, operations managers, supervisors and senior technicians:* a three-day course which covers the same ground as the two-day event, and which also explains what must be done to manage the implementation of RCM.

- *facilitators:* facilitators should be introduced to RCM on a three-day course such as the one described above, and should then undergo ten days of intensive practical training before starting to work with groups. This practical training should involve the application of RCM to real life assets in the latter stages.

(Aladon Ltd and its worldwide network of licensees have trained more than ten thousand people around the world on RCM courses of this nature. They have conducted courses for organisations in virtually all major industrial sectors, and are able to provide further practical support in the field. At the time of publication, these courses are available in English and Spanish, and will shortly be available in a variety of other languages.)

11 What RCM Achieves

The application of RCM results in the outcomes which are summarised in Part 1 of this chapter. Achieving these outcomes requires a great deal of time and effort, especially if RCM is implemented as described in Parts 4 to 6 of Chapter 10.

However, if it is applied correctly, it yields returns which far outweigh any of the costs involved. Some applications have paid for themselves in as little as two weeks, although the payback period is usually a matter of months The wide variety of ways in which RCM pays for itself are discussed at length in Part 2 of this chapter.

11.1 The Outcomes of an RCM Analysis

An RCM review results in four main products or "outcomes", as follows:

- *learning about functions:* the outcome of RCM which attracts by far the most comment from those who take part is how much they learn about how the equipment is supposed to work. This applies both to new assets and to assets which have been in operation for decades. Most of this learning takes place when the review group lists functions and performance standards in the first column of the information worksheet, as shown in Figure 3.7 and again in Figure 11.1.

FUNCTION	
1	To provide an unrestricted passage for all the hot turbine exhaust gas to an outlet 10 metres above the roof of the turbine hall
2	To reduce the exhaust noise levels to ISO Noise Rating 30 at 150 metres
3	To ensure that the surface temperature of the ducting inside the turbine hall does not exceed 60°C
4	To transmit a warning signal to the turbine control system if the exhaust gas temperature exceeds 475°C and a shutdown signal if it exceeds 500°C at a point 4 metres from the turbine
5	To allow the ducting to move freely in response to temperature changes

Figure 11.1:
Learning how the equipment works

- *a better understanding of how the asset can fail* and of *the root causes of each failure:* this focuses maintenance energy on trying to solve the right problems. Not only does this help to prevent failures which occur of their own accord, but it also leads people to stop doing things which cause failures. Most of the learning in this area takes place when the group carries out the failure modes and effects analysis described in Parts 3 and 4 of Chapter 3, the results of which are recorded in the third and fourth columns of the RCM Information Worksheet as shown in Figure 3.1 on page 38.

- lists of *proposed tasks* designed to ensure that the asset continues to operate at the desired level of performance. The task selection process is described in Chapters 5 and 6, and the tasks are listed on the RCM Decision Worksheet as explained in Chapter 7. Chapter 8 describes how the majority of these tasks are then packaged in one of three ways:
  - maintenance schedules to be done by the maintenance department
  - revised operating procedures for the operators of the asset
  - a list of areas where changes (usually design changes) must be made to deal with situations where maintenance cannot help the asset to deliver the desired performance in its current configuration.

This process is summarised in Figure 11.2:

Proposed task	Initial interval	Can be done by
Check main coupling visually for loose or missing bolts	Monthly	Fitter
No scheduled maintenance	N/A	N/A
Check oil level on agitator gearbox and top up with Wonderoil 900 if necessary	Monthly	Fitter
Check main bearing for noise	Daily	Operator
No scheduled maintenance	N/A	N/A
More secure fastenings needed on main drive guard		Engineering
Log oil filter differential pressure and report if it is above 18 psi	Weekly	Operator
etc...		

MAINTENANCE SCHEDULE
Machine Nº 254-07

FREQUENCY	TO BE DONE BY
Monthly	Fitter

1: Check main coupling visually for loose or missing bolts
2: Check oil level on agitator gearbox and top up with Wonderoil 900 if necessary
3: etc...

OPERATING PROCEDURE
Machine Nº 254-07

Every day:
1: Check main bearing for noise
2: etc...

Every Monday:
1: Log oil filter differential pressure and report if it is above 18 psi
2: etc...

SUGGESTED MODIFICATIONS
Machine Nº 254-07
1: More secure fastenings needed on main drive guard
2: etc...

- greatly improved **teamworking**. Part 3 of Chapter 10 explained how the participants in RCM review meetings gain a much better understanding of what each member of the group should be doing, what the group as a whole is trying to achieve, and how well each group member is able to play his or her part in achieving it. In so doing, this process changes most groups from a collection of highly disparate individuals into teams.

11.2 The Benefits of RCM

None of these outcomes are of any use unless they help the organisation to achieve its objectives. These of course vary considerably from one organisation to another, but all will include at least one of the following:
- greater safety and environmental integrity
- improved operating performance
- greater maintenance cost-effectiveness
- longer useful life of expensive items
- greater individual motivation.
How RCM contributes to the fulfilment of each of these objectives is discussed in the next part of this chapter.

Greater Safety and Environmental Integrity

The ways in which RCM leads to improved safety and environmental protection are summarised in the following paragraphs:

- the *systematic review of the safety and environmental implications of every evident failure before considering operational issues* means that safety and environmental integrity become – and are seen to become – top priorities.

- from the technical viewpoint, *the decision process dictates that failures which could affect safety or the environment **must** be dealt with* in some fashion – it simply does not tolerate inaction. As a result, tasks are selected which are designed to reduce *all* equipment-related safety or environmental hazards to an acceptable level, if not eliminate them completely. The fact that these two issues are dealt with by groups which include both technical experts and representatives of the "likely victims" means that they are also dealt with realistically.

- the structured approach to protected systems, especially the concept of the hidden function and the orderly approach to failure-finding, leads to substantial improvements in the maintenance of protective devices. This *greatly reduces the probability of multiple failures* which have serious consequences. (This is perhaps the most powerful single feature of RCM.)

- the thorough review of failure effects and the default action which must be taken if routine maintenance is unable to prevent critical failures frequently leads to *the provision of additional protection* which reduces unacceptable risks to an acceptable level.

- the *overall reduction in the number and frequency of routine tasks* (especially invasive tasks which upset basically stable systems) reduces the risk of critical failures occurring either while maintenance is under way or shortly after start-up.

This issue is particularly important if we consider that preventive maintenance played a part in two of the three worst accidents in industrial history (Bhopal, Chernobyl and Piper Alpha). One was caused directly by a proactive maintenance intervention which was currently under way (checking safety systems at Chernobyl). On Piper Alpha, an unfortunate series of incidents and oversights might not have turned into a catastrophe if a crucial relief valve had not been removed for preventive maintenance at the time.

The most common way to track performance in the areas of safety and environmental integrity is to record the number of incidents which occur. This is usually done by recording the number of lost-time accidents per million man-hours in the case of safety, and the number of excursions (incidents where a standard or regulation is breached) per year in the case of the environment. While the ultimate target in both cases is usually zero, the short-term target is always to better the previous record.

To provide an indication of what RCM has achieved in the field of safety, Figure 11.3 shows the number of accidents per million take-offs recorded each year in the commercial civil aviation industry over the period of development of the RCM philosophy (excluding crashes caused by sabotage or military action). The percentage of these crashes which were caused by equipment failure also declined. Much of the improved reliability is of course due to the use of superior materials and greater redundancy, but most of these improvements were driven in turn by the realisation that maintenance on its own could not extract the required level of performance from the assets as they were then configured. As explained in Chapter 12, this shifted attention from a heavy reliance on fixed time overhauls in the 1960's to doing whatever is necessary to avoid or eliminate the *consequences* of failures, be it maintenance or redesign (the cornerstone of the RCM philosophy). It also reduced the number of crashes which might otherwise have been caused by inappropriate maintenance interventions.

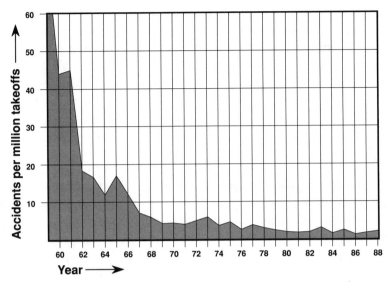

Figure 11.3:
Safety in the civil aviation industry

Improved Operating Performance

From the operational viewpoint, equipment performance usually consists of three elements, as follows:

- *availability* (sometimes called uptime), which is a measure of the amount of time the equipment is capable of operating at all
- *efficiency*, which contrasts the rate at which the equipment is operating with the rate at which it should be operating
- *yield*, which measures how much of the output of a machine conforms to the required quality standards (or in the case of equipment used to provide a service, for what percentage of the uptime it provides a service of the required standard).

This suggests that overall plant performance can be determined by multiplying these three factors, as follows:

    plant performance = availability x efficiency x yield.

(As discussed on pages 98 - 102, a large number of variables affect the extent and relative importance of each of these factors. They also vary widely from industry to industry, so it is only possible to discuss them in the most general terms.)

A number of other methods can be used to measure plant performance. For instance, the *mean time between failures* of the system as a whole was suggested in Part 3 of Chapter 9. However, this is useful only as a basis for tracking trends or comparing the performance of different assets. In a fully-loaded 24-hour, 7-day operation which produces a limited number of products, a good measure of plant performance is simply to note the *total output of the plant compared to budget*. In energy-intensive plants, a different but important perspective on plant performance obtained by measuring *energy efficiency* (such as fuel consumption in the case of vehicles).

In addition to all the factors mentioned above, the scope for performance improvement clearly depends on the performance at the outset. For example, an undertaking which is achieving 95% availability has less improvement potential than one which is currently only achieving 85%. Nonetheless, if it is correctly applied, RCM achieves significant improvements regardless of the starting point.

For instance, the application of RCM has contributed to the following:
- a 16% increase in the total output of the existing assets of a 24-hour 7-day milk-processing plant. This improvement was achieved in 6 months, and most of it was attributed to an exhaustive RCM review done during this period.
- a 300-ton walking dragline in an open-cast coal mine whose availability rose from 86% to 92% in six months.
- a large holding furnace in a steel mill which achieved 98% availability in its first eighteen months of operation against an expectation of 95%.

Plant performance is of course improved by reducing the number and the severity of unanticipated failures which have operational consequences. The RCM process helps to achieve this in the following ways:

- the *systematic review of the operational consequences of every failure* which has not already been dealt with as a safety hazard, together with the stringent criteria used to assess task effectiveness, ensure that only the most effective tasks are selected to deal with each failure mode.

- by relating each failure mode to the relevant functional failure, the information worksheet provides a tool for *quick failure diagnosis*, which leads in turn to *shorter repair times*. (In fact, when we analyse the relationship between functions, functional failures and failure modes, we are actually carrying out a three-level fault-tree analysis.)

- the emphasis placed on on-condition tasks helps to ensure that *potential failures are detected before they become functional failures*. This helps reduce operational consequences in three ways:

- problems can be rectified at a time when stopping the machine will have the least effect on operations
- it is possible to ensure that all the resources needed to repair the failure are available before it occurs, which shortens the repair time
- rectification is only carried out when the assets really need it, which extends the intervals between corrective interventions. This in turn means that the asset has to be taken out of service less often.

For instance, the example concerning tyres on page 130 shows that the tyres need to be taken out of service 20% less often for retreading if on-condition maintenance is used instead of scheduled restoration. In this case, the effect on the availability of the vehicle would be marginal, because removing a tyre and replacing it with a new one can be done very quickly. However, in cases where the corrective action requires extensive downtime, the improvement in availability could be substantial.

• the previous example suggests that a greater emphasis on on-condition maintenance can *reduce the frequency of major overhauls*, with a corresponding long-term increase in availability. In addition, a comprehensive listing of all the failure modes which are reasonably likely together with a dispassionate assessment of the relationship between age and failure, reveals that *there is often no reason at all to carry out routine overhauls at any frequency*. This leads to a reduction in previously scheduled downtime without a corresponding increase in unscheduled downtime.

For instance, a comprehensive RCM review enabled a major integrated steelworks to eliminate all fixed-interval overhauls from its steel-making division. In another case, the intervals between major overhauls of a stationary gas turbine on an oil platform were increased from 25 000 to 40 000 hours without sacrificing reliability.

• in spite of the above comments, it is often necessary to plan a shutdown or an overhaul for any of the following reasons:
- to prevent a failure which is genuinely age-related
- to rectify a potential failure
- to rectify a hidden functional failure
- to carry out a modification.

In these cases, the highly disciplined review of failure modes and the need for preventive or corrective action which is part of the RCM process leads to shorter shutdown worklists, which leads in turn to *shorter shutdowns*. Shorter shutdowns are easier to manage and hence more likely to be completed as planned.

- short shutdown worklists also lead to *fewer infant mortality problems* when the plant is started up again after the shutdown, because it is not disrupted as much. This too leads to an overall increase in reliability.

- the *elimination of superfluous plant* and hence of superfluous failures. As mentioned in Chapter 3, it is not unusual to find that between 5% and 20% of the components of a complex plant are utterly superfluous, but can still disrupt the plant when they fail. Eliminating such components leads to a corresponding increase in reliability.

- by using a group of people who know the equipment best to carry out a systematic analysis of failure modes, it becomes possible to *identify and eliminate chronic failures* which otherwise seem to defy detection, and to take appropriate preventive action.

- as explained on page 237, RCM provides an opportunity for those who participate in the process to *learn quickly and systematically how to operate and maintain new plant*. This enables them to avoid many of the errors which would otherwise be made as a result of the learning process, and to ensure that the plant is maintained correctly from the outset.

  At least four organisations with whom the author has worked in the UK and the USA achieved what each described as "the fastest and smoothest start-up in the company's history" after applying RCM to new installations. In each case, RCM was applied in the final stages of commissioning. The companies concerned are in the automotive, steel, paper and confectionery sectors.

Greater Maintenance Cost-effectiveness

In most industries, maintenance is now the third highest element of operating costs, behind raw materials and either direct production labour or energy. In some cases, it has risen to second or even first place. As result, controlling these costs has become a top priority.

However, the rate at which mechanisation and automation are taking place often means that the amount of maintenance work to be done is growing at such a pace that it is not possible to seek a reduction in absolute maintenance costs. RCM helps to reduce, or at least to control the rate of growth of these costs in the following ways:

Less routine maintenance:

Wherever RCM has been correctly applied to an existing fully-developed preventive maintenance system, it has led to a reduction of 40% to 70%

in the perceived routine maintenance workload. This reduction is achieved partly by a reduction in the number of tasks, but mainly by an overall increase in the intervals between tasks. It also suggests that if RCM is used to develop maintenance programmes for new equipment or for equipment which is currently not subject to a formal preventive maintenance programme, the routine workload will be 40% – 70% lower than if the maintenance programme were developed by any other means.

Note that in this context, "routine" or "preventive" or "scheduled" maintenance means any work undertaken on a cyclic basis, be it the daily logging of the reading on a pressure gauge, a monthly vibration reading, an annual functional check of a temperature switch or a five-yearly fixed-interval overhaul. In other words, it covers scheduled on-condition tasks, scheduled restoration, scheduled discard tasks and scheduled failure-finding.

For example, RCM has led to the following reductions in routine maintenance workloads when applied to existing systems:
• a 50% reduction in the routine maintenance workload of a confectionery plant
• a 62% reduction in the number of low-frequency maintenance tasks which needed to be done per year on a machining line in an automotive engine plant
• a 50% reduction in the routine maintenance requirements of the 11 kV transformers in an electrical distribution system.

Note that the reductions discussed above are only reductions in *perceived* routine maintenance requirements. In the case of many PM systems, fewer than half of the schedules issued by the planning office are actually completed. This figure is often as low as 30%, and sometimes even lower. In these cases, a 70% reduction in the routine workload will only bring what is issued into line with what is actually being done, which means that there will be no reduction in actual workloads.

Ironically, the reason why so many traditionally-derived PM systems suffer from such low schedule completion rates is that much of the routine work is perceived – correctly – to be unnecessary. Nonetheless, there can be no doubt that if only a third of the prescribed work is being done in any system, that system is wholly out of control. A zero-based RCM review does much to bring situations like these back under control, and it does so without increasing actual workloads above current levels.

Better buying of maintenance services

Applying RCM to maintenance contracts leads to savings in two areas.

Firstly, a clear understanding of failure consequences allows buyers to specify response times more precisely – even to specify different response times for different types of failures or different types of equipment. Since rapid response is often the most costly aspect of contract maintenance, judicious fine-tuning in this area can lead to substantial savings.

Secondly, the detailed analysis of preventive tasks enables buyers to reduce both the content and the frequency of the routine portions of maintenance contracts, usually by the same amount (40% - 70%) as any other schedules which have been prepared on a traditional basis. This leads to corresponding savings in contract costs.

Less need to use expensive experts

If field technicians employed by equipment suppliers attend RCM meetings as suggested on page 237, the exchange of knowledge which takes place leads to a quantum jump in the ability of the craftsmen employed by the users to solve difficult problems on their own. This leads to an equally dramatic drop in the need to call for (expensive) help thereafter.

Clearer guidelines for acquiring new maintenance technology

The criteria used to decide whether a preventive task is technically feasible and worth doing apply directly to the acquisition of condition monitoring equipment. If these criteria are applied dispassionately to such acquisitions, a number of expensive mistakes can be avoided.

Most of the items listed under "improved operating performance".

Most of the items listed in the previous section of this chapter also improve maintenance cost-effectiveness. How they do so is summarised below:

* *quicker failure diagnosis* means that less time is spent on each repair
* *detecting potential failures before they become functional failures* not only means that repairs can be planned properly and hence carried out more efficiently, but it also reduces the possibility of the expensive secondary damage which could be caused by the functional failure
* the *reduction or elimination of overhauls* together with *shorter work-lists for the shutdowns which are necessary* can lead to very substantial savings in expenditure on parts and labour (usually contract labour)
* *the elimination of superfluous plant* also means the elimination of the need either to prevent it from failing in a way which interferes with production, or to repair it when it does fail

- *learning how the plant should be operated* together with *the identification of chronic failures* leads to a reduction in the number and severity of failures, which leads to a reduction in the amount of money which must be spent on repairing them.

The most spectacular case of this phenomenon encountered by the author concerned a single failure mode caused by incorrect machine adjustment (operator error) in a large process plant. It was identified during an RCM review and was thought have had cost the organisation using the asset just under US$1 million *in repair costs alone* over a period of eight years. It was eliminated by asking the operators to adjust the machine in a slightly different way.

Longer Useful Life of Expensive Items

By ensuring that each asset receives the bare minimum of essential maintenance – in other words, the amount of maintenance needed to ensure that the "can" stays ahead of the "want" – the RCM process does much to help ensure that just about any asset can be made to last as long as its basic supporting structure remains intact and spares remain available.

As mentioned on several occasions, RCM also helps users to enjoy the maximum useful life of individual components by selecting on-condition maintenance in preference to other techniques wherever possible.

Greater Motivation of Individuals

RCM helps to improve the motivation of the people who are involved in the review process in a number of ways. Firstly, a clearer understanding of the functions of the asset and of what he or she must do to keep it working greatly enhances the competence and hence the confidence of each individual.

Secondly, a clear general understanding of the issues which are beyond the control of each individual – in other words, of the limits of what he or she is expected to achieve – enables them to work more comfortably within those limits. (For instance, no longer is the maintenance foreman automatically held responsible for every failure, as so often happens in practice. This enables him – and those about him – to deal with future failures more calmly and rationally than might otherwise be the case.)

Thirdly, the knowledge that each group member played a part in formulating goals, in deciding what should be done to achieve them and in deciding who should do it leads to a strong sense of ownership.

This combination of competence, confidence, comfort and ownership means that the people concerned are much more likely to want to do the right job, and to do it right the first time.

Better Teamwork

In a curious way, teamwork seems to have become both a means to an end and an end in itself in many organisations. The ways in which the highly structured RCM approach to maintenance problem analysis and decision making contributes to teambuilding were summarised on page 236. However, not only does this approach foster teamwork within the review groups themselves, but it also improves communication and co-operation between:
• production or operations departments and the maintenance function
• management, supervisors, technicians and operators
• equipment designers, vendors, users and maintainers.

A Maintenance Database

The RCM Information and Decision Worksheets constitute a comprehensive maintenance database which provides a number of additional benefits in its own right. These are as follows:

• *adapting to changing circumstances:* the RCM database makes it possible to track the reason for every maintenance task right back to the functions and the operating context of the asset. As a result, if any aspect of the operating context changes, it is easy to identify the tasks which are affected and to revise them accordingly. (Typical examples of such changes are new environmental regulations, changes in the operating cost structure which affect the evaluation of operational consequences, or the introduction of new process technology.) Conversely it is equally easy to identify the tasks which are *not* affected by such changes, which means that time is not wasted reviewing these tasks.

In the case of traditionally-derived maintenance systems, such changes often mean that the whole maintenance programme has to be reviewed in its entirety. As often as not, this is seen as too big an undertaking, so the system as a whole gradually falls into disuse.

• *more accurate drawings and manuals:* the RCM process usually means that manuals and drawings are read in a completely new light. People start asking "what does it do?" instead of "what is it?", which leads them to spot a surprising number of errors which may have gone unnoticed in as-built drawings (especially process and instrumentation drawings). This happens most often if the operators and craftsmen who work with the machines are included in the review teams.

- *reducing the effects of staff turnover:* all organisations suffer when experienced people leave or retire and take their knowledge and experience with them. By recording this information in the RCM database, the organisation becomes much less vulnerable to these changes.

  For example, a major automotive manufacturer was faced with a situation where a plant was to be shut down and most of the workforce had chosen not to move with the equipment to the new site. However, by carrying out a comprehensive RCM analysis of the equipment before it was moved, the company was able to transfer much of the knowledge and experience of the departing workers to the people who were recruited to operate and maintain the equipment in its new location.

- *the introduction of expert systems:* the information on the Information Worksheet in particular provides an excellent foundation for an expert system. In fact, many users regard this worksheet as a simple expert system in its own right, especially if the information is stored in a simple proprietary computerised database and sorted appropriately.

An Integrative Framework

As mentioned in Chapter 1, all of the issues discussed above are part of the mainstream of maintenance management, and many are already the target of improvement programmes. A key feature of RCM is that it provides an effective step-by-step framework for tackling *all* of them at once, and for involving everyone who has anything to do with the equipment in the process. Consequently, when assessing whether it is worth embarking on an RCM implementation programme, it is worth also asking how much more time and effort would be needed to tackle each of the issues described above separately. (In most cases, the answer is an order of magnitude more.)

How RCM Should Not be Applied

If it is applied correctly, RCM yields results very quickly, especially if an intensive project is undertaken as described on page 246. However, not every application of RCM yields its full potential. Some even achieve little or nothing. In the author's experience, the main reasons why this happens are as follows:

- *the analysis is performed at too low a level.* This causes a whole series of problems which are listed in detail on page 303 of Appendix II. Most important among these are that the analysis takes far longer than it should, it results in a massive increease in paperwork and the quality of the decisions deteriorates markedly. As a result, people start finding the process tedious and hence lose interest, it costs much more than it should and it does not achieve as much as it could.

- *too hurried or too superficial an application.* This is usually the result of insufficient training and practice, or too heavy an emotional investment in the status quo on the part of key participants. It often results in a set of tasks which are almost the same as they were to begin with.

- *a tendency to place too much emphasis on failure data* such as MTBF's and MTTR's. This issue is discussed at length in Part 3 of Chapter 9. Such data are nearly always over-emphasised at the expense of properly defined and quantified performance standards, the thorough evaluation of failure consequences and the correct use of data such as P-F intervals. It results in lop-sided and sometimes superficial analyses.

These comments suggest that the surest way to achieve most if not all of the positive benefits of RCM is to apply the process at the right level, and to do so on a formal basis using groups of properly trained people who have an intimate first-hand knowledge of the equipment under review.

12 A Brief History of RCM

12.1 The Experience of The Airlines

In 1974, The United States Department of Defense commissioned United Airlines to prepare a report on the processes used by the civil aviation industry to prepare maintenance programmes for aircraft. The resulting report was entitled *Reliability-centred Maintenance*

Before reviewing the application of RCM in other sectors, the following paragraphs summarise the history of RCM up to the time of publication of the report by Nowlan and Heap[1978]. The italicised paragraphs quote directly from their report.

The Traditional Approach to Preventive Maintenance

The traditional approach to scheduled maintenance programs was based on the concept that every item on a piece of complex equipment has a "right age" at which complete overhaul is necessary to ensure safety and operating reliability. Through the years, however, it was discovered that many types of failures could not be prevented or effectively reduced by such maintenance activities, no matter how intensively they were performed. In response to this problem, airplane designers began to develop design features that mitigated failure consequences – that is, they learned how to design airplanes that were "failure tolerant". Practices such as the replication of system functions, the use of multiple engines and the design of damage tolerant structures greatly weakened the relationship between safety and reliability, although this relationship has not been eliminated altogether.

Nevertheless, there was still a question concerning the relationship of preventive maintenance to reliability. By the late 1950's, the size of the commercial airline fleet had grown to the point at which there was ample data for study, and the cost of maintenance activities had become sufficiently high to warrant a searching look at the actual results of existing practices. At the same time the Federal Aviation Agency, which was responsible for regulating airline maintenance practices, was frustrated by experiences showing that it was not possible to control the failure rate of certain unreliable types of engines by any feasible changes in either the content or frequency of scheduled overhauls. As a result, in 1960 a task force was formed, consisting of representatives from both the FAA and the airlines, to investigate the capabilities of preventive maintenance.

The work of this group led to the establishment of the FAA/Industry Reliability Program, *described in the introduction to the authorising document as follows:*

> *"The development of this program is towards the control of reliability through an analysis of the factors that affect reliability and provide a system of actions to improve low reliability levels when they exist. In the past, a great deal of emphasis has been placed on the control of overhaul periods to provide a satisfactory level of reliability and overhaul time are not necessarily directed at associated topics; therefore, the subjects are dealt with separately."*

This approach was a direct challenge to the traditional concept that the length of time between successive overhauls of an item was an important factor in controlling its failure rate. The task force developed a propulsion-system reliability program, and each airline involved in the task force was then authorised to develop and implement reliability programs in the area of maintenance in which it was most interested. During this process, a great deal was learned about the conditions that must exist for scheduled maintenance to be effective. Two discoveries were especially surprising:

- **Scheduled overhaul has little effect on the overall reliability of a complex item unless the item has a dominant failure mode**
- **There are many items for which there is no effective form of scheduled maintenance**

The History of RCM Analysis

The next step was an attempt to organise what had been learned from the various reliability programs and develop a logical and generally applicable approach to the design of preventive maintenance programs. A rudimentary decision-diagram technique was devised in 1965, and in June 1967 a paper on its use was presented at the AIAA Commercial Aircraft Design and Operations Meeting. Subsequent refinements of this technique were embodied in a handbook on maintenance evaluation and program development, drafted by a maintenance steering group formed to oversee development of the initial program for the new Boeing 747 airplane. This document, known as MSG-1, was used by special teams of industry and FAA personnel to develop the first scheduled-maintenance program based on the principles of reliability-centred maintenance. The Boeing 747 maintenance program has been successful.

Use of the decision-diagram technique led to further improvements, which were incorporated two years later in a second document, MSG-2: Airline Manufacturer Maintenance Program Planning Document.

MSG-2 was used to develop the scheduled maintenance programs for the Lockheed 1011 and the Douglas DC10 airplanes. These programs have also been successful. MSG-2 has also been applied to tactical military aircraft; the first applications were for aircraft such as the Lockheed S-3 and P-3 and the McDonnell F4J. A similar document prepared in Europe was the basis for the initial programs for such aircraft as the Airbus Industrie A-300 and the Concorde.

The objective of the techniques outlined in MSG-1 and MSG-2 was to develop a scheduled-maintenance program that assured the maximum safety and reliability of which the equipment was capable and also provided them at the lowest cost. As an example of the economic benefits achieved with this approach, under traditional maintenance policies the initial programme for the Douglas DC-8 airplane required scheduled overhaul for 339 items, in contrast to seven such items in the DC-10 program. One of the items no longer subject to overhaul limits in the later programs was the turbine propulsion engine. Elimination of scheduled overhauls for engines led to major reductions in labour and materials costs, and also reduced the spare-engine inventory required to cover shop maintenance by more than 50%. Since engines for larger airplanes then cost more than US$1 million each, this was a respectable saving.

As another example, under the MSG-1 program for the Boeing 747, United Airline expended only 66 000 manhours on major structural inspections before reaching a basic interval of 20 000 hours for the first heavy inspections of this airplane. Under traditional maintenance policies it took an expenditure of more than 4 million manhours to arrive at the same structural inspection interval for the smaller and less complex Douglas DC-8. Cost reductions of this magnitude are of obvious importance to any organisation responsible for maintaining large fleets of complex equipment. More important:

• *Such cost reductions are achieved with no decrease in reliability. On the contrary a better understanding of the failure process in complex equipment has actually improved reliability by making it possible to direct preventive tasks at specific evidence of potential failures.*

Although the MSG-1 and MSG-2 documents revolutionised the procedures followed in developing maintenance programs for transport aircraft, their application to other types of equipment was limited by their brevity and specialised focus. In addition, the formulation of certain concepts was incomplete. For example, the decision logic began with an evaluation of proposed tasks, rather than an evaluation of the failure consequences that determine whether they are needed, and if so, their actual purpose. The problem of establishing task intervals was not addressed, the role of hidden-function failures was unclear, and the treatment of structural maintenance was inadequate. There was also no guidance on the use of operating information to refine or modify the initial program after the equipment entered service or the information systems needed for effective management of the on-going program.

All these shortcomings, as well as the need to clarify many of the underlying principles, led to analytic procedures of broader scope and their crystallisation into the logical discipline now known as Reliability-centred Maintenance.

RCM is known as MSG-3 within the aviation industry, and to this day it remains the process used to develop and refine maintenance programmes for all major types of aircraft.

12.2   RCM in Other Sectors

Since 1978, RCM has been applied extensively by the US Navy. In 1984, three nuclear power undertakings in the United States commenced a series of pilot applications under the auspices of the Electric Power Research Institute in San Diego[(1988)]. The EDF in France have also used RCM to develop maintenance programmes in nuclear power facilities. A number of other projects have been undertaken, most notably on a group of Norwegian oil platforms with assistance from SINTEF and the Norwegian Institute of Technology[(1991)]. All of these projects have achieved or promise to achieve improved plant reliability while reducing routine maintenance workloads, as described in Chapter 11.

In other industries, the author and his associates have assisted a number of organisations with the application of RCM. The projects concerned range from in-company awareness training for senior operations and maintenance managers to the full-scale application of RCM to all the equipment on a site. The sectors in which projects have been carried out in the five years prior to the date of publication of this book include the following:
- 3 electric power generation and distribution undertakings (9 sites)
- the world's largest public housing undertaking
- 2 railways
- 2 automobile manufacturing companies (on a total of 5 sites)
- several food manufacturing plants, including confectionery manufacturing (6 sites), vegetable processing (2 sites), milk processing (2 sites), chewing gum manufacture, edible oil processing (4 sites) and ice cream manufacture
- 2 breweries
- 5 offshore oil and gas undertakings
- 5 water utilities (on a great many sites)
- 1 manufacturer of photographic equipment (2 sites)
- 3 pharmaceutical companies
- 2 paper-making companies (6 sites)
- 2 nuclear facilities (neither involved in electricity generation)
- 5 steel mills
- a bank
- an underground railway
- 3 oil refineries
- a paint manufacturer
- an office equipment manufacturer
- 2 base metal mines
- 2 cosmetics manufacturers
- a joinery
- an aluminium processing company (2 sites)
- 2 cigarette manufacturers
- several engineering and metalworking companies.

These projects have been carried out in the United Kingdom, the Republic of Ireland, the United States, Hong Kong, Australia, Spain and Singapore. The fact that RCM has been enthusiastically received by people at all levels, and has enabled users to achieve some remarkable successes in all of these countries, suggests that it is much less affected by cultural differences than many other participative techniques of this nature.

The organisations listed opposite all became aware of and started applying RCM at different times, so implementation is more advanced on some sites than others. At this stage, the overall situation can be summarised as follows:

- in about 25% of the cases, senior managers have undergone preliminary training
- about 10% of the organisations have applied RCM to all of the equipment on at least one site
- the remaining 65% have reviewed some of their equipment, and most plan to continue using RCM to analyse most if not all of their assets.

Space does not permit a detailed consideration of the work done in each case. However, Chapter 11 provides a general summary of the results achieved to date, together with a brief review of some of the highlights.

12.3 Why RCM *2*?

There are currently three versions of the RCM decision diagram in widespread use. The first is shown on pages 91 and 92 of the report by Nowlan and Heap[1978]. This is the version first used by the author, and it is also the version originally used by most other RCM practitioners.

The second version of the decision diagram is the official MSG3 version currently used by the civil aviation industry. It is shown as the "System/ Powerplant Logic Diagram" on pages 6 and 7 of the Maintenance Program Development Document published by the Air Transport Association of America[1988].

The environment and the evolution of RCM 2

The author used a very slightly modified version of the Nowlan and Heap diagram between 1983 and 1990. During this period, the environment became more and more of an issue. In the early days, facilitators were advised to treat environmental hazards in the same way as safety hazards. However, in practice this meant that many environmental problems which did not pose an immediate and direct threat to safety were overlooked. The environment can also be a highly contentious issue which does not lend itself to subjective evaluation in the same way as safety.

As a result, in 1988 the author began working with a number multi-national organisations to develop a more precise approach to failures which threatened the environment. This culminated in the addition of question E to the RCM 2 decision diagram in 1990. The use of standards and regulations as a basis for this decision removed the element of subjectivity. However, the whole issue was still accorded much the same priority as safety in recognition of the high and rising priority which society places on the environment, as discussed at length in Part 2 of Chapter 4. The addition of this question alone changed the decision diagram enough to warrant changing its name to RCM 2.

Other changes incorporated in RCM 2

When RCM 2 was launched in September 1990, a number of other changes were incorporated into the decision process which had been under development for several years. These were as follows:

- question H was amended to remove a number of ambiguities which arose when the airline-oriented version of this question was used in industry.

- question S was also altered to remove possible ambiguities surrounding the meaning of the word "safety".

- the italicised extension was added to question O because many users tended to interpret this question too narrowly.

- questions H1/S1/O1/N1 were modified to make them easier to understand.

- the term "scheduled restoration" was substituted for "scheduled rework" in questions H2/S2/O2/N2 because "rework" has a different meaning in manufacturing companies. This frequently caused confusion. ("Scheduled restoration" is now also used in the MSG3 decision diagram.)

- the terms "technically feasible" and "worth doing" were substituted for "applicable" and "effective". This was done because the way in which the latter terms were used was slightly contrived in this context and frequently required a great deal of explanation.

- the small but significant number of situations where failure-finding was either impossible or impractical led to the development and addition of formal selection criteria for this task. It also led to the development and addition of the secondary default decision process for hidden functions which is explained on page 143.

- the questions on the revised decision diagram were re-coded to eliminate the possibility of confusion with analyses carried out using its predecessors, and the decision worksheet was revised accordingly. The decision worksheet was also modified to provide more space for task descriptions.

- the basis upon which the probability of a multiple failure is calculated was changed. Previously, it was calculated by multiplying the probability of failure of the protected function by the probability of failure of the protective device. As explained in Part 1 of Chapter 4, it is now calculated by multiplying the probability of failure of the protected function by the probability that the protective device will be in a failed state.

    The reason for this change is that the former calculation focuses on the probability of two events occurring during a single mission during which it is impossible to gain access to the plant (to say the least, it is difficult to gain access to a failed aircraft engine at 35 000 feet over water), whereas the latter calculation is better suited to plant which is continuously accessible.

With the possible exception of the question concerning environmental consequences, none of these changes represent a significant departure from the philosophy underlying the original Nowlan and Heap decision diagram. The key differences between the two diagrams and between them and MSG 3 are summarised in the next section of this chapter. However, it must be stressed that the changes have all been made to improve clarity and user-friendliness, and in the case of questions H4 and H5, to plug a small gap in the logic.

    The nett effect of these changes has been to make a technique which is already extraordinarily robust at the theoretical level even more robust, and to make it quicker and easier to use into the bargain.

Comparing the three main decision diagrams

Following the development of RCM 2, it is worth closing by comparing the three main decision diagrams. The key areas in which they differ are:

- the way in which lubrication is handled
- whether or not any formal distinction is made between multiple failure which affect safety and those which do not, and if so, how these distinctions are handled
- the application of formal task selection criteria to failure-finding tasks and the default action to be taken if a suitable task cannot be found

ISSUE	NOWLAN & HEAP	MSG 3	RCM 2
Lubrication	Treated separately	A question about lubrication is incorporated at the head of every task selection column	Lack of lubrication is treated like any other failure mode, except for total loss lubrication which is treated separately (seepage 154)
Multiple failures which affect safety	Not handled as a separate issue	Asks if the multiple failure could affect safety right after asking if the failure is evident. Yes and no answers lead to two separate columns: "Yes" defaults to compulsory redesign, "no" to desirable redesign	Asks if the multiple failure could affect safety at the foot of the hidden function column (question H4) and leads to the same defaults as MSG3
Failure-finding	Failure-finding is a compulsory default action if no preventive task can be found: does not specify criteria for deciding whether failure-finding is technically feasible and worth doing	Asks about failure-finding before seeking preventive tasks: Specifies failure-finding task selection criteria	Seeks to prevent failures before considering failure-finding because the latter implies that components can spend time in the failed state. Specifies failure-finding task selection criteria
Safety consequences	Encourages users to select the first appropriate preventive task without considering subsequent categories	Encourages users to consider tasks from all categories before making a selection	As for Nowlan and Heap
The environment	Not considered	Not considered	Considered in question E

Table 12.1: Comparing Nowlan & Heap, MSG3 and RCM 2

- the methods of selecting tasks meant to prevent failures which have safety consequences
- the approach to failures which could affect the environment.

The differences themselves are summarised in Table 12.1 opposite.

Appendix I:
Condition Monitoring Techniques

1 Introduction

Chapter 5 explained at length that most failures give some warning of the fact that they are about to occur. This warning is called a *potential failure*, and is defined as an *identifiable physical condition which indicates that a functional failure is either about to occur or in the process of occurring*. On the other hand, a *functional failure* is defined as *the inability of an item to meet a specified performance standard*. Techniques to detect potential failures are known as *on-condition* maintenance tasks, because items are inspected and left in service *on the condition* that they meet specified performance standards. The frequency of these inspections is determined by the *P-F interval*, which is the interval between the emergence of the potential failure and its decay into a functional failure.

Basic on-condition maintenance techniques have existed as long as mankind, in the form of the human senses (sight, sound, touch and smell). As explained in Chapter 5, the main technical advantage of using people in this capacity is that they can detect a very wide range of potential failure conditions using these four senses. However, the disadvantages are that inspection by humans is relatively imprecise, and the associated P-F intervals are usually very short.

But the sooner a potential failure can be detected, the longer the P-F interval. Longer P-F intervals mean that inspections need to be done less often and/or that there is more time to take whatever action is needed to avoid the consequences of the failure. This is why so much effort is being spent on trying to define potential failure conditions and develop techniques for detecting them which give the longest possible P-F intervals.

However, Figure A1.1 shows that a long P-F interval means that the potential failure must be detected at a point which is higher up the P-F curve. But the higher we move up this curve, the smaller the deviation from the "normal" condition, especially if the final stages of deterioration are not linear. The smaller the deviation, the more sensitive must be the monitoring technique designed to detect the potential failure.

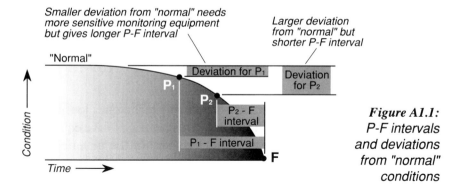

Figure A1.1:
P-F intervals
and deviations
from "normal"
conditions

2 Categories of Condition Monitoring Techniques

Most of the smaller deviations tend to be beyond the range of the human senses and can only be detected by special instruments. In other words, equipment is used to *monitor the condition* of other equipment, which is why the techniques are called *condition monitoring*. This name distinguishes them from the other types of on-condition maintenance (performance monitoring, quality variation and the human senses).

As mentioned in Chapter 5, condition monitoring techniques are really no more than highly sensitive versions of the human senses. In the same way as the human senses react to the symptoms of a potential failure (noise, smells, etc), so condition monitoring techniques are designed to detect specific symptoms (vibration, temperature, etc). For the sake of simplicity, these techniques are classified according to the symptoms (or *potential failure effects*) which they monitor, as follows:

- *dynamic effects.* Dynamic monitoring detects potential failures (especially those associated with rotating equipment) which cause abnormal amounts of energy to be emitted in the form of waves such as vibration, pulses and acoustic effects.

- *particle effects.* Particle monitoring detects potential failures which cause discrete particles of different sizes and shapes to be released into the environment in which the item or component is operating.

- *chemical effects.* Chemical monitoring detects potential failures which cause traceable quantities of chemical elements to be released into the environment.

- *physical effects.* Physical failure effects encompass changes in the physical appearance or structure of the equipment which can be detected directly, and the associated monitoring techniques detect potential failures in the form of cracks, fractures, the visible effects of wear and dimensional changes.

- *temperature effects.* Temperature monitoring techniques look for potential failures which cause a rise in the temperature of the equipment itself (as opposed to a rise in the temperature of the material being processed by the equipment).

- *electrical effects:* Electrical monitoring techniques look for changes in resistance, conductivity, dielectric strength and potential.

An enormous variety of techniques has been developed and more are appearing all the time, so it is not possible to produce an exhaustive list of all the techniques available at any time. This appendix provides a very brief summary of about sixty of the techniques currently available. Some of these are well-known and well-established, while others are in their infancy or even still under development.

However, whether or not any of these techniques is technically feasible and worth doing in any context should be assessed with the same rigour as any other on-condition task. To help with this process, this appendix lists the following for each technique:

- the potential failure conditions which the technique is meant to detect (*conditions monitored*)
- the equipment it is designed for (*applications*)
- the P-F intervals typically associated with the technique (*P-F interval*) – for obvious reasons, this can only be a very rough "ballpark" guide
- how it works (*operation*)
- the training and/or level of skill needed to apply the technique (*skill*)
- the advantages of the technique (*advantages*)
- the disadvantages of the technique (*disadvantages*).

Finally, before considering specific techniques, it is worth noting that a great deal of attention is being focused on condition monitoring nowadays. Because of its novelty and complexity, it is often regarded as being completely separate from other aspects of scheduled maintenance. However, we should not lose sight of the fact that condition monitoring is only another form of scheduled maintenance. When it is used, it should be designed into normal schedules and schedule planning systems wherever possible, and not made subject to expensive parallel systems.

3 Dynamic Monitoring

A Preliminary Note on Vibration Analysis

Equipment which contains moving parts vibrates at a variety of frequencies. These frequencies are governed by the nature of the vibration sources, and can vary across a very wide range or *spectrum*. For instance, the vibration frequencies associated with a gearbox include the primary frequencies of rotation of the shafts (and their harmonics), the tooth contact frequencies of different gear sets, the ball passing frequencies of the bearings and so on.

If any of these components starts to fail, its vibration characteristics change, and vibration analysis is all about detecting and analysing these changes.

This is done by measuring how much the item as a whole vibrates, and then using spectrum analysis techniques to home in on the frequency of vibration of each individual component in order to see whether anything is changing.

However, the situation is complicated by the fact that it possible to measure three different characteristics of vibration. These are amplitude, velocity and acceleration. So step one is to decide which of the characteristics is going to be measured – and what measuring device is going to be used – and then step two is to decide which technique will be used to analyse the signal generated by the measuring device (or sensor).

In general, amplitude (or displacement) sensors tend to be more sensitive at lower frequencies, velocity sensors across the middle ranges and accelerometers at higher frequencies. The strength of the signal at any frequency is also influenced by how closely the sensors are mounted to the components which emit the signal at that frequency.

The rest of this part of this chapter looks in more detail at the ways in which the signals can be analysed.

3.1 Broad Band Vibration Analysis

Conditions monitored: Changes in vibration characteristics caused by fatigue, wear, imbalance, misalignment, mechanical looseness, turbulence, etc.

Applications: Shafts, gearboxes, belt drives, compressors, engines, roller bearings, journal bearings, electric motors, pumps, turbines, etc.

P-F interval: Limited warning of failure

Operation: Monitors the vibration of the equipment as a whole and provides basic information for check or trend monitoring. An initial arrangement might be an accelerometer and a vibration meter with amplification circuitry for a meter calibrated in vibrational units. The reading is closely related to the RMS of the vibrations at the location of the accelerometer but does not discriminate between various frequencies. Such meters have a constant frequency response over the range 20 Hz to 1000 Hz

Skill: To use the equipment and record the vibration: a suitably trained semi-skilled worker

Advantages: Can be used by inexperienced personnel: Cheap and compact: Can be portable or permanently installed: Effective in detecting elementary defects: Minimal data logging: Interpretation and appraisals can be based on published condition acceptability criteria such as VDI 2056 from Germany

Disadvantages: Only a crude overall measurement: No frequency content: Defect identification limited.

3.2 Octave Band Analysis

Conditions monitored and Applications: As for broad band vibration

P-F interval: Days to weeks depending on application

Operation: Fixed contiguous octave and fractional octave filters divide the frequency spectrum into a series of bands of interest, which have a constant width when plotted logarithmically. The average output from each filter is measured successively, and the values are displayed by a meter or plotted on a recorder

Skill: To operate equipment and interpret results: a suitably trained technician

Advantages: Simple to use when the measurement parameters have been previously determined by an engineer: Fully portable, allowing on-site measurement and analysis: Relatively small investment required: Good detection capabilities using fractional octave filters: Recorder provides a permanent record

Disadvantages: Limited information for diagnostic purposes: Diagnostic ability also limited by logarithmic frequency scale: Relatively long analysis time.

3.3 Narrow Band Frequency Analysis - Constant Bandwidth

Conditions monitored: As for broad band vibration, and to identify multiple harmonics and sidebands

Applications: As for broad band vibration, and development, diagnostic and experimental work – especially vibrations associated with rotating machines such as gearboxes

P-F interval: Usually from several weeks to months

Operation: An accelerometer detects the vibration and converts it into an electrical signal which is amplified and fed into an analyser. A constant bandwidth between 3.16 Hz and 100 Hz, and a frequency range of between 2 Hz and 200 Hz is chosen. Both linear and logarithmic frequency sweeps may be selected, but linear is chosen when identifying harmonics. In order to make more detailed investigations of peaks, bandwidths and frequency ranges can be changed to suit requirements

Skill: To operate equipment: a suitably trained and experienced technician. To interpret results: an experienced senior technician

Advantages: Simple to use when the measurement parameters have been set: Good for large frequency ranges and for detailed investigation at high frequencies: Identifies multiple harmonics and side bands which occur at constant frequency intervals

Disadvantages: Not portable: Relatively long analysis time: Quite expensive and quite highly skilled.

3.4 Narrow Band Frequency Analysis – Constant Percentage Bandwidth

Conditions monitored: Shock and vibration

Applications: As for broad band vibration

P-F interval: Usually several weeks to months

Operation: High resolution narrow bandwidth frequency analysis is performed by sweeping through the desired frequency range, of 2 Hz to 200 Hz, using a constant percentage filter bandwidth (1%, 3%, 10% and $^1/_3$ octave) which separates closely spaced frequencies. A constant percentage filter bandwidth as narrow as 1% allows very fine resolution which in turn facilitates detailed examination. Continuous sweeping through the frequency range is used with a level recorder

Skill: To operate equipment: a suitably trained and experienced technician. To interpret results: an experienced senior technician

Advantages: Better stability and more accurate calibration at low frequencies than constant bandwidth analyser: Level recorders provide a permanent record: Simple to use: Good detection capabilities at 1% bandwidth: Measurement of short duration shock impulses: Can be used for distortion measurements

Disadvantages: Equipment not portable: Analysis takes a long time: Equipment relatively expensive.

3.5 Real Time Analysis

Conditions monitored: Acoustic and vibrational signals; measurement and analysis of shock and transient signals

Applications: Rotating machines, shafts, gearboxes etc

P-F interval: Several weeks to months

Operation: A signal is recorded on magnetic tape and played back through a real-timer analyser. The signal is sampled and transformed into the frequency domain. A constant bandwith spectrum is produced, measured at 400 equally spaced frequency intervals across a frequency range selectable from 0-10 Hz to

0-20 kHz. A high resolution mode can be selected, and scan can also be adjusted to give a "slow motion" analysis, allowing any changes in the baseband spectrum to be observed as the time window is stepped along

Skill: To operate equipment and interpret results: an experienced engineer

Advantages: Analyses all frequency bands over the entire analysis range simultaneously: Instantaneous graphical display of analysed spectra is continuously updated: No need to wait for level recorder readout: Suited to analysis of short duration signals such as transient vibration and shock: X-Y recorders provide a permanent record

Disadvantages: Equipment not portable and very expensive: Needs high level of skill: Off-line analysis.

3.6 Proximity Analysis

Conditions monitored: Misalignment, oil whirl, rubs, imbalance/bent shafts, etc.

Applications: Shafts, motor assemblies, fans, etc.

P-F interval: Days to weeks

Operation: In the basic mode, a signal from a transducer operates as the ordinate against a time base. With a single impulse, sinusoidal curves indicate imbalance, bent shafts, oil whirl, misalignment, adhesive bearing rubs. Two signals produce a polar diagram which provides more characteristic information on an X-Y diagram. More information can be obtained by introducing a phase-indicating mark on the wave forms of the oscilloscope display. These marks are generated at the rate of one per revolution by a pick up incorporated in the shaft-speed tachometer

Skill: Equipment operation and interpretation of results: a suitably trained and experienced technician

Advantages: Can be used for balancing: Equipment portable: Very simple to use

Disadvantages: P-F interval short: Long analysis time: Diagnostic ability limited.

3.7 Shock Pulse Monitoring

Conditions monitored: Surface deterioration and lack of lubrication

Applications: Rolling element bearings, pneumatic impact tools, valves of internal combustion engines

P-F interval: Depends on the application, but usually several weeks to months

Operation: An accelerometer detects shock waves, and the signal is passed through a band pass filter which selects only frequencies exceeding 10 kHz. This high frequency input is converted into square pulses. The peak values of these pulses are read off as a measure of bearing damage

Skill: A suitably trained and experienced technician

Advantages: Long P-F intervals: Equipment portable: Simple to use

Disadvantages: Not suitable for slow-moving machinery with high levels of product impact noise unless "adaptive noise cancelling" is also used.

3.8 Kurtosis

Conditions monitored: Shock pulses

Applications: Rolling element bearings and gears

P-F interval: Several weeks to months

Operation: Kurtosis is a statistical concept relating to the "peakiness" of the distribution of vibration amplitude. The condition of the bearing is related to the kurtosis value displayed on a meter, independent of bearing speed. The idea behind kurtosis is that some components degenerate as a result of the loss of gross surface area, so that progressively increasing periodic impulses are generated. A statistical distribution of such curves in the first order produces a normal form of distribution which tends to ignore the peaks of the shock. If the "statistical moments" are analysed in much the same manner as when obtaining first and second moments of area, the higher area moments become more sensitive to the tails of the distribution curve and so register the size and frequency of the peaks that need to be monitored as a basis for condition appraisal.

Skill: A suitably trained semi-skilled worker

Advantages: Applicable to any materials with hard surfaces: Equipment portable: Very simple to use

Disadvantages: Limited application and significantly affected by impact noise from other sources: Considered by some users to be too sensitive.

3.9 Acoustic Emission

Conditions monitored: Plastic deformation and crack formation caused by fatigue, stress and wear

Applications: Metal materials used in structures, pressure vessels, pipelines and underground mining excavations

P-F interval: Several weeks depending on application

Operation: Audible stress waves, due to crystallographic changes, are emitted from materials subjected to loads. These stress waves are picked up by a transducer and fed via an amplifier to a pulse analyser, then either to an X-Y recorder or to an oscilloscope. The displayed signal is then evaluated

Skill: Equipment operation and interpretation of results: A suitably trained and experienced technician

Advantages: Remote detection of flaws: Covers entire structures: Measuring system set up very quickly: High sensitivity: Requires limited accessibility to test objects: Detects active flaws: Only relatively low loads are required: Can sometimes be used to forecast failure load

Disadvantages: The structure has to be loaded: A-E activity is highly dependent on materials: Irrelevant electrical and mechanical noise can interfere with measurements: Gives limited information on the type of flaw: Interpretation of results may be difficult.

3.10 Ultrasonic Leak Detection

Conditions monitored: Leaks and other sources of very high frequency noise

Applications: Chemical plants, high pressure gas mains, underground tanks, steam condensers, refrigeration equipment, heat exchangers, pressurised telephone cables, compressed air systems, watertight compartments in ships, pressurised compartments in aircraft, ovens under pressure or vacuum, boilers and vacuum brake systems, air operated contactors on electric traction control, valve operation in compressors and internal combustion engines, radiation from faulty electrical appliances, high voltage corona discharge, etc

P-F interval: Highly variable depending on the nature of the fault

Operation: Ultrasonic energy is generated by molecular collisions when gas is forced through a small orifice. The ultrasonic energy is picked up by a high frequency ceramic microphone. The signal is amplified and used to provide a visual indication of a moving coil meter as well as an audible signal on headphones

Skill: A suitably trained semi-skilled worker

Advantages: Can be used in very noisy areas (headphones screen the ambient noise): Microphone highly directional and enables the operator to detect a leak or other source of noise at long range: Equipment portable

Disadvantages: Does not indicate size of leak: Underground tanks can only be tested under vacuum.

4 Particle Monitoring

4.1 Ferrography

Conditions monitored: Wear, corrosion and fatigue

Applications: Enclosed lubricating and hydraulic oil systems such as gearboxes, engine sumps, hydraulics, etc.

P-F interval: Usually several months

Operation: Wear particles are separated magnetically from lubricating oils onto an inclined glass slide by means of an instrument known as a ferrograph. The particles are distributed along the length of the slide according to their size. The slide, known as a ferrogram, is treated so that the particles adhere to the surface when the oil is removed. The total density of particles and the ratio of large to small particles indicate the type and extent of wear, and the analysis is done by a technique known as bichromatic microscopic examination. An electron microscope can also be used to determine particle shapes and provide an indication of the cause of the failure

Skill: To draw the sample and operate the ferrograph: a suitably trained semi-skilled worker. To analyse the ferrogram: an experienced technician

Advantages: More sensitive than emission spectrometry at early stages of engine wear: Measures particle shapes and sizes

Disadvantages: Not an on-line technique: Measures only ferromagnetic particles: Requires an electron microscope for in-depth analysis

4.2 Graded Filtration

Conditions monitored: Particles in lubricating oils (such as iron, copper, lead, chromium, aluminium, silicon, etc) caused by wear, fatigue and corrosion

Applications: Enclosed lubricating and hydraulic oil systems, such as gearboxes, engine sumps, hydraulics, etc

P-F interval: Usually from several weeks to months

Operation: An oil sample is diluted and passed through a series of calibrated-membrane filters. The particles collected are counted under a microscope in size groups for each element, and their statistical distribution is shown in the form of a graph. Analysis of the particle distribution profiles indicates whether wear is normal or not

Skill: Sampling: a laboratory assistant. Examination of particle distribution profiles: an experienced laboratory technician or engineer

Advantages: Can determine whether wear is normal or not: Relatively cheap: Can be used to compare one item with another

Disadvantages: Not an on-line technique: Specialist skills required to interpret test results: Identification of particle elements difficult

4.3 Magnetic Chip Detection

Conditions monitored: Wear and fatigue

Applications: Equipment with enclosed lubricating systems, such as gearboxes, engine sumps, aircraft engines, turbines, compressors, etc.

P-F interval: Days to weeks

Operation: A magnetic plug is mounted in the lubricating system so that the magnetic probe is exposed to the circulating lubricant. Fine metal particles suspended in the oil, and metal flakes from fatigue break up are captured by the probe. The probe is removed regularly for microscopic examination of the particles adhering to it. An increase in the quantity and size of particles indicates imminent failure. The debris has different characteristics (shape, colour and texture) depending on its source

Skill: To collect the sample: a suitably trained semi-skilled worker. To analyse the debris: a suitably trained and experienced technician

Advantages: Cheap method of monitoring the contamination of liquids: Low powered microscope only required for the analysis of debris: Some probes can be removed without loss of lubricant

Disadvantages: Short P-F interval: High skill needed to interpret the debris

4.4 X-Ray Fluorescence

Conditions monitored: Wear; damage to air filters

Applications: Enclosed lubricating and hydraulic oil systems, such as gearboxes, engine sumps, hydraulics, etc.

P-F interval: Usually several months

Operation: An oil sample is exposed to a source of radiation which causes contaminants to emit characteristic X-rays. The rate of X-ray emission and its spectrum identify the type and quantity of the contaminants. X-ray fluorescence can analyse the same metallic elements as atomic absorption spectrometry with the exception of lithium and magnesium. In addition, sulphur, iodine, bromine and chlorine (often present in anti-wear additives) can be analysed

Skill: To draw sample: a suitably trained semi-skilled worker. To operate equipment: a suitably skilled technician. To interpret result: an experienced engineer

Advantages: Can detect very small traces of impurities

Disadvantages: Not as accurate in the parts per million range as atomic absorption spectrometry: The instrument is very expensive

4.5 Blot Testing

Conditions monitored: Wear, fatigue and sometimes corrosion particles

Applications: Circulating oil systems, such as gearboxes, engine sumps, hydraulics, compressors, etc.

P-F interval: A few days to a few weeks

Operation: A drop of oil is deposited on filter paper. The oil initially spreads out, mainly on the surface, so that large particles will remain within a circular corona of a small radius. This removes many organometallic and detergent-dispersant additives. Further dispersion leads to oil penetration and filtration through the paper, so circular zones corresponding to the size of particles transported by the filtering oil are clearly defined. A period of 24 hours is needed for the oil to "blot" fully, after which the results may be analysed photometrically

Skill: Oil blotting: a suitably trained semi-skilled worker. Analysis: a suitably experienced technician

Advantages: Provides a record: Easy to set up

Disadvantages: 24 hours needed for the oil to blot: Considerable skill needed to analyse the oil blots.

4.6 LIDAR (LIght Detection And Ranging)

Conditions monitored: Presence of particles in the atmosphere

Applications: Quality and dispersion of plumes of smoke from smokestacks

P-F interval: Highly variable depending on the application

Operation: Single wavelength light is directed to the area under investigation. The quantity of particulate matter is assessed by measuring backscatter. Locations are determined by triangulation based on readings taken from two points.

Skill: An experienced engineer

Advantages: A remote sensing technique which can cover large areas

Disadvantages: Very expensive: Requires a high level of skill.

5 Chemical Monitoring

5.1 Spectrometric Oil Analysis Procedure

Conditions monitored:
• Wear: the following wear metals are measured in lubricating oils:
  - Iron from gears, cylinder liners, etc
  - Copper from bearings, bushes and cooling systems
  - Lead from petrol, bearings, bushes and lubricants
  - Chromium from rings and sometimes liners
  - Aluminium from piston bearings
  - Molybdenum from piston rings
  - Tin from bearings in some engines
  - Silver and zinc associated with some locomotive engines
  - Nickel associated with aircraft engines

- Leaks: the following elements are measured in lubricating oils:
  - Silicon from leaks in induction systems
  - Sodium from cooling water additives in oil
  - Copper from cooling water in oil
  - Boron from coolant leaks in oil
- Corrosion (in certain cases)

Applications: Circulating oil systems

P-F interval: Usually several weeks to months

Operation: Contaminants in an oil sample are measured by emission or atomic absorption spectrometry. *Emission spectrometry* excites the metallic impurities in the sample with a direct high voltage (15 000 V), causing impurities to emit characteristic radiations which can be analysed. *Atomic absorption spectrometry* works on the principle that every atom absorbs light of its own specific wavelength. The oil sample is diluted and vaporised in an acetylene flame, and the presence of each element is determined using a light source of the right wavelength. In this way, wear particles are identified, quantified and qualified so that the source of deterioration can be located. Graphs of wear rates for each metal show improving or deteriorating conditions.

Skill: To draw the sample: a suitably trained semi-skilled worker. To operate the spectrometer: a suitably trained laboratory technician. To analyse the test results: an experienced chemical analyst

Advantages: Atomic absorption spectrometer comparatively cheap: More reproducible at low concentrations: Emission spectrometry much faster than AAS

Disadvantages: Atomic absorption spectrometer slow and laborious: Emission spectrometer expensive.

5.2 Gas Chromatography

Conditions monitored: Gases emitted as a result of faults, such as sulphur hexafluoride, nitrogen, air, hydrogen, etc

Applications: Nuclear power systems, turbine generators and is well suited to sulphur hexafluoride and nitrogen sealed systems

P-F interval: Highly variable depending on the nature of the fault

Operation: Gases are selectively absorbed by passing them through columns of finely divided absorbent material, such as diatomaceous earth. The separate gases are then desorbed by the passage of an inert carrier gas through the column. Light gases appear first from the column and more complex gases last

Skill: A suitably trained laboratory technician

Advantages: High sensitivity detection (one part in 1000 million, by volume): Once the equipment has been set up, can be operated by a laboratory assistant

Disadvantages: Adequate samples for sensitive analyses are difficult to obtain: In large systems any fault gases may be rapidly diluted: Considerable skill needed to interpret results: Equipment not portable: Wide range of applications required to justify purchase: Not widely used in the maintenance environment.

5.3 Liquid Chromatography

Conditions monitored: Changes in lubricant properties such as alkalinity, acidity, ash, flash point, insolubles, viscosity, etc

Applications: Enclosed oil systems such as transformers, engine sumps, compressor sumps, hydraulic systems, etc

P-F interval: Depends on the rate of lubricant degradation and the application, but usually several weeks

Operation: Liquids are selectively absorbed by passing through a column of finely divided absorbent material. The separate liquids are then desorbed by passing a mixture of two solvent liquids, with different polarities, through the column. Light liquids appear first from the column and complex liquids last. The analysis appears on a strip chart recorder, or a screen, and the area under each peak is measured to determined the respective liquid concentrations

Skill: A suitably trained laboratory technician

Advantages: High sensitivity: Quick sampling and analysis: Strip chart provides a permanent record

Disadvantages: Considerable skill is needed to interpret results: Equipment not portable: Wide range of applications required to justify purchase: Not an on-line monitoring technique: Not widely used in maintenance.

5.4 Infra-red Spectroscopy

Conditions monitored: the presence of gases such as hydrogen, sulphur hexafluoride, nitrogen, methane, carbon monoxide and ethylene; fluid degradation

Applications: As for liquid chromatography

P-F interval: Highly dependent on the application

Operation: The atoms of a molecule vibrate about their equilibrium positions with different but precisely determinable frequencies. A sample, placed in a beam of infra-red light, absorbs these characteristic frequencies. The absorption bands, plotted against wavelength, specify the infra-red spectrum. The position of the absorption points on the wavelength scale is a qualitative characteristic and conclusions can be drawn from the intensity of the absorption bands

Skill: To operate a pre-set infra-red spectrometer: a trained laboratory assistant. To interpret and evaluate the results: an experienced laboratory technician

Advantages: Rapid analysis: High sensitivity: Can be operated by laboratory assistant when equipment is pre-set: Graphs provide a permanent record

Disadvantages: Considerable experience and skill needed to analyse results: Laboratory based equipment: Wide range of applications required to justify the cost of the equipment.

5.5 Fluorescence Spectroscopy

Conditions monitored: Changes in the properties of oils, such as alkalinity, acidity, insolubles, etc.

Applications: As for liquid chromatography

P-F Interval: Several months

Operation: A sample is irradiated and degradation products such as oxidants luminesce as fluorescence and phosphorescence spectra according to the molecular structure

Skill: A trained and experienced laboratory technician

Advantages: Sensitive assessment of oxidation products

Disadvantages: Considerable skill and experience needed to analyse results: Laboratory based equipment: The equipment is expensive

5.6 Ultra-violet and Visible Spectroscopy

Conditions monitored, applications and P-F interval: As for fluorescence spectroscopy

Operations: A sample is subjected to intense ultra-violet light and the molecular structure of the sample produces a spectrum of characteristic wavelengths. The concentrations of some anti-oxidants and their oxidation products can be determined by the direct absorption at specified wavelengths of each characteristic element

Skill, advantages and disadvantages: As for fluorescence spectroscopy.

5.7 Thin-layer Activation

Conditions monitored: Wear

Applications: Turbine blades, engine cylinders, shafts, bearings, electrical contacts, rails and cooling systems

P-F interval: Months

Operation: A thin layer of atoms in the surface of the material to be monitored is made radioactive by bombarding it with a beam of charged particles. Monitoring systems are calibrated to take radioactive decay into account. Material losses of up to 1 μm can be measured up to four years after activation

Skill: To take readings: a suitably trained semi-skilled worker

Advantages: Wear can be measured during normal plant operation even with substantial intervening material

Disadvantages: Components have to be removed to be activated unless coupons can be used: Reactivation is required every four years.

5.8 Electro-chemical Corrosion Monitoring

Conditions monitored: Corrosion of material embedded in concrete

Applications: Structural steel pylons, gantries, etc

P-F interval: Months

Operation: Small currents are passed between the structure and a probe inserted in the ground nearby. These currents affect the potential of the structure at any point where corrosion is taking place. The changes in the potential are measured by a half-cell in contact with the ground and close to the structure. The degree of corrosion is directly related to the current required to displace the leg potential. High currents indicate the need for a physical inspection.

Skill: A suitably trained technician

Advantages: Structures do not have to be excavated for inspection unless this technique reveals a real need to do so

Disadvantages: Does not measure the extent or precise location of corrosion: Ground must be moist.

5.9 DIAL (DIfferential Absorption LIDAR)

Conditions monitored: The chemical composition and dispersal of gases in the atmosphere

Applications: Gases emitted by smokestacks and leaks in tanks or pipelines

P-F interval: Minutes to months, depending on the application

Operation: Similar to LIDAR (see 4.6 above), except that two differential wavelengths are used. One wavelength is set to correspond to a given gas, so one wavelength is absorbed and the other reflected. The quantity of gas present is determined by measuring the amount of light reflected. The location of the gas can be determined by triangulation based on readings taken from two points.

Skill: An experienced engineer

Advantages: Can cover large areas

Disadvantages: Must be calibrated for individual gases: Very expensive and unlikely to be economic for a single site: Operating the equipment requires a high level of skill.

6 Physical Effects Monitoring

6.1 Liquid Dye Penetrants

Conditions monitored: Surface discontinuities or cracks due to fatigue, wear, surface shrinkage, grinding, heat-treatment, corrosion fatigue, corrosion stress and hydrogen embrittlement

Applications: Ferrous and non-ferrous materials such as welds, machined surfaces, steel structures, shafts, boilers, plastic structures, compressor receivers, etc.

P-F interval: Several days to several months, depending on the application

Operation: The liquid penetrant is applied to the test surface and sufficient time is allowed for penetration into surface discontinuities. Excess surface penetrant is removed. A developer is applied which draws the penetrant from the discontinuity to the test surface, where it is interpreted and evaluated. Liquid penetrants are categorised according to the type of dye (visible dye, fluorescent or dual sensitivity penetrants) and the processing required to remove them from the test surface (water washable, post emulsified or solvent removed).

Skill: To apply penetrant: suitably trained semi-skilled worker. Interpretation: suitably experienced technician

Advantages: Visible dye penetrant kits are very cheap (but the more expensive fluorescent kits are far more sensitive): Detects surface discontinuities on non-ferrous materials

Disadvantages: Fluorescent penetrants require a darkened area for inspection: Highly qualified personnel required to evaluate results: Not an on-line monitoring technique: Monitors surface-breaking defects only: Cannot test materials with very porous surfaces.

6.2 Electrostatic Fluorescent Penetrant

Conditions monitored and applications: As for liquid dye penetrants

P-F interval: Slightly longer than liquid dye penetrants

Operation: As for liquid penetrant dyes, except that opposing electrostatic polarity must be induced between the workpiece and testing materials

Skill: Application of the penetrant: a suitably trained semi-skilled worker. Interpretation and evaluation: a suitably experienced technician

Advantages: The polarity ensures more complete and even deposition of penetrant and developer than with ordinary penetrants, which gives greater sensitivity

Disadvantages: As for ordinary fluorescent penetrants.

6.3 Magnetic Particle Inspection

Conditions monitored: Surface and near-surface cracks and discontinuities caused by fatigue, wear, laminations, inclusions, surface shrinkage, grinding, heat treatment, hydrogen embrittlement, laps, seams, corrosion fatigue and corrosion stress

Applications: Ferromagnetic metals such as compressor receivers, welds, machined surfaces, shafts, steel structures, boilers, etc.

P-F interval: Days to months depending on the application

Operation: A test piece is magnetised and then sprayed with a solution containing very fine iron particles over the area to be inspected. If a crack exists, the iron particles will be attracted to the magnetic flux leaking from the area caused by the discontinuity and form an indication. These leakage fields act as local magnets. The indication is then interpreted and evaluated. Fluorescent magnetic particle sprays provide greater sensitivity and inspection should be carried out under ultra-violet light in a darkened booth.

Skill: Application: a suitably trained semi-skilled worker. Interpretation: a suitably experienced technician

Advantages: Reliable and sensitive: Very widely used

Disadvantages: Detects only surface and near-surface cracks: Time consuming: Contaminates clean surfaces: Not an on-line monitoring technique.

6.4 Strippable Magnetic Film

Conditions monitored: Surface discontinuities and cracks caused by fatigue, wear, surface shrinkage, grinding, heat treatment, hydrogen embrittlement, laminations, corrosion fatigue, corrosion stress, laps and seams

Applications: Ferromagnetic metals such as compressor receivers, welds, machined surfaces, shafts, gears, steel structures, boilers, etc.

P-F interval: Several weeks to months

Operation: A self curing silicon rubber solution containing fine iron oxide particles is poured into or onto the area under inspection and a magnetic field induced by a magnet. The magnetic particles in the solution migrate to cracks under the influence of the magnetic field. After curing, the rubber is removed as a plug from holes or as a coating from surfaces. Cracks appear on the cured rubber as intense black lines. Investigation of small cracks may need a low powered microscope

Skill: Application of solution: suitably trained semi-skilled worker. Evaluation: experienced technician

Advantages: Can be used to examine areas with limited visual access: Provides a record of developing cracks

Disadvantages: Detects only surface cracks: Not an on-line technique.

6.5 Ultrasonics - Pulse Echo Technique

Conditions monitored: Surface and below surface discontinuities caused by fatigue, heat treatment, inclusions, lack of penetration and gas porosity in welds, lamination; The thickness of materials subject to wear and corrosion

Applications: Ferrous and non-ferrous materials related to welds, steel structures, boilers, boiler tubes, plastic structures, shafts, compressor receivers, etc.

P-F interval: Several weeks to several months

Operation: A transmitter sends an ultrasonic pulse to the test surface. A receiver amplifier feeds the return pulse to an oscilloscope. The echo is a combination of return pulses from the opposite side of the workpiece and from any intervening discontinuity. The time elapsed between the initial and return signals and the relative height indicate the location and severity of the discontinuity. A rough idea of the size and shape of the defect can be gained by checking the workpiece from another location

Skill: A suitably trained and experienced technician

Advantages: Applicable to the majority of materials

Disadvantages: Difficult to differentiate types of defects.

6.6 Ultrasonics - Transmission Technique

Conditions monitored, applications and P-F interval: As for pulse echo technique

Operation: A transmitter emits continuous waves from one transducer which are passed right through the test piece. Discontinuities reduce the amount of energy reaching the receiver and so their presence can be detected

Skill and advantages: As for pulse echo technique

Disadvantages: As for pulse echo technique: Problems of modulation associated with standing waves cause false readings to be obtained

6.7 Ultrasonics - Resonance Technique

Conditions monitored, application and P-F interval: As for pulse echo technique. (Also used for testing the bond strength between thin surfaces)

P-F interval: As for pulse echo technique

Operation: A transmitter is moved over the test surface and the signal observed. Resonance in the absence of discontinuities keeps the transmitted signal high. Discontinuities cause the transmitted signal to fade or disappear

Skill, advantages, and disadvantages: As for pulse echo technique

6.8 Ultrasonics - Frequency Modulation

Conditions monitored, applications and P-F interval: As for pulse echo

Operation: A transducer is used to send ultrasonic waves continuously at changing radio frequencies. Echoes return at the initial frequency and interrupt the new changed frequency. By measuring the phase between frequencies the location of the defect can be determined

Skill, advantages and disadvantages: As for pulse echo technique

6.9 Coupon Testing

Conditions monitored: General and localised erosion and corrosion such as metal loss and pitting

Applications: As for electrical resistance method, except paper mills

P-F interval: Several months

Operation: Coupons are usually produced from mild, low carbon steel or from a grade of material that duplicates the wall of a vessel or pipe. The coupons are carefully prepared, weighed and measured before exposure. After the coupons have been immersed in the process stream for a period of time (several weeks to several months) they are removed and checked for weight loss and pitting. From these measurements, relative metal loss from the pipe wall can be calculated and pitting can be estimated

Skill: A suitably trained craftsman

Advantages: Very satisfactory when corrosion is steady: Useful in hazardous areas where electrical devices are prohibited: Fairly cheap: Indicates corrosion type: Very widely used

Disadvantages: Long duration of exposure required: Response to dangerous corrosive conditions is slow: Use of coupons is labour intensive: Corrosion rate determination usually takes several weeks: Provides no allowance for unusual or temporary conditions: Coupons inadequate for pulp and paper industry.

6.10 Eddy Current Testing

Conditions monitored: Surface and sub-surface discontinuities caused by wear, fatigue and stress; detection of dimensional changes through wear, strain and corrosion; determination of material hardness

Applications: Ferrous materials used for boiler tubes, heat exchanger tubes, hydraulic tubing, hoist ropes, railway lines, overhead conductors, etc

P-F interval: Several weeks depending on the application

Operation: A test coil carrying alternating current at 100 kHz to 4 MHz induces eddy currents in the part being inspected. Eddy currents detour around cracks, becoming compressed, delayed and weakened. The electrical reaction on the test coil is amplified and recorded on a cathode ray tube or a direct reading meter

Skill: A suitably trained and experienced technician

Advantages: Applicable to a wide range of conducting materials: Can work without surface preparation. High defect detection sensitivity: strip chart recorder provides a permanent record

Disadvantages: Poor response from non-ferrous materials.

6.11 X-ray Radiography

Conditions monitored: Surface and sub-surface discontinuities caused by fatigue, stress, inclusions, lack of penetration in welds, gas porosity, intergranular corrosion and stress corrosion. Semi-conductor discontinuities such as loose wires, etc

Applications: Welds, steel structures, plastic structures, metallic wear components of engines, compressors, gearboxes, pumps, shafts, etc

P-F interval: Several months

Operation: A radiograph is produced by passing x-rays or gamma rays through materials which are optically opaque. The absorption of the initial x-ray depends on thickness, nature of the material and intensity of the initial radiation. When the film is exposed to these rays, the areas exposed become dark when the film is developed. The degree of darkening depends on the amount of radiation reaching the film. The film will be darkest where the object is thinnest. A crack, inclusion or a void is observed as a dark patch.

Skill: Use of equipment: a suitably trained and skilled technician. To interpret the results: a highly skilled technician or engineer

Advantages: Provides a permanent record: Detects defects in parts or structures not visually accessible: Most widely applied x-ray technique

Disadvantages: Sensitivity often low for crack-like defects: Two-sided access sometimes needed

6.12 X-ray Radiographic Fluoroscopy

Conditions monitored, applications and P-F interval: as for X-ray radiography

Operation: The transmitted radiation produces a fluorescence of varying intensity on the coated screen instead of darker patches. The brightness of the image is proportional to the intensity of the transmitted radiation

Skill: As for x-ray radiography

Advantages: Quick results: Has a scanning capability: Detects defects in parts or structures not visually accessible: Most widely applicable technique: Low cost

Disadvantages: No record produced: Generally inferior image quality: Less sensitive than X-ray radiography

6.13 Rigid Borescopes

Conditions monitored: Surface cracks and their orientation, oxide films, weld defects, corrosion, wear, fatigue

Applications: Internal visual inspection of narrow tubes, bores and chambers of engines, pumps, turbines, compressors, boilers, etc in automotive, shipbuilding, aircraft, power generation, chemical and related industries.

P-F interval: Several weeks depending on application

Operation: Light is channelled from an external light source along a flexible fibre cable to the borescope. Using very high light intensity (300 W) photographs can be taken

Skill: A suitably trained and experienced craftsman

Advantages: Inspection done with clear illumination: Parts not visible to the naked eye can be photographed and magnified

Disadvantages: Provides surface inspection only: Resolution limited: Lens systems relatively inflexible: Operators can suffer from "optic eye" during prolonged inspection.

6.14 Cold Light Rigid Probes

Conditions monitored, applications and P-F interval: As for rigid borescopes (also used in combustible and heat sensitive areas)

Operation: White light of high intensity is channelled from a cold light supply unit (150 W) into a flexible fibre cable, through which it is transmitted by total reflection into a rigid borescope. The probe contains a lens relay system sheathed by glass fibres through which the light passes to the working tip. No light is wasted and no heat is emitted. Forward, fore-oblique, sideways and retro-viewing versions of these probes are available. Probe diameters range from 1.7

mm to 10 mm and lengths from 8 cm to 133 cm. Parts which are not visible to the naked eye can be photographed and magnified or recorded by a miniature video camera coupled to the endoscope

Skill: As for rigid borescopes

Advantages: As for rigid borescopes. No heat is generated when cold light supply used: Detailed inspection of surface finish in inaccessible areas can be obtained without dismantling: Photographs provide permanent records: Equipment portable: With the use of the video camera/endoscope technique, inspection time is reduced to a quarter of the time required for direct viewing

Disadvantages: As for rigid borescope: Probe inflexible: Not an on-line monitoring technique

6.15 Deep-Probe Endoscope

Conditions monitored, applications and P-F interval: As for rigid borescopes. (Also used for the inspection of pipework in boilers and heat exchangers)

Operation: These are special modular endoscopes available in lengths of up to 21 m. They are made of stainless steel and screw together to provide a viewing system which can penetrate bores with severely restricted entry. Illumination is provided by a high intensity quartz halogen light

Skill: As for rigid borescopes

Advantages and disadvantages: As for rigid borescopes

6.16 Pan-view Fibrescopes

Conditions monitored, applications and P-F interval: As for rigid borescopes

Operation: White light of high intensity from a cold light supply unit is transmitted by total internal reflection through a flexible fibre cable into a fibrescope. The fibrescope contains optical fibres bundled together to form flexible light pipes. The fibrescope has a remotely controllable prism built into its tip which can be made to view forwards or sideways as required. The instrument can be inserted using forward viewing and can be stopped to take a detailed sideways look at any passing defect by simply rotating a control knob built into the side of the eyepiece. Adaptors can be used to take photographs or mount TV viewers or cine cameras. An ultra-violet light of high intensity can also be used with fluorescent penetration to detect minute flaws in inaccessible areas.

Skill: As for rigid borescopes

Advantages: As for cold light rigid probes: Flexibility makes more detailed inspections possible

Disadvantages: Not an on-line monitoring technique: Provides surface inspection only: Resolution limited: Operators can suffer from "optic eye" during prolonged inspections: Ultra violet fibrescopes are expensive

6.17 Electron Fractography

Conditions monitored: The growth of fatigue cracks

Applications: Metallic components in aircraft, motor vehicles, industrial equipment, etc

P-F interval: Depends on the application

Operation: Every fracture has its own "fingerprint", in that the history of the fracture process is imprinted on the fracture surface. By studying a replica of the fracture with an electron microscope, it is possible to establish the causes and circumstances of failure

Skill: Replica of the fracture surface: suitably trained technician. Analysis and reading: experienced engineer

Advantages: Failures can be analysed with a high degree of certainty: No damage caused to fracture surface when replica is made

Disadvantages: Electron microscope is expensive: High degree of specialisation required to read the results: Not an on-line monitoring technique: Inaccessible components must be dismantled.

6.18 Strain Gauges

Conditions monitored: Strain

Applications: Large civil structures such as bridges, tunnels, the load bearing elements of large buildings

P-F interval: Weeks to months

Operation: Resistance wire, foil and semi-conductor strain gauges work on the principle that when an electrical conductor is stretched, its electrical resistance increases. By bonding the conductor to provide intimate mechanical contact with the surface under test, any strain on that surface will be reflected in a change of the resistance in the strain gauge. Sensitive indicating or recording equipment is needed to monitor the strains in most structures

Skill: Operation of equipment: a suitably trained craftsman: Interpretation of results: a structural engineer

Advantages: Readily attached to almost any surface

Disadvantages: The strain gauge must be compatible with both the material under test and the environment in which it is operating.

7 Temperature Monitoring

7.1 Thermography

Conditions monitored: Temperature variances caused by wear, fatigue, leaks, poor electrical connections, changes in heat transfer characteristics due to de-lamination of laminated materials, etc.

Applications: Power transmission lines, transformers, electrical switchgear, building insulation, refractories, hydraulics, bearings, gas mains (dirt accumulations), plastics, tyre defects, continuous processes such as glass, paper, metal, plastics and rubber manufacture

P-F interval: A few days to several months depending on the application

Operation: Thermography is based on the principle that all objects above absolute zero (-273°C) emit infra-red radiation. This energy is detected by an infra-red camera which produces a live thermal picture. Variations in the surface temperature are seen as light and dark areas. The thermal picture can be recorded by a video-camera attached to the display screen

Skill: Operation of equipment: suitably trained craftsman. Interpretation of results: suitably trained and experienced technician

Advantages: Stationary or moving objects can be examined at any distance without touching or influencing the temperature of the object: Photographs and videotapes provide a permanent record: Examinations are carried out at safe distances from dangerous gases and high temperatures: Equipment portable and quick to use

Disadvantages: Equipment expensive: Needs specialist to interpret results: Wide range of applications are needed to justify cost of the equipment.

7.2 Fibre Loop Thermometry

Conditions monitored: Temperature variations caused by insulation deterioration, leaks, blocked cooling systems, etc

Applications: Pipelines, engines, transformer windings, power cables

P-F interval: Hours to months

Operation: Light is passed down a fibre-optic cable. A certain amount of back-scatter is always reflected back towards the light source and diminishes the strength of the outgoing signal. There is a direct mathematical relationship between the time it takes the light to travel down the cable for a given distance, the amount of backscatter and the temperature of the cable. This relationship can be used to determine the temperature at given points along the cable.

Skill: A suitably trained and experienced technician

Advantages: Unaffected by the presence of electromagnetic interference: Operable in hazardous environments: Can reach inaccessible locations: Combines temperature sensing and data transmission in a single component (the cable): Continues functioning even if a cable break occurs: Accurate up to 4 km

Disadvantages: Uneconomic in small installations

7.3 Temperature Indicating Paint

Conditions monitored: Surface temperature

Applications: Hot spots, insulation failure

P-F interval: Weeks to months, depending on the application

Operation: A silicon-based paint which changes colour as temperatures rise. The colour starts out green, changes to blue at 204°C and turns white at 316°C. The colours do not change back again as the temperature drops

Skill: No training required for observers

Advantages: Very simple to use: Provides a permanent record of the highest temperature reached

Disadvantages: Colours do not change back again: Only useful at two fixed temperatures: Service life of each coat only one to two years (provided it does not change colour in the interim)

8 Electrical Effects Monitoring

8.1 Linear Polarisation Resistance (Corrator)

Conditions monitored: The rate of corrosion in electrically conductive corrosive fluids

Applications: Cooling water systems, municipal water systems, nuclear power heat exchange waters, geothermal power generating systems, desalination plants and pulp and paper mills

P-F interval: Depends on the application and the rate of corrosion. Usually several months in most applications

Operation: Corrosion rate is measured by the electro-chemical polarisation method with two or three probes and a measuring instrument. The principle is based on the fact that small voltage applied between a metal specimen and a corrosive solution will produce a current. The ratio of voltage to current is inversely proportional to the corrosion rate so it provides a measure of the corrosion rate increase.

Skill: A suitably trained craftsman

Advantages: Provides a direct indication of the corrosion rate and pitting tendency: Measures corrosion as it occurs: Some instruments provide a record of the corrosion condition: Automatic detection and control available: Sensitive to corrosion rates as low as a fraction of a mil per year: Portable equipment available: Rapid measurement: Interpretation normally easy

Disadvantages: Portable equipment does not provide a permanent record: Readings must be adjusted when taken in high sensitivity corrosive media: Gives no information on total corrosion

8.2 Electrical Resistance (Corrometer)

Conditions monitored: Integrated metal loss (i.e. total corrosion)

Applications: Petroleum refineries, process plants, gas transmission plants, underground or undersea structures, cathodic protection monitoring, abrasive slurry transport, water distribution systems, atmospheric corrosion, electrical generating plants, paper mills, etc.

P-F interval: As for linear polarisation resistance

Operation: The system is composed of a probe and an instrument to read the probe. The probe consists of a wire, strip or tube of the same metal as that in the plant being monitored. The electrical resistance of the probe, which is measured by a bridge circuit, increases as the probe cross-section decreases with corrosion. This increase in resistance enables total metal loss to be read out which is easily converted to corrosion rate.

Skill: As for linear polarisation method

Advantages: When plotted against a time scale, yields both corrosion rate and total metal loss: Can be used in any environment: Portable equipment available: On-line monitoring possible: In-plant equipment provides permanent records: Interpretation normally easy

Disadvantages: Gives no indication of whether the corrosion rate at a particular time is high or low: Portable equipment provides no permanent record

8.3 Potential Monitoring

Conditions monitored: Corrosive states of plant (active or passive) such as stress-corrosion cracking, pitting corrosion, selective phase corrosion, impingement attack etc.

Applications: Electrolyte environments such as chemical process plants, paper mills, electrical generating plant, pollution control plants, desalination plants, etc.; best suited to materials of stainless steel, nickel-based alloys and titanium

P-F interval: Depends on the material and the rate of corrosion

Operation: This technique takes advantage of the fact that, from the point of view of corrosion, a metal which is in a passive state (low corrosion rate) has a noble corrosion potential, while the same metal in an active state (higher corrosion rate) has a much less noble potential. The potential changes when passivity breaks down, and measurements can be made using a voltmeter of about 10 megohm input impedance and full-scale deflection of 0.5 to 2 volts

Skill: Usually a trained technician, but sometimes needs an experienced engineer

Advantages: Monitors localised attack: Fast response to change

Disadvantages: Small potential changes can be influenced by changes in temperature and acidity: Does not give a direct measure of corrosion rate or total corrosion: Not widely used: Expert assistance may be required for interpretation.

8.4 Meggers and Other Voltage Generators

Conditions monitored: Resistivity of insulation

Applications: Electrical circuits

P-F interval: Months to years

Operation: Test voltages from 250 volts to 10 kV are required to carry out resistivity tests. Measurement is based on the ratiometer principle using two moving coils connected mutually at right angles within a permanent magnetic field. The control coil is in series with a constant resistance and the deflecting coil in series with the resistance of the insulation to be measured. The amount of deflection is a function of the resistance of the insulation

Skill: Craftsmen or engineers depending on the voltages applied

Advantages: A simple and very well-understood technique

Disadvantages: Cannot be carried out on-line.

9 A Note on Leaks

With the exception of ultrasonic leak detection, a topic which has not been covered in much detail in this Appendix is leaks, especially in underground storage tanks. This is because a publication which provides a comprehensive description of 36 different leak detection methods is already available. It is called "Underground Leak Detection Methods - A State of the Art Review", and is in the form of a report prepared in 1986 by Shahzad Niaki and John Broscious of the IT Corporation in Pittsburgh and commissioned by the Hazardous Waste Engineering Research Laboratory, Edison, New Jersey. Copies of the report are available from the National Technical Information Service, a division of the United States Department of Commerce based in Springfield, Virginia, USA.

Appendix II
Levels of Analysis

An issue which often causes problems in the early stages of the implementation of RCM – and which also affects the amount of time and effort required – is the level in the equipment hierarchy at which the analysis is performed. It needs careful consideration because an analysis carried out at too high a level can become too superficial, while one done at too low a level can become unintelligible. This appendix considers the implications of carrying out the analysis at different levels.

Starting at a low level

When applying RCM for the first time, most analysts tend to start at a low level in the equipment hierarchy.

For example, when thinking about the failure modes which could affect a motor vehicle, a possibility which comes to mind is a blocked fuel line. The fuel line is part of the fuel system, so it seems sensible to address this failure mode by raising a Worksheet for the fuel system. This might look as shown in Figure A2.1:

RCM II INFORMATION WORKSHEET © 1990 ALADON LTD	UNIT or ITEM *Engine*			
	ITEM or COMPONENT *Fuel system*			
FUNCTION	**FUNCTIONAL FAILURE** *(Loss of Function)*		**FAILURE MODE** *(Cause of Failure)*	
1 To transfer fuel from the fuel tank to the engine at a rate of up to 1 litre per minute	A Unable to transfer any fuel at all		1 No fuel in tank 3 Fuel filter blocked 7 Fuel line blocked by foreign object 12 Fuel line severed ... etc	

Figure A2.1: Failure modes of a fuel system

This example indicates that if the analysis is carried out at this level, the blocked fuel line might be the seventh failure mode to be identified out of a total of perhaps fifteen or twenty.

When the decision worksheet has been completed for this sub-system, the RCM review group proceeds to the next system, and so on until the maintenance requirements of the entire vehicle have been reviewed.

This approach seems to be straightforward enough until we consider that the vehicle can actually be sub-divided into a great many sub-systems – the cooling system, the exhaust system, the engine control system, the air intake system, the braking system, the lighting system, the wheels, the seats and so on. If a separate analysis is carried out for each sub-system, a series of problems begin to arise. Among these are the following:

- the further down the hierarchy one progresses, the more difficult it becomes to conceptualise and define performance standards. (One could also ask who actually cares about the precise amount of fuel passing through the fuel system as long as the fuel economy of the vehicle is within reasonable limits and the vehicle has enough power.)

- at a low level, it becomes equally difficult to visualise and hence to analyse failure consequences.

- the lower the level of the analysis, the more difficult it becomes to decide which components belong to which system (for instance, is the accelerator part of the fuel system or the engine control system?)

- some failure modes can cause many sub-systems to cease to function simultaneously (such as a failure in the supply of power to an industrial plant). If each sub-system is analysed on its own, failure modes of this type are repeated again and again.

- control and protective loops can become very difficult to deal with in a low-level analysis, especially when a sensor in one sub-system drives an actuator in another through a processor in a third.

  For instance, a rev limiter which reads a signal off the flywheel in the "engine block" sub-system might send a signal through a processor in the "engine control" sub-system to a fuel shut-off valve in the "fuel" sub-system.

  If special attention is not paid to this issue, the same function ends up being analysed three times in slightly different ways, and the same failure-finding task prescribed more than once for the same loop.

- a new worksheet has to be raised for each new sub-system. This leads to the generation of vast quantities of paperwork for the analysis of the entire vehicle, or the consumption of equally large amounts of computer memory space. The associated manual or electronic filing systems have to be very carefully structured if the information is to remain manageable. In short, the whole exercise starts to become much more extensive and much more intimidating than it needs to be.

The main reason for this tendency to carry out RCM analyses at very low levels in the equipment hierarchy is a belief that a failure mode which affects a component can only be identified at the level of that component. In fact, this is not so. Failure modes can be identified at any level, as the next sections of this chapter demonstrate.

Starting at the top

Instead of starting the analysis towards the bottom of the equipment hierarchy, we could start at the top.

For example, the primary function and desired performance standards of the truck first mentioned on page 47 was listed as follows: *"To transport up to 40 tonnes of material at speeds of up to 75 mph (average 60 mph) from Startsville to Endburg on one tank of fuel."*

The first functional failure associated with this function would be "Unable to move at all". Four of the failure modes which could cause this functional failure are those already identified in Figure A2.1, except that they would now appear on the RCM Information Worksheet as shown in Figure A2.2.

RCM II INFORMATION WORKSHEET © 1990 ALADON LTD	**UNIT or ITEM**	*40 tonne truck*	
	ITEM or COMPONENT		
FUNCTION	**FUNCTIONAL FAILURE** *(Loss of Function)*	**FAILURE MODE** *(Cause of Failure)*	
1 To transfer up to 40 tonnes of material from Startsville to Endburg speeds of up to 75 mph (average 60 mph) on one tank of fuel	A Unable to move at all	18 No fuel in tank 42 Fuel filter blocked 73 **Fuel line blocked by foreign object** 114 Fuel line severed ... *etc*	

Figure A2.2: *Failure modes of a truck*

The main advantages of starting the analysis at this level are as follows:
- functions and performance expectations are much easier to define
- failure consequences are much easier to assess
- it is easier to identify and analyse control loops and protective circuits as a whole
- there is less repetition of functions and failure modes
- there is no need to raise a new information worksheet for each new sub-system as there is in the case of lower-level analyses, so analyses carried out at this level consume far less paper.

However, the main disadvantage of performing the analysis at this level is that there are hundreds of failure modes which could render the truck effectively unable to move. These range from a flat front tyre to a sheared crankshaft. So if we were to try to list all the failure modes at this level, it is possible that we would overlook several altogether.

For instance, we have seen how the blocked fuel system might have been the seventh failure mode out of fifteen to be identified in the analysis carried out at the "fuel system" level. However, at the truck level, Figure A2.2 shows that it might have been 73rd out of perhaps 200 failure modes.

Intermediate levels

The problems associated with both high- and low-level analyses suggest that it may be sensible to carry out the analysis at an intermediate level. In fact, we are almost spoiled for choice, because most assets can be sub-divided into a great many levels and the RCM process applied at any one of these levels.

For example, Figure A2.3 shows how the 40 tonne truck could be divided into at least five levels. It traces the hierarchy from the level of the truck as a whole down to the level of the fuel lines. It goes on to show how the primary function of the asset might be defined at each level on an RCM Information Worksheet, and how the blocked fuel line could be identified at each level.

However, given the choice of five (sometimes more) possibilities, how do we select the level at which to start?

The answer can be found yet again in the fact that any asset is acquired to fulfil specific functions. These are the functions which are usually specified in the top level of the analysis. Since the objective of maintenance is to ensure that the asset continues to fulfil these functions at the desired level of performance, they should be specified for every asset.

For example, the reason why an operator acquires a truck is to carry goods from A to B, not to pump fuel along a fuel line. Although the latter function contributes to the former, the overall performance of the asset – and hence of its maintenance – is always judged at the top level. For instance, the chief executive of a truck fleet is much more likely to ask "how is truck X performing?" than "how is the fuel system on truck X performing?" (unless of course he knows that a particular fuel system is causing problems).

For this reason, an RCM review group should always start by specifying the primary and secondary functions and performance standards of the asset at the top level. This also serves to define the context in which all the lower level systems are operating.

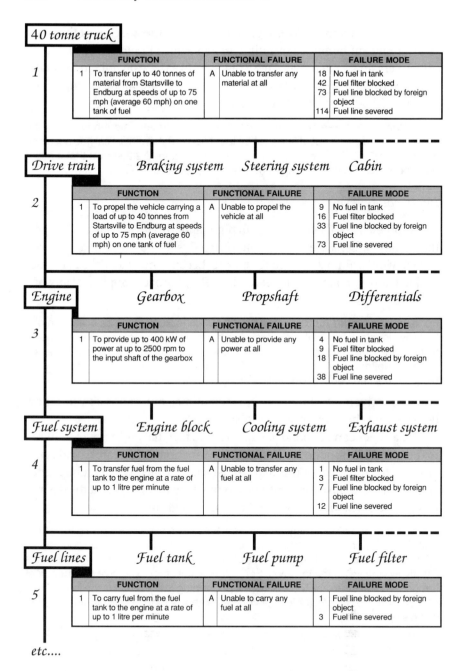

40 tonne truck

		FUNCTION		FUNCTIONAL FAILURE		FAILURE MODE
1	1	To transfer up to 40 tonnes of material from Startsville to Endburg at speeds of up to 75 mph (average 60 mph) on one tank of fuel	A	Unable to transfer any material at all	18	No fuel in tank
					42	Fuel filter blocked
					73	Fuel line blocked by foreign object
					114	Fuel line severed

Drive train   *Braking system*   *Steering system*   *Cabin*

		FUNCTION		FUNCTIONAL FAILURE		FAILURE MODE
2	1	To propel the vehicle carrying a load of up to 40 tonnes from Startsville to Endburg at speeds of up to 75 mph (average 60 mph) on one tank of fuel	A	Unable to propel the vehicle at all	9	No fuel in tank
					16	Fuel filter blocked
					33	Fuel line blocked by foreign object
					73	Fuel line severed

Engine   *Gearbox*   *Propshaft*   *Differentials*

		FUNCTION		FUNCTIONAL FAILURE		FAILURE MODE
3	1	To provide up to 400 kW of power at up to 2500 rpm to the input shaft of the gearbox	A	Unable to provide any power at all	4	No fuel in tank
					9	Fuel filter blocked
					18	Fuel line blocked by foreign object
					38	Fuel line severed

Fuel system   *Engine block*   *Cooling system*   *Exhaust system*

		FUNCTION		FUNCTIONAL FAILURE		FAILURE MODE
4	1	To transfer fuel from the fuel tank to the engine at a rate of up to 1 litre per minute	A	Unable to transfer any fuel at all	1	No fuel in tank
					3	Fuel filter blocked
					7	Fuel line blocked by foreign object
					12	Fuel line severed

Fuel lines   *Fuel tank*   *Fuel pump*   *Fuel filter*

		FUNCTION		FUNCTIONAL FAILURE		FAILURE MODE
5	1	To carry fuel from the fuel tank to the engine at a rate of up to 1 litre per minute	A	Unable to carry any fuel at all	1	Fuel line blocked by foreign object
					3	Fuel line severed

etc....

Figure A2.3: *Functions and failures at different levels*

The next step is to identify failure modes at an appropriate level. This level will vary for different systems and sub-systems, although in general, complex systems which are likely to suffer from a large number of failure modes will tend to be analysed at lower levels.

For instance, it may be possible to analyse the entire braking system at level 2 as shown in Figure A2.3, but it may be necessary to analyse the engine at level 3 or even level 4. The entries for these two sub-systems might appear on the top-level information worksheet as shown in Figure A2.4. "Analysed separately" means that separate worksheets will be raised for the braking system and the engine.

40 tonne truck

	FUNCTION		FUNCTIONAL FAILURE		FAILURE MODE	FAILURE EFFECTS
1	To transfer up to 40 tonnes of material from Startsville to Endburg at speeds of up to 75 mph (average 60 mph) on one tank of fuel	A	Unable to transfer any material at all	1	Engine fails	Engine analysed separately
				2	Vehicle stolen	etc..
				3	etc...	
		B	Unable to achieve 75 mph	1	Clutch slipping	etc...
				2	etc...	
		C	etc...			
2	To be capable of stopping in a controlled manner within a distance of 100 m from a speed of 75 mph	A	Unable to stop at all	1	Brakes fail	Braking system analysed separately
		B	Unable to stop in a controlled manner	1	Road slippery and ABS system failed	etc....
				2	etc...	
		C	Unable to stop in 100 m from 75 mph	1	etc...	

Figure A2.4: "Analysed separately"

Bearing in mind that it is easier to identify failure consequences at higher levels, a good general rule is to carry out the analysis one level higher than at first seems sensible (if not two). Complex sub-systems should only be broken out when this is absolutely unavoidable. (Note also the comments about "black-boxing" in the next section of this Appendix.)

Complex Failure Modes

The questions of levels of analysis also apply to the definition of failure modes themselves, but in a slightly different way.

Chapter 3 mentioned that it is important to identify the root cause of each functional failure in enough detail to ensure that time and effort are not wasted treating symptoms instead of causes. However, it is equally important to ensure that too much time is not wasted on the analysis itself by going into too much detail (so-called "analysis paralysis"). Decisions most often have to made in this area when dealing with small, complex components which can themselves suffer from a number of different failure modes. These components can be treated in one of three ways:

- list only one failure mode for the component in the form of one statement such as "motor fails" (the so-called "black box" approach)

- list individually all the lower level failure modes which might cause the component to fail

- raise a separate worksheet and analyse all the functions, functional failures, failure modes and effects of the component at a lower level.

For example, consider an item which could stop completely as a result of the failure of a small gearbox. On the information worksheet for this item, this gearbox failure could be listed in one of three ways:

FAILURE MODE	FAILURE EFFECT
1 Gearbox fails	Motor trips and alarm sounds in control room. Downtime to replace gearbox 3 hours
OR	
1 Gearbox bearings seize	Motor trips and alarm sounds in control room. Downtime to replace bearings 4 hours
2 Gear teeth stripped	Motor does not trip but machine stops. Downtime to replace gears 6 hours
3 Gearbox seizes due to lack of oil	Motor trips and alarm sounds in control room. Downtime to replace bearings 4 hours
......*etc*	
OR	
1 Gearbox fails	Gearbox analysed separately.

Other examples of components or assemblies of this type are small electric motors, small hydraulic systems, control loops, protective circuits and complex couplings.

There is no universal approach to the issue of black-boxing, so each case has to be dealt with on its merits. However, a component or assembly should have the following characteristics before it is treated as a black box:

- it is not subject to detailed diagnostic and repair routines when it fails, but is simply replaced and either discarded or subjected to later repair

- it is quite small but quite complex

- it does not have any dominant failure modes

- it is not likely to be susceptible to any form of failure prevention in the first place.

In some cases, a complex assembly might suffer from one or two dominant failures which are readily preventable, and a number of less common
failures which may not be worth preventing because the frequency and/
or the consequences of the failures do not warrant it.

For example, a small electric motor operating in a dusty environment might be
certain to fail due to overheating if the grille covering its cooling fan gets blocked,
but failures for other reasons might be few, far between and not very serious if they
do occur. In this case, the failure modes for this motor might be listed as follows:
• motor fan blocked by dust
• motor fails (for other reasons).

The failure of services (electricity, water, steam, air, gases, vacuum, etc)
are always treated as a single failure mode from the point of view of the
asset which is supplied by that service. This is because detailed analysis
of these failures is always beyond the scope of the asset in question. As
a result, such failure modes are noted for information purposes ("Power
supply fails"), their effects recorded and then they are analysed in detail
when that service is analysed as a whole.

Bibliography

Davis D J (1952): "An Analysis of Some Failure Data". *Journal of the American Statistical Association*, **47 (258)**, 113 - 150

Gaertner J P (1989). *Demonstration of Reliability-Centered Maintenance*. Palo Alto, California: Electric Power Research Institute

Maintenance Steering Group - 3 Task Force (1988). *Maintenance Program Development Document MSG-3*. Washington DC: Air Transport Association (ATA) of America

Moubray J M (1989). "Maintenance and Product Quality". *International Conference on Total Quality*, Hong Kong: 16 - 17 November 1989

Moubray J M (1989). "Maintenance and Safety - a Proactive Approach". *Annual Conference of the Accident Prevention and Advisory Unit of the UK National Health and Safety Executive*, Liverpool, UK; 19 May 1989

Moubray J M (1988). "Developments in Reliability-centred Maintenance". *The Factory Efficiency & Maintenance Show and Conference*, NEC, Birmingham, UK; 27 - 30 September 1988

Moubray J M (1988). "Maintenance Management - The Third Generation". *The 9th European Maintenance Congress*, Helsinki, Finland; 24 - 27 May 1988

Moubray J M (1987). "Reliability-centred Maintenance". *A Conference on Condition Monitoring*, Gol, Norway; 2 - 4 November 1987

Nelson W (1982). *Applied Life Data Analysis*. New York: Wiley

Niaki S and Broscious J A (1985). *Underground Tank Leak Detection Methods – A State-of-the-Art Review*. Springfield, Virginia: National Technical Information Service, US Department of Commerce

Nowlan F S and Heap H (1978). *Reliability-centered Maintenance*. Springfield, Virginia: National Technical Information Service, US Department of Commerce

O'Lone O G et al (1989). "Special Report: The World Airline Fleet Grows Older". *Aviation Week and Space Technology*, **131 (4)**, 42 - 95

Resnikoff H L (1978). *Mathematical Aspects of Reliability-centered Maintenance*. Los Altos, California: Dolby Access Press

Sandtorv H and Rausand M (1991). "RCM - Closing the Loop between Design Reliability and Operational Reliability". *Maintenance*, 6(1), 13 - 21

Index